Praise for first edition of Medicine

"The book illustrates why the medic
universally held Netter in high esteem.... The author has brought
her creative, extremely hardworking father to life."
—*Publishers Weekly*

"Netter was... the best known medical illustrator in the world...
among the Olympians of medical education."
—*The New York Times*

"Francine Mary Netter captures her father in a very personal
and professional light, describing in detail the fascinating life
and work of one of medicine's truly great medical illustrators... a
beautiful memoir."
—*Clinical Anatomy*

"—a wonderful story."
—*Family Medicine*

"Francine Netter has done an admirable job of documenting her
father's remarkable career."
—*The Atlantic*

"Fascinating account of how Dr. Netter became a medical artist
and how he changed medical education with the use of his extraordinary illustration and communication skills."
—*AMI News*

Medicine's Michelangelo

MEDICINE'S MICHELANGELO

The Life & Art of Frank H. Netter, MD

by his daughter

FRANCINE MARY NETTER

with a foreword by William L. Roper, MD, MPH

SECOND EDITION

 Turkey Creek Press

Medicine's Michelangelo: The Life & Art of Frank H. Netter, MD, second edition

Published by Turkey Creek Press, Raleigh, North Carolina 27612

www.turkeycreekpress.com

First edition was published in hardcover by Quinnipiac University Press, 2013.

Copyright © 2013, 2020 Francine Mary Netter. All rights reserved.

ISBN: 978-1-7330058-0-7 trade paperback

Design and composition: Dick Margulis www.dmargulis.com

Cover illustration: "Skull: Anterior View," Frank H. Netter, *Atlas of Human Anatomy*, Ciba-Geigy, Summit, New Jersey, 1989, plate 1, courtesy of Elsevier.

First printing

MANUFACTURED IN THE UNITED STATES OF AMERICA

CONTENTS

ILLUSTRATIONS

Chapter 15: The East Side

Chapter 17: Ciba-Geigy

Chapter 19: Point Manalapan

FOREWORD

Dr. Frank Netter helped me through medical school

FRANK NETTER, MD, TAUGHT me and generations of other physicians the splendid details of the human body. Through his many works of medical art we learned anatomy and much more. I never met this giant of medicine, who left us in 1990, but his amazing life and work come alive in this fascinating book by his daughter, Francine Mary Netter. She tells a tale that is rich in detail and realistic—we see the real Frank Netter.

We learn about this complex man, who was artist, then physician, then medical artist—and through his decades of work we meet a host of famous physicians, practically a "who's who" of medical science from the 1930s to the 1990s. Frank Netter's collaborations with them led to his extensive set of books, published by the international pharmaceutical giant, Ciba-Geigy.

I am amazed at how timeless his work is—he was entirely up to date in many areas and had a way of steering clear of details that were not necessary and might have dated his art. Many of his drawings from the 1970s and 1980s are still highly relevant despite the incredible progress in medical science.

One of Frank Netter's great contributions was to make learning easier by incorporating so many elements that are not nearly so well captured by any combination of photographs, diagrams, pathways and description. It is all there in every Netter drawing. He was a great medical artist whose pictures combine art and science. Dr. Netter's works live on even now, more than two decades after him, in *Netter's Anatomy Atlas* and many other publications.

And now this new book brings insight into the man behind the medical artistry. As I read it, I vividly recalled the impact his pictures had on me as a young medical student four decades ago.

I believe you too will enjoy this story of Frank Netter—his life and times and his art.

WILLIAM L. ROPER, MD, MPH
Interim President of the University of North Carolina System,
formerly Dean of the School of Medicine, Vice Chancellor for Medical
Affairs, and Chief Executive Officer of the UNC Health Care System
at the University of North Carolina at Chapel Hill

Medicine's Michelangelo

INTRODUCTION

FRANK NETTER WAS THE quintessential New Yorker. He knew his way around among the skyscrapers and the parks and the historic sites. Give him a street address and he could tell you the cross street and how best to get there, and he could generally recommend a nice place in the vicinity to have lunch.

He stood 5′ 10″ tall, at least he had in his younger days, and maintained a trim figure. His hair, black with just a touch of gray at the temples, he wore parted in the center and combed back in waves off his face. With dark eyes, olive skin, and aquiline nose, he was a handsome man. If in winter you had seen him walking down Fifth Avenue in his camel-colored cashmere overcoat and tan felt fedora, you might have taken him for a stockbroker or a lawyer or even the physician he was. But underneath that conservative, citified exterior he favored a dashing, debonair, sometimes outlandish style befitting the artist.

Therein lies the conundrum, for he was both physician and artist. "The doctors consider me an artist, and the artists consider me a doctor," he told his young colleague Dr. Frederick Kaplan. I am kind of in the territory between the two."[1]

On the top floor of the mansion where we lived when I was a child, Daddy had a large art studio where he spent his days and nights making pictures. I remember him working long hours in his studio and emerging with a shadow of a beard, which scratched when he kissed me. If you had asked me then, I would have told you that Daddy spent all his time painting. But I can now tell you with certainty that that was not the case. For each picture he made, and he made over 4000 of them for Ciba Pharmaceuticals alone, he spent most of his time studying, thinking, and planning.

With some frequency I used to go up to the studio to see him, to watch him draw and paint, and simply to be with him. Daddy would tell me about the medicine in the picture he was making at the time. If he made a picture of the heart, he explained to me how it worked to circulate the blood. If it was a picture of the intestines, he taught me about digestion. He never held anything back because of my young age. The pictures told the story and made it all clear to me. We talked about all the various things that fathers and daughters discuss; and I learned much about my father and a great deal about art and medicine.

During those visits to the studio, I would explore the interesting paraphernalia he had there, his paints and the sable brushes I enjoyed washing for him, and the human skeleton wired together and hanging at the corner of his drawing board. In a far corner I once found a notebook from his medical school days, filled with anatomical sketches done in colored pencil. I marveled that he had saved it. And we talked about that notebook, and about his career too.

It was not Frank Netter's youthful aspiration to be a medical illustrator. As a young art student he had doubted his own talent, and he went reluctantly into medicine at the urging of his mother. As a medical student, he made anatomical pictures merely for his own edification, but his classmates soon were asking for his pictures, as were his professors, for he depicted the sense of the thing, not just the lines and shadows.

When the advertising managers at the pharmaceutical companies found out that as a young surgeon he could make pictures that appealed to doctors, medical illustration then found him, grabbed him, and catapulted him to the zenith of medicine. His pictures showed the latest thinking in anatomy, pathology, embryology, and physiology and helped doctors help their patients. Frank Netter's was the art of healing.

Ciba Pharmaceuticals asked in 1952 for his exclusive services to provide "anatomical, medical, surgical, and pathological illustrations for use in promotional literature and . . . in *The Ciba*

Collection of Medical Illustrations."[2] That contract ran 10 years, but they renewed it several times, first for 10 years more, then another 10 years, and another.

In 1986, at the age of 80, Frank Netter came to the Fifth Avenue law offices of his cousin, Richard Netter, to sign yet another contract with his patron, Ciba. The negotiation had been arduous. Ciba was ready to call it quits, but they came back and tried one more time, and when Frank agreed to sign, it heralded publication of his award-winning classic, *Atlas of Human Anatomy.*[3] Here they were, less than a mile from the tenement on West 53rd Street where Frank Netter had been born, but it was a long way indeed.

Netter Family Tree

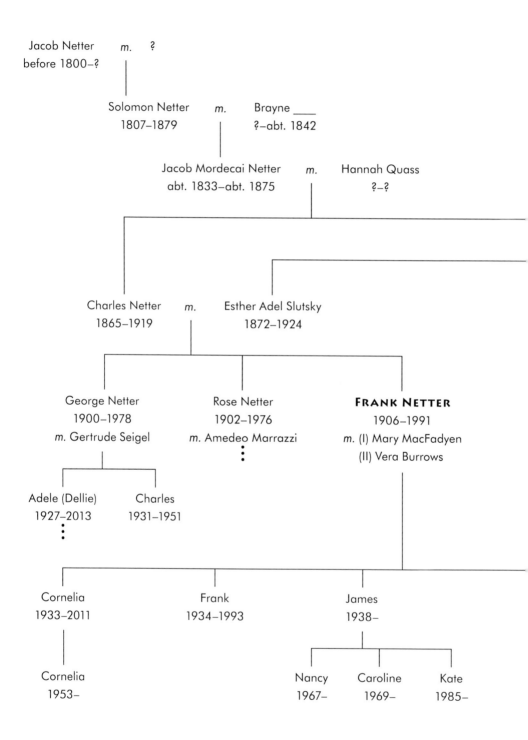

Jacob Netter   *m.*   ?
before 1800–?

Solomon Netter   *m.*   Brayne ____
1807–1879   ?–abt. 1842

Jacob Mordecai Netter   *m.*   Hannah Quass
abt. 1833–abt. 1875   ?–?

Charles Netter   *m.*   Esther Adel Slutsky
1865–1919   1872–1924

George Netter   Rose Netter   **FRANK NETTER**
1900–1978   1902–1976   1906–1991
m. Gertrude Seigel   *m.* Amedeo Marrazzi   *m.* (I) Mary MacFadyen
      ⋮   (II) Vera Burrows

Adele (Dellie)   Charles
1927–2013   1931–1951
⋮

Cornelia   Frank   James
1933–2011   1934–1993   1938–

Cornelia   Nancy   Caroline   Kate
1953–   1967–   1969–   1985–

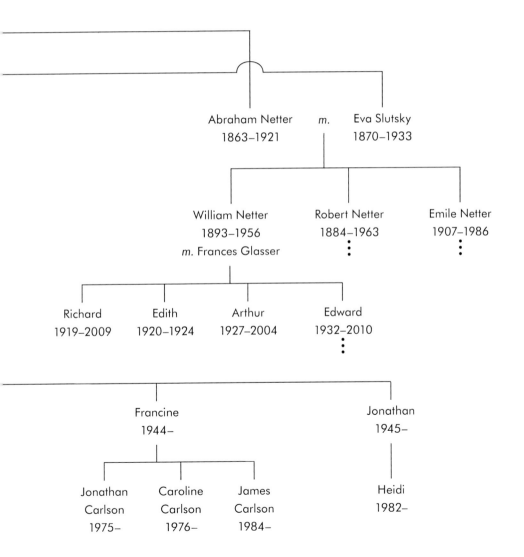

Abraham Netter
1863–1921

m.

Eva Slutsky
1870–1933

William Netter
1893–1956
m. Frances Glasser

Robert Netter
1884–1963

Emile Netter
1907–1986

Richard
1919–2009

Edith
1920–1924

Arthur
1927–2004

Edward
1932–2010

Francine
1944–

Jonathan
1945–

Jonathan
Carlson
1975–

Caroline
Carlson
1976–

James
Carlson
1984–

Heidi
1982–

CHAPTER 1

NEW YORK CITY

THE NETTERS TRACE THEIR lineage back to the Alsatian wine-growing region of eastern France, where the walled village of Bergheim sits on a hillside above the Rhine Valley. A sandstone-and-ironwork fountain anchors the central market square, and in summer, flowers spill from window boxes on the half-timbered houses clustered along narrow streets. From the village ramparts there is a view of a hilltop fortress that fell into ruin after 1633.

Before the French Revolution, the Netters had lived in France for generations. According to the 1784 census, there were 17 families with the name of Netter living in Alsace.[1] Frank Netter's earliest known antecedent was Jacob Netter, born sometime before 1800. After the rise of Napoleon, Jacob left Alsace and traveled to Jerusalem, where his son, Solomon, and grandson, Jacob Mordecai Netter, were born. By 1843 Solomon, fleeing a cholera epidemic that swept through the old city, had resettled his family in Vienna, where he had a little shop and devoted himself to his occupation as a book merchant.[2]

In 1857, the scholarly young Jacob Mordecai Netter left Vienna and traveled the world from community to community, teaching, making friends, some of whom gave him lodging, and learning from them. In mid-October 1857 he was in Bombay, where he befriended Reuben Sassoon, of the prominent Sassoon family who had amassed a fortune in international trade with India and China.[3] Reuben ran the Sassoon shipping office in Hong Kong and arranged transportation for Jacob on a Sassoon steamship to the island of Macau, which served as Jacob's hopping-off point en route to Canton. But the south of China was embroiled in a brutal revolt, the Taiping Rebellion,[4] and in late June 1858, Jacob fled for his life across the bay to Hong Kong, which was, he wrote in his journal, "securely under the flag of Britain."[5]

From Hong Kong, on a tall ship packed with young Chinese men rushing to the gold fields of California, Jacob crossed the great Pacific Ocean on a voyage of 74 days. He passed his time at sea reading the small book he carried with him[6] and writing in his journal. He arrived in San Francisco in January 1859 and preached there on April 4, the Saturday before Passover.[7] In mid-May he set out on a journey of nearly five months across the vast North American continent—by stagecoach, wagon, or horseback—traversing desert, mountains, and the Great Plains to the relative civilization of Missouri, and continued east on a network of riverboats and railroads to Utica, New York.[8]

It was here that he observed immigrants discarding ethnic divisions. No longer were they confined by who they were, but were free to pursue what their talents permitted. "At the moment, the parts of this great nation are split apart into factions and are opposed in their desires," wrote Jacob in his journal, alluding to slavery and the impending American Civil War. "But if they unite, ridding that wide land of its abominations and disgusting things, they will be aroused in their strength to spread their wings to other parts of the earth. The spirit of their ideas will remain before the nations."[9]

He spent the autumn months in Utica before returning to Europe,[10] crossing the Atlantic Ocean on a sea voyage of 40 days.[11] In 1860 Jacob published *Quails from the Sea*,[12] based on his travel journal, including political commentary and expounding on the ethical ideals of humility, charity, kindness, and good works.

Jacob married a young woman from Vilna, Hannah Quass, and soon after took her to live in Constantinople, the vibrant capital of the Ottoman Empire—he was, after all, an Ottoman subject by birth. Their two sons, Abraham and Charles, were born there in 1863 and 1865, but when Jacob died in about 1875, Hannah returned with her children to her family in Vilna, in Russian Poland. After Tsar Alexander III rose to power in 1868, the pogroms and anti-Semitic deprivations led to mass migrations to the United States; and in 1888, Charles, 22, and Abraham, 24, no doubt dreaming of their father's tales of adventure, joined the tens of thousands of emigrants. They left not only Europe but also their father's religion behind, because it seemed to them that more people had been persecuted and killed in the name of religion than anything else.[13]

ᘓᕼᘓᕼᘓᕼᘓ

Charles went first, wending his way to Hamburg and booking passage on the SS *Bohemia* of the Hamburg-America Line for the 14-day Atlantic crossing.[14] The 350′ long *Bohemia* could accommodate 100 first-class passengers and, in cramped quarters, 1200 third-class passengers. On the day Charles debarked, June 15, 1888, no fewer than eight ships teeming with immigrants arrived in New York Harbor. Every day, more ships arrived carrying more immigrants. The tugboats worked six days a week, pushing the masses of future citizens to the docks at the Castle Garden immigration depot. The following year, Abraham sailed from Liverpool, England, paying the equivalent of about $20 for steerage passage on the *Celtic*, a steamship of the White Star Line.[15] Accommodating 1000 third-class passengers, she arrived in New York on May 20, 1889. The brothers gathered with the other Jews on New York's Lower East Side, where the crowded and often squalid tenements served as the starting point for the climb to respectability. Charles found work as a cigar packer,[16] and Abraham, at a newsstand.[17]

In 1890, sisters Eva and Esther Adel Slutsky[18] fled the poverty of Vilna and came to New York. They might have known the Netter brothers in Europe, or perhaps they met them for the first time on the Lower East Side. In any case, Abraham and Eva married in 1891, and Charles and Esther married in 1897. By 1895, Abraham and Charles had both become naturalized citizens.[19]

The two Netter families were incredibly close. They lived near each other,[20] and in a formal photo taken in 1904 of Esther and

Photo: Esther Slutsky Netter, c. 1895.

Charles's two children, George and Rose (ages 4 and 1), together with Eva and Abraham's two sons, William and Robert (ages 8 and 6), the four children look as if they all belong to one family.

In the tenement where Esther and Charles lived, at 200 West 53rd Street, Frank Henry Netter[21] was born on April 28, 1906. He was named after two heroes of American history, Benjamin Franklin and Patrick Henry. The Netters gave all their children American names. As did thousands upon thousands of immigrants from diverse backgrounds, they threw off old ethnic traditions, spoke English at home, and assimilated themselves into the melting pot of their new country.

ᐒᐤᐒᐤᐒ

Charles and Abraham had a stationery store in the theater district, on New York's West Side. They sold cigars and tobacco, newspapers, and the more popular magazines. It was a cramped little store with a register on a high counter near the door, a typical family-owned business on a busy corner. Inside, the aroma of tobacco infused the newsprint and permeated the place.

One of Frank's earliest memories was of the day, when he was about 2 years old, that his father brought him to the store and sat him on the counter beside the register. Frankie watched the people come into the store, pick up a newspaper, maybe read the headlines, take out some money, and give it to his father, who was standing behind the counter. Next to the register was a mechanical cigar cutter for cutting the tip off a cigar. Little Frankie watched as one man after the other put cigars in the cigar cutter, heard it click each time, and saw the men take out the cigars and put them in their mouths. And into the cutter he stuck his pinky finger, it clicked, and he screamed, no doubt causing some excitement in the store. As a result, the fingernail on that pinky forever grew crooked.[22]

The Netters' economic arrangements were quite simple—if one of the families needed money, they had only to go to the register drawer in the store and take what they needed. In practice, how-ever, each took only the smallest amount, thereby leaving more for the others.[23] Family members came and went between the two apartments,[24] and at mealtimes there was always food to share with whichever of them happened to be present.[25]

They eventually managed to purchase a few acres of land in West Milford, in northern New Jersey. There was a small ramshackle cabin with an outhouse on the property. Netter Castle, they called it. Every summer either Esther or Eva would take the children from both families on the train to Netter Castle. They would play ball and picnic and swim and be in the fresh air.[26]

Except for those times in the country, Charles and Abraham were at the store every day, and Eva and Esther took turns as sales clerk. When a child was old enough, he helped by stocking the shelves or working behind the counter before and after school. Frank was often in the store, together with his siblings and double first cous-ins. George, the scholar, spent many a day in the store, standing behind the counter with his schoolbooks, study-ing his lessons.[27]

As a youngster in the store, Frank never missed looking in the newspa-per at the funnies—*Boob McNutt,* a comic strip by Rube Goldberg about a nincompoop who got into all kinds of crazy situations; *The Katzenjammer Kids,* originated by Rudolph Dirks; *Mutt and Jeff,* by Bud Fisher, about the

Photo: Frank and George H. Netter, at Netter Castle, c. 1917.

antics of a short dimwit and a tall lunatic; and *Bringing Up Father*, by George McManus, which had an appealing art nouveau look to it. Frank would take a pencil and copy the comics or copy what he saw in the magazines, trying to do it himself.[28]

The cover of the July 4, 1916, issue of *Leslie's Weekly* magazine featured James Montgomery Flagg's image of Uncle Sam with the caption "What are you doing for preparedness?" It became Flagg's ubiquitous "I Want You for U.S. Army" poster, which began appearing all over town, soon followed by more than 40 other Flagg creations, as the United States geared up to enter World War I. J.C. Leyendecker's pictures of a debonair young man advertised Arrow shirts, and every December one of his "New Year's Baby" pictures was on the cover of *The Saturday Evening Post*. That year the *Post* also began featuring covers by young Norman Rockwell, including "Boy with Baby Carriage," "Shall We Dance?" and others. C. Coles Phillips's cover art featured his glamorous "Fade Away Girl" series, and Maxfield Parrish's luminous creations adorned ads for Ferry seeds and Fisk tires. It was the Golden Age of Illustration, and while people did not always recognize the names of these artists, they recognized the pictures.

In the store, Frank pored over those pictures. "I used to look at the pictures in the magazines and wonder who made them," he recalled years later. "I thought these must be the most wonderful people in the world. That's the remarkable thing. It wasn't the pictures themselves that I admired but the thought of the people who *made* the pictures, [and] I wanted to draw pictures good enough to be published in magazines.

"My father introduced me to a man he knew who made cartoons for the newspaper," Frank remembered, "and this man . . . showed me how to draw a pig and an elephant and a cat. And I drew those pictures over and over again." After a time, Frank grew bored with drawing animals. Frank wrote in his notes:

> I wanted to draw *people*. But the artist had not shown me how to draw people. So I began to look at the people I saw on the

street, at the expression on their faces. Some were serious and some were intent and some were just placid and some were jovial. And I looked at the positions they took. Some were bent over and some were straight up and some were bent in different directions. And I looked at the way they moved. Some leaned forward when they walked, some leaned backward. Some bent their knees and some walked sort of "goose stepped." And I tried to put these people on paper . . . I was just a little kid and I couldn't do it as well as the pictures I saw in the magazines. But I knew that I wanted to be an artist.[29]

When he was 11 years old, Frank drew a picture of his mother. She was sitting in a chair peeling potatoes and had dozed off. As she slumped over the bowl in her lap, he took a pencil and paper and drew her picture. In it, the table is before her and the bowl is in her lap. Her facial features are hidden; only her figure is depicted. He used only lines to create the outline and the shading, but that picture remains a real and genuine picture of life, one he framed and kept always.

The Artist's Mother,
Frank H. Netter,
pencil on paper, 1917,
from the collection of
Adele Netter Bendes.

ᐁᶻᶜᶻᶜᶻᶜᶻᐁ

George graduated from high school in 1918. A series of photos taken in the living area of the family's apartment shows George, in a trim new suit, holding his rolled diploma. He was 6′ tall and towered over his father, Charles. A white iron bed frame in an alcove is in the background of the picture, a testament to their close living quarters. George entered Columbia University that fall, but in the summer of the following year, Charles died in that small apartment from carcinoma of the pancreas.[30]

Then came the influenza epidemic, which hit New York City between 1918 and 1920, striking the hale and hearty as well as the weak. The disease was characterized by sudden onset and rapid progression. Thousands died from the pneumonia associated with the infection. And it was perhaps the flu that killed Frank's uncle Abraham. He died of pneumonia in April 1921, at his home in the Bronx.[31] That summer George, himself recovering from an illness, accompanied his grieving aunt Eva to a resort community in the Catskill Mountains.

Gertrude Seigel (Gertie) was a girl of 19 who was vacationing with her sister and her aunt at a nearby guesthouse,[32] a nice respite from where she lived with her parents in the Bronx.[33] She was picking wild strawberries, she remembered, when tall, handsome George came walking toward her; that is how they met. The weather was clear, and the fresh air in the mountains made for pleasant walks in the country. And when they returned to the city, George continued to court Gertie, although his studies at Columbia occupied much of his time.

After Charles and Abraham died, the sisters closed the stationery store. Eva was left with only her youngest child, 12-year-old Emile, as her two older sons were grown and in a law practice together. At age 48, Esther was left with three children, George (19), Rose (16), and Frank (13), who was just starting high school.

CHAPTER 2

ART STUDENT

FRANK ENTERED DEWITT CLINTON High School in the fall of 1919. Although part of the New York City public school system, it was then an all-boys school at 59th Street and 10th Avenue.[1]

The student-run publication was a monthly magazine called the *Magpie* that featured articles about the school, some fiction and poetry, and pictures students had drawn. Frank walked in to the *Magpie* editorial office[2] and spoke to staff members about getting his pictures published. "They looked at the samples of my work which I had brought along," Frank remembered, "and told me that they weren't very good but that the faculty art supervisor would help me."[3]

The advisor was Bernard I. Green,[4] an American Impressionist who taught in high schools and professional schools and exhibited at various galleries and in other venues, including the National Academy of Design. He had somewhat rigid ideas about art, Frank remembered. "Almost every afternoon for a while I went to this teacher's room. He gave me pen and ink and Bristol board and told me that I must learn technique. For about a week he had me draw evenly spaced neat pen lines." Frank complained, saying that he wanted to draw pictures, not straight lines, and Green answered that before he could make pictures, he must first learn technique. "But he did make the concession thereafter of letting me practice swirls and curves in addition to the evenly spaced lines. I got awfully tired of this—and eventually I quit going there. I guess he thought I was very unappreciative."[5]

Frank kept making pictures, and eventually the *Magpie* began publishing some of them. "They were not very good pictures," he recalled, "but I got a thrill out of seeing them published."[6] By his senior year in high school, Frank's pictures appeared in every issue of the *Magpie* magazine. Working primarily in pencil or pen and ink, he illustrated stories and essays written by other students.[7] He made pictures of people in all sorts of situations to enhance the stories. One of a gangster, for example, had the caption, "Don't move! I've got you covered."[8] Another of a woman and man in a disheveled room had the caption, "She noticed that he held a beautiful silver-and-gold candy box."[9] In another, the drawing of a man walking down the street is more cartoon-like, with little shading.[10] For still another, he made pictures within pictures—a seascape, a still life, and a triplet of the interior of a bookstore.[11] For the April 1923 *Magpie* cover, Frank made a picture of a lad in a baseball uniform. He is winding up for the pitch, one foot up in the air, and teetering on a chair trying to catch a glimpse of himself in the mirror over his mother's dressing table.[12]

The January 1923 issue of the *Magpie* was dedicated to the senior class, and for that, Frank made decorative divider pages for various sections of the magazine, including "Senior Histories,"[13] portraying a student in profile sitting on the floor, knees up to hold the pad of paper on which he was writing or drawing. He made a cartoon for a section entitled "Faculty"[14] showing a knock-kneed, cross-eyed, bald character wearing an oddly proportioned black suit, vest, string tie, and spats, and standing with one hand on his hip, the other on his cane, as he glared through pince-nez perched on his long nose. For the "Organizations" section he portrayed a medley of musical instruments, sports equipment, books, camera, art supplies, and radio equipment.[15]

"First Pitch of the Season," Frank H. Netter,
Magpie, *April 1923, cover, courtesy of DeWitt*
Clinton High School and Gerard Pelisson.

As a senior, Frank was inducted into the Arista League, an honor society whose slogan was "Character, Service, and Scholarship." In 1923, the league staged a production of *The Pirates of Penzance*. It is likely that Frank painted the stage sets, but exactly what role he played in the production is lost to history. Frank's other extracurricular activities during his high school years included running on the cross-country and track teams.[16]

"Faculty," Frank H. Netter, Magpie, January 1923, page 9, courtesy of DeWitt Clinton High School and Gerard Pelisson.

❧❧❧❧❧

New York in the 1920s was a wonderful place for a teenager interested in art. On the subway or the El, for just a nickel fare, Frank could get almost anywhere he wanted to go—to pore over art books at the library or to see some of the world's finest art at the galleries and museums. "I used to frequent the Metropolitan Museum of Art. I really haunted the place," Frank wrote in his notes. "I used to go there and study the paintings and marvel at the beautiful work displayed there. One of my favorites was [Diego] Velázquez, the great Spanish painter. Also, I admired John Singer Sargent [for] the freshness, the freedom, the ease of brushwork."[17]

It might have been through Bernard Green or a fellow student at school that Frank learned of the National Academy of Design, at that time located uptown at Amsterdam Avenue and 109th Street. Founded nearly 100 years earlier by outstanding artists to further fine art in America, the National Academy offered art education and opportunities for exhibition. Professional artists, some of whom were quite well known, taught at the National Academy School of Fine Arts. The formal curriculum offered a progression of drawing classes, beginning with the Antique Class, where the student learned to draw figures by copying plaster casts of antique sculptures, advancing to the Life Class, where live models posed nude for the more accomplished student studying figure drawing.

The National Academy School charged no tuition, but there was a high standard for admission. Frank went to see them and asked about taking classes. He showed them his portfolio, and in October 1923 they admitted him to the evening Antique Class. "I was in seventh heaven," Frank recalled. "Now I knew I was going to be an artist. What more wonderful thing could happen to me in this world?"[18] During the day, Frank went to high school, and in the evening, he went to the National Academy.

After a time Esther asked him where he was going every evening, and he confessed to her that he wanted to be an artist and was going to art school at night. Frankie was always drawing, and Esther liked his pictures, but she worried about his future. She wanted him to learn a profession, as his siblings were doing. George was at Columbia Law School and on the *Columbia Law Review*. Rose was at Hunter College[19] and planning to study medicine. Esther hoped Frankie would become a physician or an engineer. Then his future would be secure.

Esther told Frank that art was very nice but it was no way for a young man to earn a living. She told him that artists cannot sell their paintings, at least not until they are dead, and only if they have talent. You need talent to be an artist, she said. How do you know if you have any talent? "I don't know if I have talent," he answered, "but I know I want to be an artist. I want to make pictures." But she envisioned artists as living desolate lives, and she did not want that for him. They are drunkards, she said, starving in an unheated garret and carousing with nude models. "At the moment this did not sound like such a bad life to me but I assured my mother [that I would] not do those things. 'I will work hard at my pictures and I will sell them to magazines and newspapers and to advertising agencies and I will make plenty of money and live very respectably . . . I might even be a famous artist some-day.' . . . [But] I could see that she was very skeptical and did not at all foresee such a future for me."

Nevertheless, Esther consented to let him study art if he prom-ised he would do his homework in the afternoons and go to the National Academy only on those nights when he had completed his schoolwork. Frank continued to study at the National Acad-emy whenever he could make time. "I remembered what I had promised my mother, [but] my interest was not in schoolwork," recalled Frank. "My love was pictures. I could hardly wait to get to art school at night."[20]

⊙⟡⊙⟡⊙⟡⊙

During the fall of 1923, while Frank was still in high school, he studied at the National Academy[21] with various artists: Charles Louis Hinton, a sculptor and illustrator of children's books who later became dean of the National Academy School; Charles Courtney Curran, known for his Impressionist paintings of young women in light-filled landscapes; George Elmer Browne, a master of composition and color who most often painted landscape and marine scenes, portraits, and figures; George Laurence Nelson, popular for portraits and colorful floral paintings; and American Impressionist Ivan Olinsky, known for his realistic portraits and fine figure paintings.[22]

At that time, too, Robert Henri was teaching at another of New York's bastions of art education, the Art Students League. Henri was a leading proponent of the so-called Ashcan School art move-ment or style that advocated using everyday life as subject matter. He taught that technique should never in itself be an end, and pro-moted the philosophy "Paint what is real to you." Although there is no indication that Frank ever studied under Henri, as an adult he had in his private library a copy of Henri's book on his teachings, *The Art Spirit.*[23]

In due course, Frank was admitted to the National Academy's Life Class, the advanced drawing class with high admission standards. He wrote in his notes:

> Now, I had arrived! I admired the work of the other students. I was awed by it. I thought, "Oh! If I could only draw like that!"

Then one evening, the other students gathered round to admire a drawing Frank had made.

> I was surprised, because my picture seemed to me so inadequate, so far short of what I would have liked to do . . . and the little model wearing only a thin kimono over her nude body sat down next to me and said, "Oh, I think it's lovely." And I was so conscious of her body. I was conscious of my being an artist. I suddenly felt that I was all the evil things my mother had thought that an artist was. But I liked it. I liked this semi-nude girl alongside of me admiring my drawing. And the students standing there also admiring [my drawing] and hardly noticing this girl . . . there was no matter of sex in it. There was only greatness and beauty and accomplishment. And at that moment I knew I must go on making pictures.[24]

Many National Academy instructors advocated the strict guidelines of the "Academic Art" tradition. They taught students to draw the human figure in exact detail and to reproduce accurately what they saw before them. One teacher in the Life Class[25] taught that an artist has more than eyes to see and a hand to draw; he also has a brain that he must use to understand, recall, and interpret. In that class, the model posed for 10 minutes while the students were to study the subject but not draw. The model then stepped down, and the students would draw what they had seen. Another time, the teacher asked the students on one side of the room to draw the model as if they were looking at her from the other side of the room. "These little stunts were designed to break the habit of sheer blind copying," Frank explained in his notes. "They trained my visual memory and my visual creativity."[26] They taught him to remember what he had seen, not exactly as would a camera, but an interpretation of it. More importantly, they taught him to understand what he saw, to discard the nonessential and distracting elements, and to create a picture with meaning and impact. Those skills he honed at the National Academy would become extremely important in his art.

∝∾∝∾∝∾

Esther still worried that Frank was wasting his time at the National Academy and neglecting his studies. At length she asked him how his art studies were progressing. Frank said he was doing all right, that he was learning about composition, design, and layout. She asked him again if he thought he had talent and could make a living selling pictures. "I don't know about talent," he remembered telling her, "but I am sure I can eventually make pictures good enough to sell and I want to be an artist."[27] But he saw that Esther was not satisfied, and she told him that she wanted to go to the art class and ask his art teacher if he had any talent, something Frank begged her not to do. In his notes he wrote:

> I did not want her to know that I was in the Life Class. I was sure she thought I was much too young to be exposed to naked women and wouldn't at all approve of my drawing nude models. That evening, I was sitting down front in the class, right close to the model who, it just so happened, had assumed what might be called a somewhat licentious pose. It was a hot, muggy night and many of the students looked pretty disheveled, ties off [and] collars open. I heard the door open and I looked around and there was my mother standing in the doorway with the instructor. I could tell by the expression on her face that she already saw me going down the pathway to a dissolute life—that she envisioned me starving in that

garret room with a beard and a turtleneck sweater and long hair, whiskey bottles strewn about and nude women draped over the furniture, smoking cigarettes in long holders, as I prepared to cut off my ear. It hurt me to think that she was worried. I was also embarrassed and I blushed. But I got up and I walked over to where she was and we went out into the hall.

My mother asked the instructor if I had talent. He answered that it was difficult to say, that I was doing quite well at my work and that time would tell. Then she asked if he thought that I could eventually be good enough to sell my pictures and make a living. At this point he fixed matters real fine by saying that this also was difficult to foretell, that sometimes an artist might go years without selling any pictures then suddenly catch on and achieve popularity. . . . I just stood there and blushed, wishing I would drop through the floor.[28]

When he got home that evening Frank promised his mother that he would pay more attention to his studies and go to college. "I would give the art business a whirl and if I didn't make a go of it I would turn to something 'respectable' like being a doctor or an engineer."[29]

In January 1924, Frank began his studies at the College of the City of New York (CCNY), which in those days charged no tuition.[30] All of the students were male. Many were children of working-class immigrants, among them Italians, Irish, Germans, Poles, and Jews from Eastern Europe; a few were African Americans; all were New Yorkers. Every day Frank took the West Side subway to 137th Street; and, carrying his briefcase of books and his portfolio of pictures, he walked up the long hill on 138th Street to Convent Avenue, where imposing grotesques, sculpted by G. Grandellis and representing the many professions of the graduates, peered down from the stone walls of the neo-Gothic buildings.

His roster included the customary first-year courses—English, history, civics, math, and science—as well as a drawing elective. In addition, he participated in extracurricular activities. He went out for cross-country and track teams, which competed against Columbia, New York University, Rutgers, and Fordham. He signed on to the art staff of the *Mercury*, which was the college comic publication, and joined the art staff of the annual *Microcosm* yearbook. In keeping with the promise he made his mother, he kept up with his studies, and in the first year he earned a solid B average and was inducted into the prestigious Soph Skull, an honor society for second year students.[31]

The National Academy was conveniently located near CCNY, and in March through April 1924, Frank took the Life Class at night with Ivan Olinsky. However, with his full college course load and roster of extracurricular activities, he did not have much time to do so.

ശ૦ଵଵ૦ଵ

Sometime after Frank graduated from high school, Esther moved with George, Rose, and Frank to an apartment on Ivy Court in Brighton Beach.[32] She wrote articles in Yiddish and might have made a few cents selling them to the Jewish newspapers. She wrote stories contrasting giving birth in Europe with giving birth in the New World, and she wrote about her dream of a camp for underprivileged children.[33] Her own children spoke neither Yiddish nor Hebrew and could not read what she wrote.

By then, Frank's double first cousin, Bill Netter, and his wife, Frances, had two children, 5-year-old Richard and a little girl, Edith. Edie was diagnosed with diabetes, which at that time, on the cusp of the introduction of insulin therapy,[34] was effectively a death sentence. Her mother weighed every drop of Edie's food, and their home was a virtual sickroom. It was not a good environment for the little boy, so for about a year Richard lived with his great aunt Esther and his father's double first cousins in Brighton Beach. Richard remembered spending many hours with his cousin Frank, watching him draw cartoons, and playing with the huge hound dog they had named Nellie.[35]

In the summer, people flocked to coastal Brooklyn for the sea breezes. It was a recreational mecca for ocean bathing or fishing and for picnics. Frank used to swim in the ocean and had a job dipping out ice cream cones and serving up hot dogs with mustard and sauerkraut in the seaside community of Sheepshead Bay,[36] not far from where they lived in Brighton Beach.

The first time George brought Gertie home to meet his mother, they rode the subway from the Bronx to Brooklyn. "When we got to the house," Gertie recalled, "his mother was at the top of the stairs—they lived in an apartment upstairs—and when we got there she said, 'So you're Georgie's girl!' and . . . she threw her arms around me and kissed me, which I thought was wonderful because in my family we did very little kissing."[37]

George and Gertie became engaged in February 1924, and her mother planned a big engagement party. But on the day of the party, Edie died. She was only 4 years old. So they canceled the engagement party and packed up all the food Gertie's mother had prepared for the party and took it over to the Netters' for Edie's funeral gathering.[38]

෨෩෨෩෨෩෨

On the first day of August 1924, Esther entered Broad Street Hospital, where she underwent a hysterectomy for a prolapsed uterus. The procedure itself was straightforward, although the drip ether anesthesia had awful side effects—patients would retch, sometimes fiercely enough to rip out their sutures. But it was septicemia that made Esther deathly ill after the operation. It would be 5 more years before Alexander Fleming discovered the antibacterial properties of *Penicillium* mold and another generation before the clinical use of antibiotics. Esther was 52 years old when she died on August 3, 1924. She was buried the next day beside Charles at Mount Carmel Cemetery.[39] Frank cried and cried for days. He swore that nobody should have to suffer as his mother had.[40] At 18,

Frank was an orphan, though he had Rose, George, his aunt Eva, and his cousins.

At the end of the summer, the owner of the hot dog stand asked Frank to become his business partner. If Frank had any money, he said, they could open another stand down the beach and build a chain of hot dog stands. Frank thought it was a sound, profitable venture. Nathan's hot dog stand in Coney Island, just to the west, was opening new branches and becoming famous. But Frank remembered the promise to his mother that he would go to college, and he told the owner that yes, he had saved some money, but he was going back to school.[41] He went with his siblings to live with Eva on West 94th Street.[42] It was only a short ride on the subway to CCNY.

But Frank was overcome with grief. His grades fell precipitously—he received a D in math and only a C in an art elective—and he stopped going to the National Academy. In the spring semester his grades improved, and he took the course of study leading to the bachelor of science degree—math, chemistry, physics, and biology—as well as the four courses in military science required of all students. And he took all the art electives he could fit into his schedule. From then on, Frank customarily received B's in his subjects, except for art, where he received straight A's.[43]

๑๏๏๏๏๏๏๏๏

To make some money the following summer, in 1925, Frank landed a job as an artist in a resort hotel in the cool green hills of the Catskill Mountains, 90 miles north of New York City. The resort had a summer theater where it staged professional productions to entertain the hotel guests, and the artists painted the stage sets. Frank liked the idea of getting out of the hot city for the summer, all expenses paid. His title was assistant scenic artist, and although he did not know anything about painting stage sets, he was willing to learn from the experienced head scenic artist, who would show him what to do.

Frank went up to the luxury resort at the beginning of the summer season. "It was a great place," he recalled, "with golf course, swimming pool, tennis courts, dance pavilion, theatre, and everything that one could desire for a vacation, including accommodations for about 800 guests. I was introduced to the head scenic artist who seemed to know . . . all there was to know about making stage sets."[44]

At 8:00 that first evening, "with much enthusiasm and verve,"[45] Frank reported to the stage to prepare the sets for the following night's show. The head scenic artist gave him the sketches for the sets and went off, leaving Frank alone to paint the set. Frank studied the sketches and finally made out that the set was to be a garden scene, with roses and a fountain. There was a large canvas backdrop lying flat on the floor, where it was to be painted and then hung vertically. Never before had Frank painted anything as large as this backdrop, but he mixed some paint up in a bucket and took some brushes and began to paint. He painted as fast as he could, but by daybreak he had barely finished one quarter of the backdrop.

When the head scenic artist returned after a night of drinking, he surveyed Frank's unfinished work and began working with Frank to get it done. He picked up the bucket of paint and threw it over the drop. Then he took a mop began to slop the color around. He then took another color, mixed it up, dumped it and began furiously to slop that around too. When he finished mopping he told Frank to turn on the electric fan to dry the paint. "Horrified, I stood back," remembered Frank. "It seemed like a nightmare . . . I was hopeless in the hands of this madman. The fan further diffused the paint in all sorts of odd directions"[46] across the canvas. Then came the roses. Frank carefully began to painted roses in one corner, while in the other, this maniac painted what Frank described as "blobs of red paint delivered by single brush stokes. Before I knew it, he had covered most of the required area with these blobs."[47]

Finally, Frank's superior declared the backdrop ready to be hung. "I wondered how he could even bear the prospect of looking at the mess he had created," Frank wrote in his notes, "but I helped him hoist the drop in position. Then we went down into the orchestra [section of the theater] to look at it, and with much trepidation, I raised my eyes to take in the creation. To my amazement, from where we stood, the scene gave the effect . . . [of] a beautiful garden backdrop with bits of blue sky showing through, a lovely fountain and roses in the foreground."[48] The master had not just been carelessly slopping the paint with a mop. He had visualized the big effect and executed it. Frank recalled:

> That night I learned one of the most valuable lessons I have ever had. . . . "Always keep the big effect in mind. Add the detail later as needed. Start with the detail and you are lost." We finished the set in the afternoon and that completed my lessons in scenic painting because that night my teacher was fired for being drunk and disorderly. I was made head scenic artist but felt perfectly confident because of the big lesson I had learned. Thereafter I got jobs painting stage sets every summer vacation.
>
> I was going to college, taking as many art courses as possible, and also selling quite a few pictures. Between the latter and the summer scenic painting I was doing fairly well and [even] saved a little money.[49]

ͼϘͽϘͼϘͽ

In his third year at CCNY, Frank continued to take as many art courses as he could fit into his schedule. His art teacher was Leigh Harrison Hunt, an 1877 graduate of CCNY and a senior faculty member. To understand the human form better, Dr. Hunt had studied anatomy—as did many artists including the grand masters—but he took it a step further. He completed his medical degree at Bellevue Hospital Medical College and for a short time taught both art at CCNY and pathology at Bellevue. By the time Frank studied art with him, Dr. Hunt had abandoned medicine in favor of art.[50]

On the *Microcosm* yearbook staff, Frank was the art editor. He was also the editorial board chairman for the *Mercury* comic and became known around the CCNY campus for his *Mercury* cartoons, some of which are reminiscent of the pictures in the magazines at the stationery store. He made gag panels of glamorous men

"Love Story" by Frank H. Netter, Mercury, *October 1926, page 13, courtesy of Archives and Special Collections, City College Library, City College of New York.*

in tuxedos and flapper girls, with joke lines such as "'You say his wife's a brunette? I thought he married a blonde.' 'He did but she dyed.'"[51] Another was of two sweethearts at the New York Public Library.[52] One picture he made was of a lovely young woman[53]

Quadrangle in Winter, *Frank H. Netter, charcoal on paper, 1927, from the collection of Francine Mary Netter.*

broadly smiling and shyly glancing sideways, her chin tilted to the side; but he left no indication as to who this beauty was or what her relation was to him.

Whenever Frank went to the art studio at CCNY, a crowd of art students gathered round to watch him work. Occasionally a student said he wanted to try making cartoons for the *Mercury* and asked Frank how to get started. Frank thought back to the days when he had wanted to draw pictures for the high school magazine and the teacher who had made him draw parallel lines, endlessly, to learn what he called technique. He was not going to tell anyone to do that. He remembered his response to them:

> "Go out and buy a bottle of India ink and some bristol board, and some drawing pens and a few sable brushes. Then if you want to draw in line, you use the pens and if you want to draw in tone you dilute the ink with water and brush it on. Then, you go ahead and draw whatever pictures you want as you see them." The most important requirement for a good picture is for the artist to have something worthwhile to say, something worthwhile in humor, in whimsy, in philosophy, in beauty, in science, in horror, in morality, in immorality—something. Once he has that, and he tries hard enough, he will find a way to put it on paper or on canvas.[54]

In 1927, the year Frank graduated from CCNY, the *Microcosm* carried several beautiful reproductions of drawings that he had made—landscapes of the campus, portraits of classmates and professors, and a decorative architectural border on each page. His landscapes of the campus included pictures of the General Alexander S. Webb statue[55] and a winter scene of the stone buildings in the Quadrangle.[56] For the frontispiece of the 1927 *Microcosm*, Frank made a picture after the central part of Edwin H. Blashfield's mural, *The Graduate*, which hangs at one end of the Great Hall, where many of CCNY's historic gatherings—convocations, graduation ceremonies, speeches, and presentations—took place.

Woman in a Hat, *Frank H. Netter, charcoal on paper, 1927,*
from the collection of Francine Mary Netter.

He also made a portrait in pencil of Dean Daniel Redmond,[57] to whom the volume was dedicated. The subject is looking straight at you through his spectacles, and you know that if you ever met the man, you would recognize him from that picture. Three of Frank's pencil sketches of classmates also appeared in that issue of *Microcosm*.[58] One portrait he gave to the subject, Leon Bankoff, who was a fellow student with Frank in Professor Hunt's informal art group at CCNY. To Leon it was evident even then that one day Frank would be recognized as a great artist.[59]

Photo: Frank H. Netter, Microcosm *yearbook. senior portrait, 1927, courtesy of Archives and Special Collections, City College Library, City College of New York.*

The portraits he did in 1927 captured not only the likeness of the subject but also the spirit of the person. One picture was of an old woman whose identity has been lost to time. She is wearing a hat; her eyes are downcast; and she has high cheekbones, sagging jowls, and a knowing half smile. A certain wisdom or beneficence seems to exude from her face, and she radiates beauty.

Everyone who knew Frank knew that he would do something in art, whether fine art, illustration, or cartoons. Yet Esther's admonitions haunted him. *Be a doctor!* she had said. He could hear her say it still from the grave. She had suffered so much, and she had died. It weighed on his conscience. He only wanted to help people, to do something that would "contribute in a small way to man's well-being,"[60] he remembered thinking. He would become a doctor, he decided. He would give up art, he vowed: "I had lived it, loved it, thrilled to it, but now it was finished."[61] He would live the "respectable" life Esther had wanted for him. He would go to medical school.

CHAPTER 3

MEDICAL STUDENT

RANK ENROLLED AT NEW York University (NYU) Medical College[1] in the fall of 1927. The college occupied five large buildings on the corner of East 26th Street and First Avenue, opposite the entrance of Bellevue Hospital. The facilities included lecture halls, laboratories for teaching and research, dissecting room, and library facilities. The large college clinic in the main building of the college treated on average 385 ambulatory patients per day.[2]

While many schools discriminated on the basis of ethnicity or social background, NYU and its medical school were open to all. Less than 2% of its medical students were African American, a percentage corresponding roughly with that of Frank's graduating class at CCNY. In 1927, only 5% of medical students in the 80 medical schools in the United States were women. NYU Medical College had been coeducational since 1919.[3]

The first-year class numbered 126 students, although some failed to make it to the second year. While it was still possible to gain admission without an undergraduate degree, most entering students were college graduates. Students were required to have at least completed undergraduate course work in chemistry, physics, biology, and English. One-fifth of the class had attended undergraduate school at CCNY, while a full three-fifths of the class came from what were then two campuses of New York University—Washington Square and University Heights in the Bronx.[4] The result was that most students knew their classmates from undergraduate school, while the lone student from the Midwest, for example, had to find his own way and make all new friends. Students from outside the United States were extremely rare.

The affiliation of NYU with Bellevue Hospital provided students with the opportunity to be on the wards with patients from the second year of their training. In 1927 Bellevue was not only the nation's oldest public hospital but also the largest. Bellevue had its own ambulance service that brought cases of every description to the emergency pavilion, and students were thus instructed in the treatment of a wide range of diseases, injuries, and sicknesses.

The legendary Dr. Edward Gamaliel Janeway, the renowned diagnostician at the end of the nineteenth century and former health commissioner of the City of New York, had given his last clinic at Bellevue some 23 years earlier, but a number of professors teaching at Bellevue in 1927, including Dr. John Wyckoff, professor of medicine, had themselves studied under Dr. Janeway.[5]

Dr. Menas Gregory, the head of psychiatry, was well known for advocating humane reforms in the treatment of acute mental disorders and was responsible for adopting a more benevolent attitude toward the mentally ill.[6] Under his direction, the new Psychopathic Pavilion was being constructed.

The four-year course of study began with anatomy, starting with osteology and progressing to dissection of the entire human body in the gross anatomy laboratory.[7] In the microscopical anatomy and embryology laboratory, students examined fresh and microscopic sections of adult human organs as well as developing organs of pigs. At the same time they studied physical and physiological chemistry, including blood, digestion, nutrition, and some morbidity. Finally, they studied the physiology of muscles, nerves, senses, secretion, absorption, and excretion.

The second year of study began with a continuation of physiology and the study of circulation, respiration, and metabolism. In pharmacology, they studied the effects of drugs, form and dosage, indications, and effects as poisons. Pathology, bacteriology, and immunology filled out the second-year laboratory work. Students were introduced to elementary clinical work in medicine, pediatrics, obstetrics, psychiatry, and neurology; and they were trained in surgery by working on cadavers in the laboratory.

In the third year the emphasis was on medicine and surgery, as well as on rotations through the clinical specialties, including the study of dermatology and syphilis. Fourth-year instruction took place almost entirely at the bedside on the wards and in the clinics of Bellevue Hospital. Students attended the autopsies at Bellevue Hospital and in fourth-year obstetrics delivered babies in the maternity ward and in the tenements of New York City.

Anesthesiology was not taught as a medical specialty but was considered a surgical technique. A nurse or the surgeon himself administered anesthesia to a patient. Then the surgeon had to hurry to perform the operation. Dr. Ralph M. Waters formed the first academic anesthesiology program in the nation in 1927 at the University of Wisconsin. Not until the mid 1930s, well after Frank had completed medical school, did Dr. Emery A. Rovenstine, who had done his residency training under Dr. Waters at Wisconsin, come to Bellevue to head a new department of anesthesiology. With the advent of modern anesthesia, the anesthesiologist monitored the anesthetized patient, thus freeing the surgeon to concentrate on the surgery.

Medical students at NYU when Frank was there were required to take two years of military science, to acquaint the future physicians with the organization and administration of the Medical Department of the US Army. First-year students were introduced to military organization, discipline, law, hygiene, and first aid. In the second year, they studied tactics, detachments, regiments, map reading, hospitalization, sanitation of the camps, marches, and combat orders.

Tuition was $488 per year, and many students had to work to meet expenses, which left little time for socializing. Out the door they ran to their after-school jobs, and after work they studied their books late into the night. Medical school was hard, exhausting work. Students had to undergo rigorous examinations and there were no second chances. Those who flunked did not return the following year,[8] but among those who made it, passing the yearly exams fomented an enduring camaraderie.

While his medical school classmates wrote their notes with ordinary pencils or fountain pens, Frank used colored pencils to depict anatomical structures graphically, and he soon filled his notebooks with illustrations of the human body. Dr. Harold D. Senior was the professor of anatomy and head of the anatomy department.[9] He or one of the associate professors went one evening to the anatomy laboratory to check that the bodies were covered and there found Frank making pictures of a cadaver. You should be home studying, the professor told him. You will never pass the examination if you do not read the book. But to Frank, just studying words in a book did not make sense.[10] "I had been trained graphically," Frank explained in his autobiographical notes, "and found I could best learn my subjects by making pictures."[11]

It was not long before Frank's classmates discovered value in his pictures. Many asked Frank to make pictures for them to study. Soon his professors too were asking for his drawings, not only to augment the teaching materials in the classroom but also to illustrate their publications. Thus, in addition to his summer jobs in commercial or scenic art, Frank sold anatomical pictures to make a little money and work his way through medical school. This artwork was just temporary, he reasoned. When he became a doctor, he would give up art and devote himself full time to a surgery practice.[12]

Frank pledged Phi Delta Epsilon fraternity. If it can be said that fraternity brothers are friends for life, that was certainly the case with Frank and his fraternity brother Max Som. Max was in the class ahead of Frank and was a superb student.[13] He stood about Frank's height, wore his dark hair slicked back, and had a straight profile and an energetic personality. Max was born in a small village near Vilna and came with his family to Brooklyn when he was only about two years old.[14] But because they did not know exactly when Max was born, they picked a date, December 24, 1905, for his birthday. Max always celebrated his birthday on Christmas Eve and invited friends to come and have a rousing good time.[15] Max and Frank would pal around together, talk about medicine and pictures, court the girls, and do those things that young men do.

One of Frank's classmates at NYU was Albert Sabin, who would come to develop the polio vaccine three decades later. Even as a student he was a diligent researcher and an affable fellow, and he and Frank developed a lifelong friendship, as did many classmates.

While serving on the art staff of the *Bellevue Violet* yearbook, Frank made drawings of the campus buildings and drew several portraits of professors and classmates. Many were published in the 1929 *Violet*, including his portrait of Dr. Arthur Mullin Wright, professor of clinical surgery, to whom the book was dedicated,[16] and portraits—pencil sketches—of each of the members of the *Violet*'s editorial board.[17] The *Violet* also published several of his perspective drawings: "The College"; "The Old Gate"; "The Chapel"; "The Administration Building"; "A & B Pavilion"; "From the River."[18]

Not published in the *Violet*, but perhaps done for a professor, was a pencil drawing—a beautiful rendering of hands, a doctor's hands applying a bandage to a patient's hand—signed by the artist, "Frank H. Netter, 1930."

From the Medical College campus at East 26th Street and the river, Frank captured the view in oils. The *East River* painting is an Impressionist landscape measuring 17″ × 21″. The colors of the gray-and-blue water and the pale blue sky

Bellevue "A & B Pavilion," Frank H. Netter, 1929, courtesy of Ehrman Medical Library Archives, New York University School of Medicine.

predominate. Strong perspective lines of the piers jut out into the water, and the unsleeping life on the river is clearly present in the red-sided tugboats chugging along, the gray smoke spilling from the stacks of the New York Edison Company,[19] the Williamsburg Bridge arching over the water, and the factories pouring out more smoke in the distance across the river. He signed it simply with his initials, "FHN," in block letters.

He really had his hands full, making pictures and studying medicine. Years later, he would confess that he had not been a good student and that his grades had suffered because he was so busy making pictures.[20] That he was the little brother of the brilliant Rose Netter was sure to have set high expectations among his professors.

oɤ૭ɤ૭ɤ૭

Rose Netter graduated from NYU Medical College in the class of 1927 and was the first woman intern at Beth Israel Hospital. She was seeing a handsome and bright young man who had been her classmate and was an intern at Bellevue. Amedeo Marrazzi was the only child of strict Roman Catholic parents who, according to the 1920 US census, had immigrated to New York from Italy in 1898.

Rose and Amedeo were in love and wanted to be married. Neither was religious, but their families grew entangled in ethnic stereotyping and religious prejudices. When Raffael Marrazzi, Amedeo's father, learned that Rose Netter was Jewish, he forbade Amedeo to marry "that Jewish girl." Her aunt Eva heard that Raffael had threatened to kill

Bellevue "George Washington Steps," Frank H. Netter, 1929, courtesy of Ehrman Medical Library Archives, New York University School of Medicine.

Rose and she pleaded with Rose to break off with Amedeo. And when Rose refused, Eva turned to Frank: Speak to your sister; tell her not to marry Amedeo; I am afraid for her. Frank dutifully did as his aunt asked, but his appeal did not sway Rose. On the contrary, it infuriated her.[21]

Rose went to her sister-in-law, Gertie, for help. She said that Amedeo's parents had disowned him, and that Raffael was chasing after Amedeo, threatening to kill him. Gertie did not know what to do. She and George lived in a small three-room apartment on the Grand Concourse in the Bronx. Gertie told Rose she could stay with them and sleep on the sofa in the living room. "It never occurred to me to tell her to bring Amedeo there to the apartment too," Gertie recalled. "The morals were so different then. They would have had to sleep in the same room."[22]

Rose and Amedeo eloped and from that time forward had nothing more to do with either of their families. She who came from such a close family estranged herself from them all. Rose served as house surgeon at Beth Israel—the first woman to hold that position—before going on to having a medical practice. Amedeo completed his internship at Bellevue, practiced medicine and served as a professor of pharmacology at NYU, and went on to have an illustrious career as a researcher. They had two children who grew up not knowing aunts or uncles or cousins. Yet Rose and Amedeo remained devoted to each other and throughout their lifelong marriage wrote love poems to each other, such as this excerpt of one Amedeo wrote to Rose:

> . . . I never catch the sheen that dances in your eyes
> nor match the grace of You, my Love, My Wife.[23]

∘∤∘∘∤∘∘∤∘

By 1930, Frank was living with Eva and Emile on Marble Hill Avenue,[24] just over the bridge in the Bronx, overlooking the Harlem

River. George and Gertie had moved to Far Rockaway with their daughter, Esther Adele, whom everybody called Dellie.

At NYU Medical College, Frank's classmates elected him class treasurer,[25] but he no longer served on the staff of the *Violet*, instead studying and making pictures to sell. Somehow, he did find time to paint Dellie's portrait. It shows a lovely child with dark hair and bright, dark eyes, and conveys the great affection the artist had for his subject.

In that third year of medical school, Mary MacFadyen joined the class as a transfer student from North Carolina. Mary was a tall brunette, serious, soft-spoken, with a hint of a Southern accent in her voice, which to those medical students in New York lent her an aura of the exotic. Of 127 students in the junior class at NYU Medical College in 1929, only 5 were women. She was in the Zeta Phi sorority and roomed with some of the other women on East 26th Street, not far from NYU Medical College and Bellevue Hospital. Mary appears in her yearbook photos as a serious, reserved, almost glum young woman, her unadorned hair pulled back, accentuating her high cheekbones.

Always with pencil in hand, Frank watched the Southern beauty from afar, until the day in a lunchroom when he drew her picture on a napkin and passed it to her. Thus began their courtship.[26] Together they studied the same courses and pursued the same goal. In the class picture that year,[27] taken outside on the school steps, the students sat all crowded

Healing Hands, *Frank H. Netter, pencil on paper, 1930, from the collection of Francine Mary Netter.*

together, Frank in the front row with the class officers, Mary in the second row just behind him and to his left. And as lovers do, they are leaning their bodies ever so slightly toward each other. For the senior year Mary was class treasurer, following Frank in holding that office.[28]

Dr. Frederick Freed was the clinical professor in obstetrics. He was known for his down-to-earth sensibility, wit, and practical application of scientific practices. Fourth-year clinical work in obstetrics included the requirement that each student deliver half a dozen babies.[29] Of course, if they got into trouble they could call the obstetrician, but most deliveries were normal. Frank remembered attending a birth in a tenement. The woman labored in bed late into the night, comforted by her sister, while the father and uncle waited in the hallway until the baby was delivered.[30]

∞∞∞∞∞

The 1931 *Bellevue Violet* had a poem below each graduate's photo. For Albert Sabin, the poem was prophetic:

> Walls reverberate a beautiful voice,
> It's mellow, basso, it's strong and it's choice.
> Is't Stentor? Still—not the drop of a pin,
> No; 'tis none other than the great Sabin.
> He taught the pneumococcus how to type,
> And thereby did save the white mouse's life.
> Altho he's apart and sometimes aloof,
> Soon we'll be proud to say, "I knew that goof."[31]

Mary's poem read:

> To our enigma now we come,
>   The doctor who takes care of nurses,
> The girl who's always looking glum,
> Though radiance her hair disperses.

The Scotch in her predominates,
    She's very sparing of her phrases,
Though sometimes she illuminates,
    In Southern tones, a problem's mazes.[32]

Frank's poem was a true foretelling:

He draws with pen, he draws with ink,
    He illustrates his Surg'ry notes,
He uses colors, blue and pink,
    To diagram congested throats.

He's often late, but what of that?
    He'll get there just the same.
—We introduce, with great éclat,
    Frank Netter, born to fame.[33]

ᖇᖇᖇᖇᖇᖇᖇ

Dr. Frank H. Netter and Dr. Mary MacFadyen graduated with their class and within days were married at City Hall on June 17, 1931.[34] Mary was Mrs. Frank Netter in her private life and Dr. MacFadyen in her professional life. They both interned at Bellevue Hospital, along with 17 of their classmates, including Albert Sabin. It was a close group, working long hours, caring for patients, and learning. Interns rode the ambulances and provided medical care in the various clinics at the hospital. They did not get much sleep, grabbing what they could while in the hospital.

The training at Bellevue was unsurpassed. Just about every ailment, known or unknown, and every injury passed through the doors of that big-city hospital. The interns treated disease and trauma in the young and old, patients from the myriad ethnic and cultural groups that composed the population of New York City. The young physicians also treated prisoners in the 53rd Street jail and the old Tombs prison.

Bellevue ambulances were each staffed with a driver, his helper, and an intern. Interns dressed in white coats and black, square-brimmed hats, the gold letters on the hatband declaring "Surgeon Bellevue Hospital." They carried a stethoscope, scissors, reflex hammer, and notebook and rode with the patient in the back of the boxy Bellevue ambulances, holding on to a strap overhead, like a commuter on the subway, while the ambulance drivers maneuvered through city traffic. A longstanding tradition of the ambulance service held that any physician who delivered a baby en route to the hospital had to buy drinks—never mind that it was during Prohibition—for the entire staff on duty in the emergency pavilion.[35]

σ❀σ❀σ❀σ

By midwinter of 1933, when Frank and Mary were in the second and final year of their internship, both of Mary's parents had died within six months of each other.[36] That spring, Eva came to Bellevue Hospital for treatment of metastatic breast cancer, and then she died too.[37]

But joy was to come Frank and Mary's way: Mary was expecting a baby. She continued her training at Bellevue despite her pregnancy, which in those days was considered daring, even

Photo: Frank and Mary Netter, c. 1933.

scandalous. Their first child, a healthy baby girl, had the same dark eyes as Frank, and they gave her the name Cornelia Ann, after Mary's maternal grandmother. Early photos of Frank and Mary together show the lovers with their bodies melded into one silhouette, both looking out at the camera. They were together, and their future as doctors and parents looked bright, even though the nation was in the depths of the Great Depression.

CHAPTER 4

MARY

MARY LOVED A GOOD joke. She would light up with a smile and let go with a contagious, hearty laugh that emanated from deep down in her belly. She enjoyed playing card games—canasta, hearts, or solitaire. And she read voraciously, often reclining on the sofa with a contemporary novel or a work of nonfiction.

She always wore a dress, never pants. She did not wear jewelry—not a wedding ring or wristwatch. Her meager supply of makeup she bought at the drugstore—coral red lipstick, which she said was a color that looked good on everyone, a pressed-powder compact, and a little red box of brown mascara.

Frank made a picture of her—just a small pastel—in which she is reposed naked and reading a book. He signed it in cursive script: "Frank H. Netter." Another picture, a portrait of her he painted in oils, done in predominantly dark blues, has a formal, solemn feeling; but there is a softness to her mouth and the delicate detail of her floral chiffon blouse. He signed it in block letters: "Frank H. Netter '32." He used Mary as a model many times in his medical pictures. If he had had a muse, it would have been she.

❦❦❦❦❦❦

Mary was one of nine siblings—four boys: Oscar Lee; Aubrey; Bernice (Ber′-nis), whom everyone called Doodle; and Jack, all older than Mary; an older sister, Katie, who adored Mary; and three younger sisters: Ella; Irene, whom everyone called "Renie";[1] and Evelyn, the baby of the family.

Most of their maternal ancestors had settled in coastal North Carolina before the American Revolution.[2] The McFadyens, in comparison with the other branches of the family, were relative newcomers, Angus MacFadyen having arrived in Wilmington, North Carolina, from Scotland in 1818.[3] Prior to the Civil War, Angus's son, Duncan, Mary's grandfather, had been a ferryboat captain on the Cape Fear River, which empties into the Atlantic Ocean with its treacherous shoals in the waters off the coast of southeastern North Carolina.[4] When the Union navy sought to halt the trade in and out of Southern ports, Duncan made and lost a small fortune as a blockade runner. He loaded his steamship with bales of cotton and, like a ghost in the fog, maneuvered past the Union gunboats plying the coast and set course for Bermuda or Nassau, where he traded for supplies needed by the Confederacy. He then turned his ship back toward Wilmington and, in the dark of night, slipped past the Union vessels and made a run for the inlet to the Cape Fear River, which Confederate cannon protected. Blockade running was a lucrative, albeit dangerous, business that lasted until 1865, when Wilmington fell to the Union.

Mary's maternal grandfather, Samuel Musgrave,[5] was a private in the 3rd Cavalry Regiment North Carolina.[6] He rode his horse into battles in North Carolina and Virginia, as well as in Pennsylvania at the horror of Gettysburg. Samuel was captured on December 17, 1863, and confined for 14 miserable months at the notorious Union prison at Point Lookout, Maryland. He returned to eastern North Carolina after the war and married Cornelia Ann Robbins.

Mary's parents, Oscar McFadyen and Katie Musgrave, married in the spring of 1890. Oscar worked for Metropolitan Life Insurance Company, opening offices in Portsmouth, Virginia, and Charleston, South Carolina, and by 1900 in Fayetteville, North Carolina, where Mary was born in 1905. In 1910, the family moved for the last time, to Greensboro, North Carolina.

⚘✿⚘✿⚘✿⚘

The McFadyen family home on West Lee Street in Greensboro has long since been demolished and the property given over to commercial use. The Victorian-style house was without central heat, and the winter cold permeated the upstairs bedrooms. On Christmas mornings, the perfume of oranges filled the parlor from the fresh fruit in the toe of each child's stocking.[7] In the oppressively hot North Carolina summers, the family would travel to Wrightsville Beach, near Wilmington, to splash in the ocean.

The McFadyens lived hand-to-mouth, as did all their friends and neighbors,[8] and made their own fun, laughing and joking together. Southern Baptist values—no drinking, no dancing, and no card-playing—dominated the culture. Mary played solitaire with a miniature deck of cards, which her mother explained was not a real deck of cards but just a toy.[9] Family photos of Mary and her sisters show Katie lovely and demure, Mary standing to one side, a pensive expression on her face, and Renie making a curtsey.

Sister Katie would take Mary shopping and teach her things and say how smart and what a good student she was. In 1917, when the soldiers went off to war, Doodle went with them. He was tall, barely 17, but he told the army that he was 18, and the army took him in. Mary was 12 years old and went with her mother and sister Katie to see Doodle off at the train station in Greensboro. Some of those boys had never before been away from home, never before seen the ocean they would cross—and some were never to return.

ତ⟡ତ⟡ତ⟡ତ

Mary was the only one among her sisters to attend college. To pay her way through school, she worked during school vacations as a typist in the billing office of the telephone company. She earned $11 a week, eventually getting a raise to $18 a week.[10] The old catalogs from the North Carolina College for Women[11] in Greensboro show that Mary attended for two years, 1921 through 1923.[12] She left Greensboro in the fall of 1923 to study at George Washington University, in Washington, D.C. Her

Photo: Mary McFadyen, age 16, North Carolina, 1921.

brother Aubrey worked in the patent office[13] in that city, and he might have encouraged her to come there, to earn the bachelor of arts degree.[14]

Her brother Oscar was a physician[15] practicing in Fayetteville, North Carolina,[16] and it was he who urged Mary to study medicine in Chapel Hill.[17] She began her medical studies at the School of Medicine at the University of North Carolina (UNC)[18] and roomed with the other women graduate students in the residence hall on Franklin Street. Every day, she walked past the specimen trees in the Coker Arboretum and across Cameron Avenue to Caldwell Hall, then the home of medical laboratories, classrooms, and library facilities.

The medical curriculum at UNC[19] was a two-year preclinical program, offering basic science training. Anatomy instruction in the dissection laboratories and the science curriculum provided a solid foundation for the students to go on to clinical work elsewhere. Yet without the advantage of a nearby hospital, patient contact was minimal if not nonexistent. In that respect, Mary's first two years of training were different from those of the medical students at NYU, who were introduced to patient care early on.

Mary generally had fond memories of her days on the campus of UNC, although the undergraduate school was not coeducational, and there were few women students in the graduate school. In her medical school class of 33, 2 were women. She recalled her first day in medical school, when a professor had looked straight at her and announced that nobody gets by on a pretty face. She often told that story and how she went on to get the highest marks in the class.[20]

After she completed the program at UNC, Mary transferred to NYU, where, of course, she met Frank. During her college years she wavered on the spelling of her surname,[21] adding the *a* to McFadyen, changing it to the historical spelling, *MacFadyen*,[22] then reverting to the previous spelling.[23] But at NYU[24] and forever after, it was *MacFadyen*.

As an intern on the wards of Bellevue, Mary met bias not only from colleagues but also from patients, who tended to address her as "nurse." She remembered one patient in particular who was in terrible pain with a fracture, and he asked her to send the doctor. But she hooked up the pulleys and put him in traction, which relieved his pain, and after that he addressed her as "doctor."[25]

One of the Bellevue ambulance drivers delighted in driving erratically at high speed, just to scare the doctor riding in the back, especially when the doctor was a woman. He would turn on the siren and weave in and out among the El supports, and the top-heavy vehicle would sway to and fro. One ambulance had over-turned, killing the doctor who had been riding along. As frightened as Mary might have been, she never flinched but hung on to the strap, stared straight ahead and never said a word about the driver's maneuvering, lest he do it all the more.[26]

When Mary finished her internship in medicine and surgery at Bellevue, she went to work for the New York City Department of Health. They paid her $35 a week, which at the time she thought was a fortune.[27] In that capacity, she treated women and children—mothers with infants, children in the schools, and women in the jail. She saw a wide range of cases and treated everything from venereal disease in prostitutes to poliomyelitis in schoolchildren.[28] When she became a clinical assistant at Woman's Hospital on 110th Street and Amsterdam Avenue[29] in 1934, she had an office around the corner on 110th Street.[30] She joined the New York County Medical Society, the Medical Society of the State of New York, and the American Medical Association.

☙❧☙❧☙❧

Thirteen months after Cornelia was born, Mary gave birth to the Netters' second child, a son; they called him Frankie. He was perfectly formed, a beautiful baby. Mary was, of course, knowledgeable about every stage of infant and child development. "No teeth at six months, six teeth at twelve months, twelve teeth at eighteen months," she would repeat in singsong fashion. When it came to caring for her own baby, Mary followed the advice of the experts of the time—don't pick up the baby when he cries, feed only on a schedule, and bottle feeding is best because it is scientific.

She busied herself with her career and hired caregivers for her children. In their training, doctors were admonished to leave the nursing to the nurses. Doctors gave the orders and acted with authority. And for women doctors, the rule was to provide more than good doctoring. It meant their professional survival. Nurses nurtured; doctors gave orders. And that posture spilled over into Mary's mothering. She let the caregivers do the bathing and dressing and feeding of her children, and she gave the orders. "Don't leave them alone" was her primary instruction.

CHAPTER 5

THE ART OF MEDICINE

I N 1933, FRANK JOINED the staff of The Mount Sinai Hospital as a clinical assistant on the surgical service of the outpatient department.[1] Mount Sinai was the premier Jewish hospital, and young doctors in those days were first appointed to the outpatient staff.[2] The talented Max Som, Frank's fraternity brother from NYU, had done his internship at Mount Sinai, finished a residency in otolaryngology, and in 1933, in an unusually rapid advancement, joined the inpatient staff as an adjunct laryngologist. It was at the clinic that Frank first met Joseph A. Gaines, who, like Max, had been on the house staff as an intern from 1930 to 1933. Joe was a clinical assistant for gynecology in the outpatient department; Isidor C. Rubin, who would go on to pioneer a diagnostic procedure to test for occlusion of the fallopian tubes, was at that time on the senior staff in the department of gynecology. Frank also met Samuel Klein at Mount Sinai. Sam, like Frank, was assigned to the surgical service of the outpatient department but was two years ahead of Frank. Another colleague was Arthur Sohval, an endocrinologist five years Frank's senior, who came to Mount Sinai in 1929 after completing his training at Columbia's College of Physicians and Surgeons.[3] Among those assiduous young doctors, each destined to become a leader in his chosen specialty, friendships developed and thrived.

Frank worked in the clinic on Monday, Wednesday, and Friday mornings and the other times at a medical office on Park Avenue near 53rd Street that he shared with Dr. Edward M. Livingston, who was on the surgery faculty at NYU, which is how Frank came to know him.[4] But few patients came to the office asking to see young Dr. Netter. He might have had an occasional referral for a house call, but generally he saw patients in the surgery clinic at Mount Sinai.

One day a patient, or rather the father of a patient, did come into his office asking for a doctor. He begged Frank to come on a house call to see his little boy.[5] The apartment building where the man lived was at a fancy address on Park Avenue. Frank went up the elevator to the apartment and found the child lying in a dark room. He was sick and had a tender abdomen. Turn on the lights, Frank asked. Please turn on the lights so I can see, he asked again. But the father stood motionless, a silhouette in the dark room. I am sorry, the father finally said, they turned off our electricity. So they took the boy to the hospital, where doctors removed his appendix and he survived. But here was a man living in a large apartment on Park Avenue who had no money to pay the electric bill, much less Frank's fee.

The Great Depression—it was the gravest economic debacle in modern history. Investors were ruined when the stock market crashed. Savings were wiped out when banks failed. Credit evaporated. Factory output fell 30%, and the unemployment level climbed to nearly 25%. Prices spiraled downward at 10% per year.[6] The money supply had so contracted that people hoarded what little money they had, if indeed they had any at all.

If people had money for doctors, they went not to the young man fresh out of school but to the older, established professors. Even well-known doctors had difficulty finding patients who could pay. Dr. Arthur H. Aufses, Sr., 10 years Frank's senior on the surgical staff at Mount Sinai, went out on a call in the middle of the night and returned in the morning with a 50-cent piece in his pocket.[7] It was all the patient had to give him. Times were hard for everyone. What few patients Frank had paid him what they could, sometimes with barter.

But word got around that Frank could make pictures. A doctor might ask him to make a picture for an article or a book, and someone else would see it and come asking for pictures. The pharmaceutical companies began coming to him for pictures to explain the function of the many new drugs they were developing, and they would pay him in cash. So Frank moonlighted, making pictures. He sold them, and that is what paid the rent and put food on the table. Art is very nice, his mother had said, but you cannot make a living at it. Be a doctor, she had said. When things get tough, you can fall back on medicine. In this case, when things got tough, Frank fell back on his art. But it was medical art.

Monroe Mayer knew Frank from their days together as students at CCNY. They ran into each other on the street one day in 1934, Monroe remembered, and they walked over to Frank's medical office. There were no patients in the office, but instead an easel and art supplies.[8] The sink where Frank was to wash his hands before examining patients was the sink where he washed his paintbrushes. As Frank later explained in his notes,

> Art was a temporary expediency just to tide me over. But I felt guilty spending so much time making pictures. I thought that I should be devoting my time to my medical practice. And I made up my mind that when the next advertising manager came asking for pictures I would charge an exorbitant fee, and he would go away and leave me to my surgery.
>
> Well, an advertising manager representing a large pharmaceutical company came to see me in my medical office and he wanted five pictures to illustrate the use of a new product. And he asked me how much I would charge for the pictures. I was getting about $50 for a picture at the time, which was a lot of money during the Depression. But I thought I really should not be doing this and decided to ask a ridiculous fee. I thought $300 per picture was more than enough to scare the guy away for good, so I said, "I will have to charge you $1500 for the pictures." Well, that was a very high price, he said, and he would have to get authorization for it . . . and [when he left] I was sure that I was done with art for good. But the next day he called me up and said that I should do the pictures and they would pay me $1500 for each of the five pictures. I was so shocked that I did not correct him.[9]

The economic comparative advantage of his medical art to his medical practice thus made itself clear. Medical art and the illustration of medical function, anatomy, and concepts was far more lucrative for him than his surgery practice. Frank took classes at the Art Students League in its beautiful facilities on West 57th Street. He paid the class dues of $12, and in December 1933 he took a course on lithography with George Alexander Picken.[10] Picken was still a young man then, but he became known not only as a painter of both figures and of the American scene but also for his knowledge of printmaking and graphic arts.

The demand for Frank's sable brush grew faster than the demand for his scalpel. Making pictures began to take his full attention, and in May of 1934 he resigned from Mount Sinai to devote himself full time to making pictures. Over the course of his long career as a medical illustrator, Frank would reach far more patients and help more people than he ever could have hoped to help as a surgeon. But Frank did not know that then. He only knew that he had an opportunity to earn a living.

⌖⌖⌖⌖⌖⌖

By the second half of the 1930s, pharmaceutical companies were beginning to develop some wonderful new drugs, and they asked Frank to make both educational and promotional materials to promote their products. One of the projects Frank illustrated was a booklet on Novocain[11] put out in 1936 by the Winthrop Chemical Company. It was a mere 43 pages but included 64 of Frank's pictures, signed "F. Netter, M.D."

In 1937, the Ciba Company approached Frank with the idea to create a flyer to send to doctors to advertise their new heart medicine, Digifoline, a digitalis preparation. It would be a small folder die-cut in the shape of the heart. The front cover of the flyer would be a picture of the front of the heart, and the back cover, a picture of the back of the heart. Inside would be pictures of the cross section of the heart with the advertising copy overprinted. For that flyer, Frank created four pictures: the front of the heart, the back of the heart, and two cross sections of the heart, as if sliced through and folded open. On the left-hand inside page, he added the flourish of a foxglove flower, from which digitalis is extracted. Frank's signature did not appear on those pictures.

Ciba sent this flyer out to doctors, and it received a positive response. Some doctors even wrote to Ciba saying how much they liked the heart flyer and could they please have some more of them, but without the writing all over it. So Ciba came out with a new format. Using more pictures that Frank painted, Ciba printed a larger flyer of the heart with the text printed off to the side of the pictures. The picture on the cover of this new flyer bore the artist's signature, and on the inside there was a cross section of the inside of the heart beside text excerpted from *Cunningham's Textbook of Anatomy*[12] describing the anatomy of the heart. The product information for Digifoline appeared on the back of the flyer, to the side of the picture of the back of the heart. That flyer too was well received by the doctors.

The success of the heart flyer gave the advertising managers at Ciba the idea to create flyers targeting other organs, corresponding with medications from Ciba. The stomach flyer excerpted text from *Gray's Anatomy*[13] describing the anatomy of the stomach structure, muscular coat, nerves, and pyloric valve, and on the back, product information for Trasentin, Ciba's trademark name for their antispasmodic. The picture on the inside of the flyer now bore the "F. Netter, M.D." signature. The kidney flyer, with Frank's signature on the inside, had text on the anatomy of the kidney taken from *Cunningham's Textbook of Anatomy*. The product literature, for Esidrone, a mercurial diuretic, was printed on a fold-down flap, so that when the flyer was opened the flap folded down to reveal more of the cross section of the kidney, along with Frank's paintings of microscopic sections of the medulla and cortex. Frank's signature appeared on the front of the lungs flyer, promoting Ciba's Coramine, a respiratory and circulatory stimulant. It too had the fold-down section for the product literature.

Armour Laboratories in Chicago was another of Frank's notable patrons. To promote their epinephrine preparation,[14] Armour came out with an educational pamphlet in 1938 using Frank's pictures, which he signed with an early version of what would become his distinctive "F. Netter, M.D." signature. The next year Armour published a softcover 64-page booklet on hematology,[15] giving credit on page 2: "Illustrated by Frank H. Netter, M.D." The booklet was primarily educational material; only a few pages in the back were devoted to product descriptions of Armour's liver extract preparations. Thirty years later, Frank would say of that small atlas, "It is pretty much out of date as there has been much progress in the field since I did it. Nevertheless, much of the material therein is still correct even tho [sic] we now know much more about these things."[16]

After the hematology project, Frank made pictures for two hardcover educational booklets that Armour printed, one on the pituitary[17] and one on the thyroid.[18] Armour also began to use his pictures in product advertisements, which appeared in various medical journals. In a letter that Fred Bradley of *Modern Medicine* magazine later wrote to Jim Weber at Armour, he stated that those ads were some of the most effective that Armour ever ran, and he recommended that Jim buy a beer for whoever was responsible.[19]

ᘓ᚜ᕗᘓᕗᘓᕗᕜ

As Frank's career blossomed, Mary continued to work at her medical practice. She also set up her typewriter in a small office at home and wrote a book on beauty and health. Her book, *Beauty Plus*,[20] first appeared in 1938. It included exercise routines and recipes for beauty creams. While she never exercised herself, she knew what should be done. "Do as I say, not as I do" was her philosophy. Frank provided illustrations for the book, stylized line drawings more reminiscent of the cartoons he did for the CCNY *Mercury* comic than of his better known medical pictures. The *Journal of the*

American Medical Association (JAMA), among others, gave the book a positive review.[21]

A few weeks after her book came out in 1938, Mary gave birth to their third child, a healthy baby boy. He was a curious, athletic, and cute little tyke, and she named him James Musgrave Netter after her mother's family, though he was often called Jim or Jimmy. Mary was at her typewriter soon afterward, writing a syndicated newspaper column on women's health and beauty issues. Jones Syndicate distributed her columns for publication in the *Miami Herald*, the *Philadelphia Evening Bulletin*, *The Cleveland Press*, and others, on topics such as diet and exercise,[22] thyroid pills,[23] ugly unwanted hair,[24] the benefits of laughter, and good health for lovely eyes.[25] Frank made illustrations for *A Doctor Talks of Beauty*,[26] a comic-strip format of Mary's column. Mary's writing might have reminded him of when his mother used to write for newspapers.

Frank and Mary stepped into the fast-moving New York art world, into the Society of Illustrators and the Salmagundi Club, and the haunts of the artists in the 1930s. The Salmagundi Club, which Frank joined as an artist member in 1939,[27] is housed, as it has been since 1917, in an elegant brownstone on Fifth Avenue, just north of Washington Square. That same year, Frank was elected to artist membership[28] in the Society of Illustrators, which had just moved its clubhouse into a nineteenth-century carriage house on East 63rd Street, where Norman Rockwell's original painting *Dover Coach*[29] hung over the clubhouse bar on the fourth floor. Membership in these clubs opened the door to art exhibitions and sales, painting demonstrations and classes, an extensive art library, and a social life in both the bohemian and traditional art circles.

In the dining rooms and parlors of those clubs, Frank began to rub shoulders with the successful painters, sculptors, illustrators, and cartoonists of the day, and he began to collect the art they created. Cartoonist Denys Wortman, who was president of the Society of Illustrators from 1936 to 1938 and a National Academician, was known for his Depression-era depictions published in the *New York World-Telegram*. He was succeeded by Harold von

Schmidt, whose work appeared in *Collier's Weekly*, *Cosmopolitan*, *Liberty*, *The Saturday Evening Post*, and *Sunset*. Von Schmidt also made 60 illustrations for Willa Cather's book, *Death Comes for the Archbishop*.[30]

John Richard Flanagan was a member of the Society of Illustrators and a National Academician. He was a superb pen-and-ink artist who advocated learning everything about art, and he likened drawing to a golf stroke that must all come together in one smooth movement.[31] "You must practice. You must train yourself," Frank recalled Flanagan saying.

> You must learn perspective, anatomy, proportion, light and shade, and color—everything. But when it comes to making a drawing, you cannot think of all those things. The paper is now in front of you and you must make that drawing. It must flow smoothly from you. If it does not, if your training has not been adequate, if you must stop when you make a drawing to think of all the principles and rules of art you are going to get so confused that you are going to end up with a mess.[32]

Rube Goldberg, whose cartoons Frank had admired when he was a youngster, was now one of Frank's friends from the Society of Illustrators. Rube's name became synonymous with madcap gadgets and absurd roundabout systems to accomplish simple tasks. He gave Frank a silly thing, an unusual sculpture: a bronze head looking up at a martini glass. Otto Soglow, who drew the comic *The Little King*, was also among Frank's many friends from the Society of Illustrators, as was E. Simms Campbell, the pioneering African American cartoonist who broke the color barrier with his *Cuties* series that appeared in *Esquire*, *The New Yorker*, and later in *Playboy*. It was at one of those parties, Mary recalled, that Simms told her he was "like a blueberry in a bowl of milk."[33]

"I reveled that they accepted me [as their peer]," Frank later recalled. "A group of us were having lunch [at the Society of Illustrators] one day, and another artist said to Norman [Rockwell],

'Norman, you are too good to be painting these [*Post*] covers; you should be painting for posterity.' And I will never forget what Norman said then. He said, 'I will take my glory in cash. Let posterity take care of itself.'"[34]

Many of these artists created their own Christmas cards. They would make a picture and have the card printed to send out to friends and relatives. Some were nice pictures, some were amusing cartoons, and some were quite irreverent. Simms Campbell, who had moved to Switzerland, sent one with a beautiful winter scape of the snow-capped Alps, and Rube Goldberg sent one that had a cartoon of a dozen or so sidewalk Santas waiting in line to use a urinal, with the caption "Line up for a Merry Christmas." Frank too took to making quick cartoon-like pictures for Christmas cards—mostly black-and-white pictures on card stock, with just a little red and green for accent Every year the picture told a different story about what the Netters were doing, where they lived, and what their big news was for the year.

At the Society of Illustrators shows, members staged burlesque revues featuring the artists and their models, combined with the hot jazz of such luminaries as Harlem's Cotton Club Band and the ragtime piano and outrageous slapstick comedy of Jimmy Durante. The artists' models performed in the shows and would have appeared bare-breasted except for laws prohibiting nudity. Instead, just over their nipples they wore pasties with tassels that flung every which way when they moved, producing a result more sexually provocative than nudity itself.

Frank and Mary liked to go to the Havana Madrid nightclub, with its dancing and Latin flavor, more subdued than the wild Society of Illustrators parties, and they often invited Frank's brother and sister-in-law, George and Gertie, to join them.[35]

Those were the wild days of rowdy parties and nightclubs. Here at last was the life of hard drinking and nude models against which his mother had warned him. But he was not starving, and he was not living in a cold garret. He was living in a large apartment on Fifth Avenue,[36] overlooking Central Park.

Photo: Mary and Frank Netter, c. 1938.

East River, *Frank H. Netter, oil on canvas, 1930, from the collection of Francine Mary Netter.*

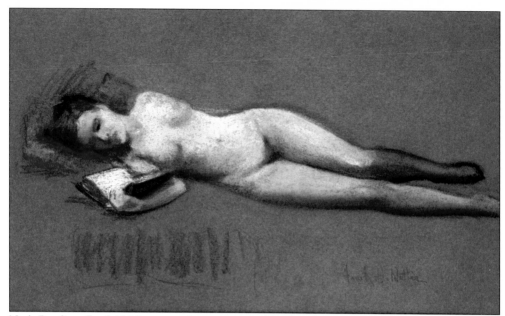

Nude Reading, *Frank H. Netter, pastel on paper, 1934, from the collection of Francine Mary Netter.*

F.NETTER

Girl with Pen, *ceramic glazes on tile, c. 1940, courtesy of the Museum of American Illustration at the Society of Illustrators.*

Mary, *Frank H. Netter, oil on canvas, 1934, from the collection of Francine Mary Netter.*

Dellie, *Frank H. Netter, oil on canvas, 1932, from the collection of Adele Netter Bendes.*

The Netter Children, *Frank H. Netter, oil on canvas, 1942, from the collection of James Netter.*

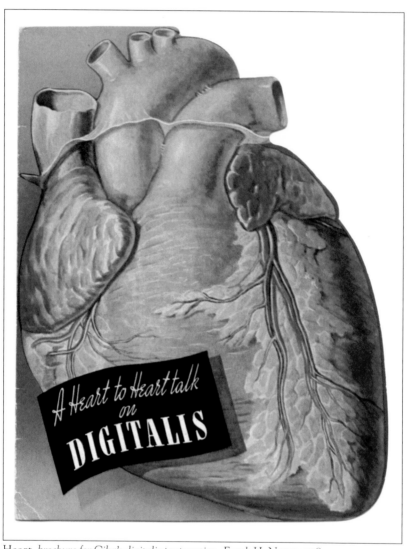

Heart, *brochure for Ciba's digitalis preparation, Frank H. Netter, 1938.*

CHAPTER 6

TRANSPARENT WOMAN

THE BAY BRIDGE, CONNECTING San Francisco with Oakland, opened in November 1936. Actually a connected roadway, it consists of one bridge on the west side between San Francisco and Yerba Buena Island, a tunnel through Yerba Buena Island, and a bridge to Oakland on the east side. The following year, in May 1937, the Golden Gate Bridge opened. It was then the longest suspension bridge in the world, connecting the northern tip of San Francisco with Marin County and with access points north to Napa and Sonoma Counties. To celebrate the completion of these two remarkable feats of engineering, the city of San Francisco and environs hosted the Golden Gate International Exposition in 1939 and 1940, an event rivaling the 1939 World's Fair in New York.

The Schering Corporation asked Frank to work on an exhibit for the exposition. Schering was developing endocrine medications and was first to commercially manufacture testosterone.[1] To showcase their work in the new field of hormones, they wanted an exhibit that would illustrate how the endocrine glands control the reproductive functions in women, including puberty, menstruation, and pregnancy. They asked Frank to come up with an idea of how best to tell the story. The one caveat was that the time for the audience to walk through and see the exhibit must be no more than 15 minutes. It would take that much time just to look at anatomical pictures of all the glands and read the descriptions of their functions—not a very interesting exhibit.

Then Frank learned of a new material just introduced in the United States by the Rohm and Haas Chemical Company, a product they called Plexiglas. "I finally decided that the only way to do it was to make a large transparent figure of a woman, showing the glands in place and through successive illuminations and flow lines, the changes they effected in the various organs, i.e., the lining of the uterus, the breasts, menstruation, pregnancy, and growth of the baby from conception to full term."[2] Frank's concept was to make pictures, paintings that would be projected onto the internal structure of the figure.

Frank made a storyboard, a series of pictures showing what would be seen at each illumination. He also had the idea to use a synchronized recording, giving the woman a voice that would tell the story of what was happening. As the pictures were illuminated, she would explain what was going on inside her body. She would tell about the hormones and how her body was changing, as shown in the successive illuminations. At a time when women generally knew, or were thought to know, relatively little about their own bodies, it was daring, if not shocking, that a woman's voice would tell the story of what was happening inside the figure.

When Frank presented the storyboard to the Schering people, they loved the idea and authorized him to proceed. Frank rented a loft in which to work and hired an assistant, Arthur Sipkin, whom Frank described as "a very dedicated and intelligent boy . . . who became my devoted right hand in the project."[3] And they began to create the *Transparent Woman*.

"Making the transparent figure was not too great a problem," Frank recalled in his notes. "I had studied sculpture along with drawing in art school, so I molded the figure in clay and then had it cast in plaster."[4] The Rohm and Haas representative told Frank that if he heated the Plexiglas, the material would soften and he would be able to mold the sheets over the plaster figure. "We set up a battery of gas burners," Frank remembered, "and held the sheets of Plexiglas over them until they were suitably soft, and then pressed and formed them over the plaster mold. And after 2 or 3 attempts we got good results."[5]

There were more than eight sections of Plexiglas that they formed in this manner—the head, the body, the arms, legs, hands, and feet—which Frank tinted lightly to give a more lifelike appearance. The next step was to make the various internal structures and organs in the same manner—clay, plaster cast, and Plexiglas. Frank and Arthur then glued all of these parts together to form the finished sculpture. "She turned out to be a really beautiful 8' tall girl,"[6] Frank recalled.

Next came the hard part, creating the successive illuminations that would show the flow of the endocrine hormones and the resulting changes in the organs—changes in the breasts and the lining of the uterus—and the growth of the baby. Frank figured that his pictures of the changing structures could be projected into the figure in proper sequence to tell the story, and he designed a system using mirrors to project the pictures into the figure from below. Frank made all the pictures to be projected, but he knew he needed help with automating the projectors, sequencing the lighting, and synchronizing the voice.

Tony Sarg was one of Frank's friends from the Society of Illustrators and the Salmagundi Club. He was an artist who did covers for *The Saturday Evening Post* but who was best known for his creations of animated window displays for Macy's and the early balloons for Macy's Thanksgiving Day Parade. Frank went to see Tony at his Times Square studio and asked his advice on how to engineer a solution to the sequencing problem. Tony knew immediately who could help, someone whom he called a projection and illumination engineer. He had helped Tony many times, and Tony was sure he could solve Frank's problem.

Frank rushed right over to see this man and showed him the sketches. After hearing Frank's explanation, he said that he certainly could work it all out. He would need Frank to send him the figure and all the sketches, and the storyboard showing the sequencing—all the work Frank had done—and he would do it. "I did that and went away happy as a lark—all my problems had been lifted off me. I was confident that I would soon have the workings for the projection and synchronized voice, and all I would have to do was plug her in."[7]

ᙏᙅᙏᙅᙏᙅ

Time was fast approaching to deliver the *Transparent Woman* to Schering. Four or five weeks had passed, and Frank had not heard from the projection engineer. He began to get a little worried and called the engineer on the phone to inquire when his figure would be ready. Almost done, he assured Frank. He would have it finished in another week. Sure enough, in a week he called to say he was done, and Frank rushed downtown to see it.

The projection engineer "pulled a pile of papers and blue prints out from a cabinet . . . and dumped it on his desk," Frank recalled. "'Here it is!' he said, 'all worked out in minute detail.'"[8] But the figure! Frank wanted to see the figure! "'Oh, we don't do that. We don't do the mechanical work. We just give all the specifications.' I felt like dying right there," Frank recalled. "I felt my heart drop down to my feet. It was like the end of the world for me."[9] The figure stood covered in dust in a closet in the back room. All Frank could do was gather the papers together and arrange to have his sculpture shipped back to his loft.

Frank and Arthur studied the drawings and pored over the specifications and notes. The notes included information as to where to get the projectors and parts, and the name of a company to supply the voice recording and the synchronization so the story would run from start to finish and make sense. Working day and night, they began to implement the mechanics themselves and got the figure working.

"It was beautiful and very effective," recalled Frank. "It really told the story. You would actually believe that that baby was growing inside of her."[10] As she spoke about her body and the changes taking place, the projected elements lit up in perfect sequence. The tinting of her skin hid the mechanical parts completely. Frank did not give her a name; she was always the *Transparent Woman*, although he did on occasion refer to her as his girlfriend.[11]

ᙏᙅᙏᙅᙏᙅ

Photo: Frank Netter with Transparent Woman *sculpture, 1938.*

The Schering people came to the loft to see her and were delighted. They insisted on having a New York showing, since the Schering corporate offices were in New York and they wanted the New York press to see her before she was shipped to California. There was not much time before the fair opened, but they arranged for a party in the ballroom of the old Vanderbilt Hotel, located on Park Avenue at 34th Street and one of the most exclusive residential hotels in New York.

They shipped the figure to the Vanderbilt and had just enough time to plug her into the electrical outlet before the event got underway. Schering executives and several members of the press attended the big party for the preview showing. Mary was there, and Frank had invited many of his artist friends as well, including Alice Caddy, who was there with her author husband, Ben Lucien Burman, for whose books she had made many illustrations. Ben was the author of *Steamboat Round the Bend*,[12] which had been made into the 1935 Will Rogers movie of the same name,[13] and of *Blow for a Landing*,[14] which received the Southern Authors Prize of 1938.[15]

Everybody was dressed up, drinking cocktails and talking. Frank was walking around, welcoming people, accepting their congratulations, when Arthur Sipkin came rushing over to him. "She won't work!" he whispered. "She won't work. They have direct current here. The lights will go on and the voice will play but the motors that run the switches will not work."[16] This once-fashionable hotel, built in 1912, was one of the last bastions of direct current in New York, a holdover from an earlier time when Edison Electric used direct current for power transmission. As the president of Schering Corporation, Dr. Julius Weltzien,[17] rose to talk at the podium, Frank slipped behind the curtain and climbed under the platform where his *Transparent Woman* statue stood waiting for her debut.

When the curtain opened, Frank was on the floor hidden under the figure, and as her recorded voice described endocrine functions, he pressed each switch to project the picture corresponding with what she was saying. At the end of those interminable 15 minutes, as he lay in those hot, dusty confines, he heard the audience's enthusiastic applause and cheers. Ben Burman, always an advocate of authors' and artists' rights, started calling, "Author, author! Creator, creator!"[18] Soon the entire audience was calling for him. Covered in grease and sweat, Frank came around front, took his bows and said a few words, albeit nothing about his ordeal on the floor.

Frank said goodbye to the *Transparent Woman*, and she was shipped to San Francisco in time for the opening of the Golden Gate International Exposition, where she had a baby every 15 minutes and received rave reviews. The reviewer of the exposition for *Ladies' Home Journal* said that she was the most popular exhibit there.[19] Another said that at nearly every show, a woman in the audience fainted, so they knew it was a hit with the crowd.[20] The *Transparent Woman* attracted audiences at the fair for the full two years, and after the close of the exposition, she went to Chicago's Museum of Science and Industry and continued having babies to a rather advanced age.

CHAPTER 7

WORLD WAR II

I N THE SUMMER OF 1940, the Netters moved from their Fifth Avenue apartment to a townhouse on East 80th Street.[1] Mary set about decorating their new house, but she knew nothing about furniture styles. "Early Ignorant" had been her decorating style, she said.[2] She frequented the antique shops along Third Avenue, buying furniture that she arranged and rearranged in their new home, and she learned about French period decor.

On the ground floor of the house there was a big bathroom for guests—the powder room. "On the walls," remembered Frank's cousin Richard, "he [Frank] had painted a fence, all around the room. It was so real looking that if you put out your hand to touch it, you were afraid you might get a splinter. And then, he painted people, at least 50 people, all peering over the fence, looking in the direction of the toilet, pointing at the toilet and laughing. I mean, if you sat on the toilet, you would get so embarrassed. It was the funniest thing."[3]

Frank and Mary had a lot of crazy stories about when they lived in that townhouse, Richard recalled. For instance, once Frank was expecting some physicians from the University of Pennsylvania to come for a conference about some pictures—medical illustrations—he was making. The men came to the door, and Frank invited them in, and they went upstairs to the living room. Frank offered them drinks, which they drank, and then they all had another as well. Frank finally asked which one of them was the medical professor. What professor? they said. It turned out that these men were selling magazines, and here was Frank entertaining them.

In 1942, Frank painted a picture of his three children, Cornelia (8) holding a doll and Jim (3) on a hobbyhorse, the two of them with their two heads together in uproarious laughter, while

Frankie (7) sat beside them, playing alone with a toy xylophone, his facial expression flat. Something was the matter with Frankie, Mary knew. He did not talk. He did not respond to her. Instead of looking at her, he looked through her. She did not know what it was, but she knew something was not right.[4] She took him to the best specialists—pediatricians, audiologists, neurologists. The description of Frankie's behavior is consistent with the definition of autism, although that disorder was then as yet undefined.[5] Mary sobbed, but as there was then a stigma associated with mental handicaps, they took Frankie to Letchworth Village in Rockland County, New York, to live out his days in an institution. But at home, Frank's painting of the three children hung in the living room over the mantle.

༺⚮⚬⚭⚮⚬⚭⚮༻

After the Japanese attacked Pearl Harbor in 1941, there was a great swell of patriotism in the United States. In New York some women who volunteered for the Red Cross would set up a table on the sidewalk on the corner of Lexington Avenue and 80th Street and would ring the bell and ask if 4-year-old Jimmy could come out and join them. He was just a little thing but cute and outgoing, and he was most effective in encouraging people to give money to the Red Cross.

And all across the country men lined up to enlist in the armed forces, or they were drafted;[6] Frank volunteered for the army, and after he was assigned to the Army Medical Museum on the National Mall, in Washington, D.C., the family moved to a rented house in Georgetown. Mary continued writing her newspaper column about women's beauty,[7] and was also commuting to New York to wind down her medical practice. But she was pregnant again, with no one to be with the children during her confinement. So Cornelia and Jimmy boarded at the Sunny Hills School,[8] located on a farm outside Wilmington, Delaware. The school had fewer than 100 students, many from military families, in grades kindergarten through high school, and taught the basic subjects—reading, writing, arithmetic, social studies, music, and art. When Frank visited the school, he saw an art display by the young art teacher whose work had a fresh quality that Frank admired.

ᘒᘒᘒ

The colonel in charge of the Army Medical Museum[9] was a pathologist named James E. Ash, and it was he who had convinced Frank to enlist and had arranged for Frank to be assigned to his organization.[10] Colonel Ash was a full colonel, short in stature, with a small white mustache, a little peculiar, as Frank recalled, but a fine pathologist.[11]

He led Frank up to the top floor of the building to a large, light, airy studio. The supplies Frank had requested were all there—the paints, brushes, sketch paper, pencils, and drawing board. Then the colonel left Frank alone in the studio, without telling him what was needed or giving him an assignment or saying what he was to do. Every morning Frank reported to the studio by 8:00 AM, and every day he stayed at the studio until 5:00 PM. He sat in the studio, read the paper, sat in the studio, and made some sketches just for fun. If he left for any reason, he left word where he would be.

After several weeks of this boredom, Frank went to the colonel and asked for some work. The colonel said there was a great deal of work and that he would let Frank know, but for now he should be patient. Frank went back to what he called his solitary confinement and took to playing solitaire and reading murder mysteries.[12] Stories by Mary Roberts Rinehart were his favorites,[13] although he became well acquainted with Dashiell Hammett's Nick and Nora Charles, with Raymond Chandler's Philip Marlowe, and with Agatha Christie's Hercule Poirot. All around him, the country was at war, and here he was idling away the time reading mystery books in this studio on the National Mall.

One morning the colonel came to the studio with Lieutenant Nison Tregor, whom he said was assigned to Captain Netter as an assistant. Frank still did not have a project on which to work, but now at least he had company, someone with whom to play gin rummy. Nicky Tregor—Frank called him Nicky—was of Russian heritage, a sculptor, actually a fine sculptor whose patrons were the cream of Russian society. He knew everybody, it seemed, not only in Russian society but also in the diplomatic world. Some of Nicky's friends came to visit him in the studio—even Joseph E. Davies, the former ambassador to the Soviet Union and third husband of cereal heiress Marjorie Merriweather Post. Nicky frequently hosted parties where he invited these celebrities to the cocktail lounge of the Mayflower Hotel and usually invited Frank and Mary to come along. Nicky always called Frank "my captain," and he would click his heels together as he introduced "my captain" to his society friends. When time came to pay the bill for these parties, Nicky always found a way of passing it off on a wealthy friend.[14]

When Colonel Ash again came to the studio, he brought with him a sergeant, who was also to be assigned to assist Captain Netter, although there was still no work assignment. The sergeant was a photographer, and he took their pictures and set up a darkroom in an adjoining closet where he processed the film and made the prints.

It had been several months when Frank, exasperated, went to the colonel begging for work. Yes, the colonel said, he had some work for Frank and his team. It was an important project, he said, as he led Frank down, down, down to the basement. Here, in the cellar, were crates and crates of bones, human bones. These are the bones from the French and Indian War, he told Frank. No one had ever separated the gunshot wounds from the arrowhead wounds, and he wanted Frank and his staff to work on it. "I could hardly believe my ears," Frank recalled. "I looked at him to see if he was kidding me, but he was dead serious. I thought, 'Is this what I enlisted in the army for; is this the way I'm going to help my country win the war?[']"[15] The army was so big and the overall effort so tremendous that Frank had gotten lost in it.

ᘛᘚᘛᘚᘛᘚ

Every morning, down to the dungeon they went. Instead of being bored to death in a bright studio on the top floor, Frank and his team were confined to a dark basement with the bones of men who had died two centuries earlier. They could not tell who had died from an arrowhead wound and who from a gunshot, but they poked around and the sergeant took photographs of the bones.

One morning they were in the studio, preparing to go down to the basement, when the telephone rang. "We looked at each other in amazement, because in all the time we had been there, the telephone had never rung. In fact we didn't even know where it was," Frank recalled.[16] It rang and rang, and they rushed around trying to locate it, until finally they found it in a cupboard, and Frank answered.

Photo: Captain Frank Netter, 1942, courtesy of Ray Olivere.

"'Captain Netter, this is General Weible,' a voice on the other end said," Frank wrote in his notes. Lieutenant General Walter Leo Weible was the deputy director and subsequently the director of training for the Army Service Forces. "'I understand that you have special qualifications for a job I want done. I want you to come over here to the Pentagon to see me about it.'"

Frank met with General Weible in his office at the Pentagon and found him to be gracious and not at all stuffy. The general took out a thick paperbound book from his desk drawer and dropped it in a thud on the desk in front of him. "'That is the army first aid manual,' he said. 'It has 280 pages, tells what to do for chigger bites and snakebites, gives 20 different types of splints for a broken arm, none of which are available in the battlefield.'"[17] The book was woefully inadequate, oversized, and overly complicated. General Weible went on to explain that the army had only eight hours of classroom time in which to teach the first aid methods the soldiers needed. He wanted Frank to prepare a manual to teach recruits how to care for their wounds or those of their fellow soldiers—a booklet for use in the classroom that was also small enough to fit in the first aid kits taken into the field. It needed to be concise and above all, "something they can remember in the stress of battle."[18]

"I was excited about this," Frank recalled. "Now I had something real to work on—something useful and worthwhile."[19] He knew he could develop pictures to teach soldiers what to do if wounded in the field. He would make pictures of various injuries, and pictures of what to do for the injuries, and the soldiers would remember the images they saw. The text for each picture would need to be only brief. He went back to his studio and started work on the first aid manual, leaving the bones from the French and Indian War once again undisturbed in the basement of the Army Medical Museum.

Frank began to put together an outline. He already knew the purpose of the work and who the audience would be. He needed to brainstorm the content and organize it into easily understood and logical groups—what war injuries might a soldier sustain, under what combat conditions, and what first aid materials might be available to the soldier on the battlefield. "That is the first rule for making illustrations," Frank explained in his notes. "You must first learn your subject, know it thoroughly before you can illustrate it intelligently."[20]

He got hold of a directory and started calling army officers and going to see them and asking questions. He talked to officers in the medical corps, in the infantry, in the artillery units, and in the tank corps. Frank explained what he was doing and asked about the various combat wounds a soldier might suffer.

Few American officers had current combat experience, but the Russians had been engaged in the conflict on the Eastern Front and knew something about war wounds. Frank made an appointment to see some Russian officers who worked at the Russian embassy. He took Nicky along to the meeting, since he spoke Russian. The Russians asked a great many questions about the project, but they did not tell Frank much. Nicky, however, made friends with the Russians and got invited to some parties at the embassy.

In the staff car on the drive back to the studio, they drove by the executive mansion. "Nicky nudged me and said, 'My captain, that is the White House,'" Frank recalled in his notes. "'I have some friends there. Let's drop in.'"[21] Nicky told the driver to drive up to the gate, which he did, and Nicky got out and waved and gestured and talked to the guards, and then he got back in the car, and the guards opened the gate and they drove right in. "I was completely flabbergasted," Frank recalled.

> We drove up to the door of the White House. . . . Nicky jumped out and began talking and gesticulating to the guards there. Then they opened the car door and I stepped out. They opened the door of the White House, and I walked in, followed by Nicky. He ran over to some lackeys there and began . . . asking about how they and their children were. . . . Then he asked, "Is Mac in? I'd like to see Mac."
>
> "Oh, yes," they answered, "Mr. MacIntyre is right there in his office." ([Marvin] MacIntyre, you may recall, was President Roosevelt's secretary.) We walked over to MacIntyre's office. The door was open and we walked in.
>
> MacIntyre, a little, dried-up-looking man, was sitting at his big desk, and Nicky ran over and grabbed his hand and said, "Hello, Mac, how are you? I never see you around anymore. You are working too hard. Why don't you come out and have cocktails with us at the Mayflower—we'll have some fun. How is your beautiful wife?" He went on and on. MacIntyre didn't get a word in edgewise. Then Nicky said, by the way, Mac, is the boss in? I'd like to see the boss."
>
> "No." MacIntyre replied. "Mr. Roosevelt is away right now." That was fortunate . . . [or] we'd have been in talking to him. Finally I nudged Nicky and said . . . "I think we should leave now. . . ."

> We started out when MacIntyre called to us. [He was] sitting
> there tapping the back of his pencil on the desk. "By the way,
> Lieutenant, what did you say your name was?"
>
> Well, I nearly fainted. "Oh, I'm Nicky Tregor, your old
> friend, and this is my captain, Captain Netter."
>
> I walked out of the White House [and got in the car to go
> back to the studio] and said to Nicky, "Are you crazy—bluffing
> your way into the White House like that—in wartime, no less.
> We could be court-martialled."[22]

But the days passed without further incident, and Frank got on
with making the sketches for the first aid manual.

ᴑᴖᴑᴖᴑᴖᴑ

Frank analyzed and researched and learned about war wounds
and the assault situation. He learned about bullet wounds, shrap-
nel wounds, and grenade wounds, and the variations on those in
different parts of the body. Of course, on the front lines, under fire,
a soldier could just try to stop the bleeding and keep his head down.
It was different in the artillery unit, miles behind the lines. In the
end, Frank concluded that three underlying principles applied to
treating all types of wounds: stop the bleeding; protect the wound;
prevent shock.

He laid out a storyboard to show the soldier simply how to treat
wounds to the arm, leg, chest, abdomen, and jaw. First, it explained
how to stop the bleeding by applying pressure or elevating a limb or,
if necessary, with the use of a tourniquet. Every soldier was issued
a small wound kit that he carried on his belt and that contained
sulfa powder, a bandage, and sulfa tablets. The soldiers were to
sprinkle the antibacterial sulfa powder on the wound, cover it with
the bandage, and take the sulfa pills. Special instructions described
treating burns, broken bones, a broken back, and heat prostration.
Pictures on shock prevention showed how to position the wounded
to keep his head low and keep him warm.

Frank made sketches to tell the story and took them took over to the Pentagon to show General Weible, who liked them very much. They were just what he wanted, he said. Frank then explained that these were only the rough sketches and he still had to make the finished paintings. Oh, no! the general said. The army considers painting to be manual labor, and since officers do not do manual labor, you cannot make the finished pictures.

As he did not have a staff of enlisted men to do the painting, Frank told the general that he knew many artists in New York whom he could ask to do it, and General Weible authorized Frank to go to New York and commission the artists to make the paintings. But getting from Washington to New York in wartime was no easy feat. Driving was impractical, what with gasoline rationing, reduced speed limits and the brownout prohibiting the use of headlights.[23] There were some regularly scheduled commercial airline flights, and there was train service, such as it was, along the northeast corridor. Frank had no luck in securing an airline reservation for a flight to New York, and he resigned himself to a long, uncomfortable train ride.

He left Nicky in charge, telling him he was going to New York for a few days. "Oh, my captain," Nicky said when he found out that Frank was going by train, "you cannot go in a coach seat. I will get you either a Pullman seat or a plane ticket."[24] And Nicky ran off to see what he could do. No sooner had Frank packed the sketches into artist portfolios than Nicky had secured Frank a first-class seat on a plane to New York. He told Frank, "My captain, would you be good enough to send a dozen roses to Miss Raisa Williamson who got the reservation for you?"[25] And he gave Frank her address. Now Frank was indebted to Nicky for the reservation and Miss Williamson was indebted to him for the roses. In that way, Nicky built up a network of people on whom he could call for favors.

In New York, Frank took the portfolios to the Society of Illustrators, where he had no trouble finding artists to paint the pictures. There was a great swell of patriotism at that time. Harold von Schmidt had resigned as president to serve as an artist–war correspondent, but several of Frank's artist friends agreed to paint the pictures for a minimal fee or even donate their services. Frank left the sketches with them to paint and returned to Washington.

The package soon arrived from New York with the completed pictures. Some exceptional artists did the work, although the artwork was unsigned.[26] The army published the pictures both as

Combat First Aid, The Infantry Journal, 1944, *cover.*

large charts used for classroom instruction and in a 4″ × 6″ booklet issued to the soldiers. The completed booklet, entitled *Combat First Aid*,[27] was a mere 100 pages. Every two pages had a picture on one page and a brief explanatory text on the facing page. Instructors used the pictures as teaching aids in the classroom, and soldiers on the battlefield could remember what they had seen in the pictures.

❧❀❧❀❧

The army had discovered the value of pictures in teaching, and demand for Frank's pictures grew quickly. Placed in charge of Graphic Training Aids for the Medical Department of the Army, Frank planned and sketched the pictures and recruited a staff of enlisted men who could paint the pictures.

He remembered the artwork he had seen at Sunny Hills School and called the headmistress, Ellen Sawin, to ask about the young art teacher, Ray Olivere. As a youngster Ray had attended the Wilmington Academy of Art under the tutelage of Frank Schoonover and N.C. Wyeth.[28] He had recently been drafted, Mrs. Sawin told Frank, and was at Camp Davis in southeastern North Carolina.

Frank contacted him there and asked if he might be interested in coming to Washington to work on the training manuals. Ray said he would love to make use of his art training for the army, so Frank got Ray assigned to him.

Another soldier–artist at the Army Medical Museum was Amerigo "Freddy" Manfredi, who, like Frank, was from New York. He served with Frank until the end of the war. Nicky made some busts of the high brass, including one of Colonel Ash. He had an assistant, Reno Gastaldi, who would set up the clay and create the basic form, and then Nicky would swoop in and put on the finishing touches. In addition to the two illustrators and two sculptors, Frank had three photographers assigned to him, and he was still having pictures painted in New York.

Under Frank's direction, Graphic Training Aids completed several projects for training the soldiers in the field, including *Survival in the Arctic, Survival in the Tropics,* and *Sanitation in the Field.* They also prepared manuals for use by medical specialists. For one manual for the training of x-ray technicians, they made over 1000 pictures showing how to take x-rays of all the different parts of the body. The pictures showed how to position the patient, the direction of view, and the distance from the patient to set the x-ray gun. In civilian life, the radiological technician coursework takes two years, but the army wanted to train x-ray technicians in a matter of months, and, using the manual Frank and his team prepared, they did.

Every morning Frank's team lined up on the lawn beside the museum for reveille before going to the studio. They were a happy bunch, joking about fighting the "Battle of Pennsylvania Avenue,"[29] and Frank was their leader. "Washington was quite wonderful back then," Ray remembered. "I was young and single, and there were five women for every guy! The Army Medical Museum was next door to the Smithsonian and just a two-block walk to the National Gallery of Art, and at lunchtime, I could go over there to hear recorded symphony music."[30] Ray worked under Captain Netter until March of the following year, when he shipped out to join the war in the Pacific, although still as an artist.[31]

Frank came to think that if illustration was so effective in the army's medical teaching, then perhaps his illustrations could be used for teaching medical techniques in civilian life. "The medical curriculum is so crowded and there is so much to learn," Frank wrote in his notes. "Medical and surgical concepts are sometimes so hard to transmit. The old methods of memorizing pages of text are no longer adequate. . . . Pictures facilitate comprehension" and "can tremendously expedite medical teaching. . . . The basic value of the picture lies in its concept," in the message it conveys.[32]

In the Surgeon General's office, Frank met a young physician, Michael DeBakey, who was already becoming highly influential in medicine and an internationally recognized cardiovascular surgeon. He supported the idea that the treatment the wounded soldier gets early on has a definite impact on his recovery, and he was a leading proponent of bringing treatment forward to the wounded[33] and of providing care in specialized medical centers to treat returning military wounded.[34] Toward that goal, Dr. DeBakey worked on a project with Frank to define the most common war injuries and the associated surgical treatment. The target audience was the medical community—the doctors who would treat these young men both early-on in the field hospitals and back in the United States when they came home.

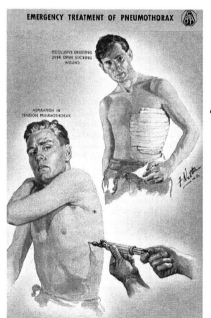

The pictures were necessarily more technical than those in the first aid manual, more anatomical and along the lines for which Frank would become famous. Frank painted all of those pictures and signed the bottom of them "F. Netter MD." The Ciba Company published them in three separate portfolios, *War Injuries of the Chest*, *War Injuries of the Abdomen*, and *War Injuries of the Extremities*, as part of a series of 14 portfolios of Frank's pictures on the pathology of various parts of the body,

Treatment of War Injuries, *Frank H. Netter, Ciba, 1943.*

which Ciba distributed to physicians as a service to the medical profession.

৵৹৵৹৵৹

In the spring of 1944, while Frank was in Washington, Mary, alone in New York, went into labor with their fourth child. Freddie Freed, Frank and Mary's former professor in obstetrics and dear friend, delivered the baby, a girl, as he had all of the Netter children. Mary named the baby Francine Mary, after both her parents, and Francine was soon the favorite of her aunts, her mother's sisters Katie and Renie, and of her aunt Gertie.

Military service ended for Frank on April 4, 1945, and he returned to New York. On August 14, Frank and Mary, who was again pregnant, and the children were on Long Island. Jimmy heard it first, and ran to tell his parents to turn on the radio. Japan had surrendered. It was V-J Day. Frank and Mary, Cornelia, Jim, and Francine got in the car and went to Times Square. Throngs of people, two million by some count, had come to celebrate. Everywhere on the streets of New York people were blowing car horns, singing and dancing, hugging and kissing. The war was over. And on December 31 of that year, their youngest child, Jonathan, was born.

Some months later, Frank met up once more with Ray Olivere at the Society of Illustrators. Ray was living in New York and launching a successful career as a commercial illustrator and artist. One project he had done was a mural at a Russian nightclub. Nicky Tregor had seen it and called him. Nicky, in his grand style, was having a party at his penthouse apartment and asked Ray to paint a mural on his terrace. And the party was fabulous, Ray remembered. Nicky invited everybody, politicians and diplomats and celebrities, and introduced Ray to them as "my sergeant." But then Nicky got into a wicked quarrel with the housekeeper—a real shouting match—and she called the cops. People were yelling—How do we get out of here?—and rushing down the back staircase, but no one was arrested.

For all his antics, Nicky Tregor was a fine sculptor, good at portraiture.[35] After the war, he prepared busts of politicians and society patrons, including a well-known bust of President Dwight D. Eisenhower, which is in the National Portrait Gallery of the Smithsonian. As for Freddy Manfredi, he went back to doing commercial illustration, which is the career he had begun before the war. Frank was back to working alone in his studio.

THE STUDIO

UP ON THE TOP floor of his home, Frank set up his studio. The best light, as every artist knows, reaches the upper floors, and it was quiet, out of the bustle of domestic activities. His was a working studio, not at all glamorous, but neither was it the unheated garret that Esther had envisioned—he had plenty of heat as well as hot and cold running water where he washed the paint off his hands and his brushes.

Under the north-facing window, he placed a table, a cabinet really, with storage for art supplies below and a place for a telephone and the thick directory that was the Manhattan telephone book. At a right angle to that table, he placed his drawing board, to which he pulled up a large, comfortable, paint-splattered, executive-style office chair. The steady north light changed little throughout the day, and when he sat in the chair at the drawing board, light from the window came across his left shoulder onto the drawing surface. His right hand, holding a pencil or brush, could then pass across the picture without casting a shadow.

Of course, he had other lighting. A large swing-arm fluorescent lamp above the drawing board directed light onto the page. And on the ceiling overhead, a bank of daylight fluorescents allowed him to work at night, which he often did, sometimes straight through until morning to finish a picture for a deadline.

Hanging next to the upper right corner of his drawing board was one of the most distinctive features of the studio—a human skeleton. This long-dead soul, his bones held together with twisted wire, was visible from all vantage points in the room.

To the right of the drawing board, completing the U-shaped work area, he placed his taboret. He had it specially built to house his paints and brushes, pencils and sharpener, water jars and palettes, and myriad supplies, all accessible at the right side. An air compressor, which drove the airbrush, resided under a corner of the taboret, next to a built-in waste container for discarded sketches. In his taboret, he had a place for everything and kept everything in its place.

Atop the taboret an enormous ashtray was filled with cigar butts and a half-smoked cigar. He would lean forward to draw or paint, pencil or brush in his right hand, cigar in his left. Then he would sit back in his chair, lift the cigar to his mouth, look at his work, and draw a puff on the cigar, the smoke encircling him. He would then lean forward again to continue his task. The odor of tobacco permeated every corner, every crevice, every piece of artwork in every part of the room.

Across the room, in the near corner, sat an upright artist's easel. More often than not, it held an unfinished oil portrait, a work in

Photo: Frank H. Netter posing at his drawing board, New York, date unknown.

progress. And the oil paints, linseed oil, oil brushes,[1] dauber, and palette sat on a small table nearby.

One long wall in his studio was devoted to his library. He had floor-to-ceiling shelving holding his reference books, medical books, numerous art books, and history and literature books. Alongside a heavily used copy of *Gray's Anatomy*[2] stood *The Complete Works of Rabelais*,[3] illustrated by Gustave Doré; *Moll Flanders*,[4] illustrated by Alexander King, who was a contemporary of Frank's from the Society of Illustrators; a small book by his friend, Rube Goldberg, *Rube Goldberg's Guide to Europe*,[5] inscribed by the author to Frank; college and medical school yearbooks; a set of the *World Book*[6] encyclopedia, given him by the publisher when he contributed an article; and *Who's Who in American Art*,[7] with an entry for Frank Netter himself. He also kept an ever-growing collection of memorabilia, photos, honors, and awards on those shelves. Unobtrusively, on the wall opposite, hung the portrait he had drawn of his mother peeling potatoes.

A waist-high cabinet along another wall held additional supplies, and its countertop served as a place to cut mats or stage completed pictures, ready and waiting to be delivered. A small round conference table and chairs made up the fourth of the quartet of workstations. Here, he could spread out his work for study or consultation with a visiting specialist. And here his children, starting from a young age, could visit and make their own pictures alongside their father.

Without assistants, without protégés, the skeleton his only companion, a solitary figure bent over the drawing board, a shadow of a beard on his face, paint on his khakis, on his shoes, on his hands and arms, making the pictures for which he became famous.

"Good (or poor) illustrations can be made in any medium,"[8] wrote Frank. Different artists "will find different media and methods best suited to their temperaments. One may prefer water-colors, another chalks or crayon, someone else oils and still another tempera . . . each artist should experiment to find in which medium or combination of media he can best express himself. In that way he can produce the most original work and achieve the greatest enjoyment out of making his pictures."[9]

Frank himself used various media, depending on the project. What he liked best to use for medical illustrations were opaque watercolors—what artists call gouache. In their versatility, he said, "they lend themselves to the most careful rendering of detail, yet may be used for broad, colorful effects."[10] He liked "beyond all question"[11] the tubes of watercolors by Winsor & Newton. His color palette generally and consistently over the years contained light and dark cadmium yellow, yellow ochre, vermilion, lamp black, titanium white, scarlet lake, alizarin crimson, ultramarine, Prussian blue, viridian green, burnt umber, and burnt sienna.

As to paintbrushes, he used Winsor & Newton top-of-the-line Series 7 sable brushes, generally only sizes 2, 4, and 7. Winsor & Newton is a British company. If he had a difficult time getting their paints and brushes during the war, he used the finest American products he could find.[12]

When Frank began to put his thoughts on paper, he would sit at his drawing board, thinking about what he was about to draw and twirling a forelock of his hair around the index finger of his left hand. He would take an inexpensive number 2 pencil, the kind used in schools and households everywhere, and roughly lay out the sketch on tracing paper, adding more and more detail as the picture came into being. Depending on the complexity of the subject, the sketch could be more or less detailed. On an intricately detailed sketch, he might use colored NuPastel color sticks to add clarity.

Then Frank would be ready to transfer the sketch to the 15″ × 20″ illustration board. He liked Whatman brand smooth—hot pressed—illustration board. Whatman was an English paper company, founded in the eighteenth century, that later went into manufacturing filtration and other products. But Whatman had made quality paper that was not only prized by artists but also used for government documents and fine stationery. Frank would take his sketch and, with a soft pencil, darken the back side of the tracing paper—although later in his career, he used a piece of graphite transfer paper under the sketch instead. Then he would position the sketch over the illustration board, securing it with tape, and with a hard pencil, a 6H pencil, he would go over the lines on the sketch and thus transfer the picture to the illustration board for painting. The pencil lines on the board were very faint and once covered by the paint were so inconspicuous that only Frank knew they were there.

After he had transferred the sketch to the board, he removed the sketch and began to paint. He would squeeze out dabs of different colored paints onto a porcelain palette, swizzle his brush in the water jar, and with a wet brush pick up a little pigment from the porcelain and transfer it to the paper palette. He would rinse the brush again in the water jar, and pick up a bit of another color and transfer that to the paper palette, where he would mix and test the colors for just the right tone and opacity. Then he would take the mixed color, a little at a time, from the paper palette onto the brush and begin to paint the board. With self-assured strokes, he washed in the color, beginning with the next-to-darkest tones. Then he added the next-lighter tones, and after that, the next-lighter still, as the picture began to unfold.

Sometimes he masked off all but a portion of the picture, taping tracing paper over the areas to be protected. He then started up the compressor, mixed a bit of paint and put it in the airbrush cup, and after testing on a palette, airbrushed the exposed area to achieve a smooth effect, leaving the covered areas untouched. At last, he added the darkest tones as accents and a little white as highlights. Then he would sit back and examine his work. He might then fix a smudge of paint that needed a touch-up or a pencil line that needed erasing. And he would sign the picture, "F. Netter, MD" and put it aside to dry.

Painting the board took a relatively short amount of time—measured in minutes and hours. By the time he came to put paint to the board, the hard work, the study and planning, had been done, and he brought the image that was in his mind to fruition on the board. He rarely, if ever, repainted a picture, having made all the decisions when the picture was still unfolding onto tracing paper. He was not one of those temperamental artists who painted pictures and then destroyed them. No, Frank Netter was a man doing a job.

He did his own legends and leader lines too. Frank cut a piece of tracing paper to the size of the illustration board, placed it over the finished, dry painting, taping it to the board at the top. It would thus flip up to reveal the finished picture, but the thin tracing paper allowed the picture to show through. On this tracing paper, he drew the leader lines and hand-printed the text. His lettering was so consistent in size that he could accurately judge the length of printed text that fit on each line, and the printed text appeared in the final product exactly on the page as did his handwritten lettering.

ᶜⁱᵒᵒᵗᵒᵒᵗᵒ

To Frank, there were three key benefits to medical illustration as a teaching device. First, it helps the student—the artist—to understand the subject, "to clarify it in his own mind"[13] and "create a mental image of it."[14] Certainly he was talking about himself, because Frank Netter the medical artist was a dedicated medical student who thoroughly studied his subject before beginning a picture.

He was fortunate to work with leading medical specialists who were responsible for some remarkable progress made in medical science during much of the twentieth century, and he tried to depict the subjects as the authors described. "But lo and behold!" he said, it sometimes happens that "when I sketch the thing out, it just does not fit together. Something is wrong because I know that if it is correct it must fit together. Then I go back to the authors and we puzzle the thing out. And sometimes they must change what they have written, or even their concepts of the subject because of what the sketch has revealed. . . . Illustrations are hard taskmasters. They force us to think clearly and logically. It is easy to talk or write around a subject we are not quite clear about, but one can scarcely leave blank spaces in the middle of a picture."[15]

Second, illustrations are a means of communication. "They serve to transmit ideas from one mind to another"[16] and help the author express his ideas. If we understand an idea, we have a mental image of it. When we make a picture of that mental image, the picture then transmits that image directly to the viewer. "The picture serves as a shortcut, so to speak. It saves us from having to translate the mental image into words, and the reader from having to translate the words back into a mental image."[17] Pictures do not depend on language and are universally understood.

Photography can also capture an image and certainly has a function in medical teaching. A photograph is a realistic reproduction of the way something actually looks. The camera creates a true image of everything in its line of sight. It does not know an artery from a vein or a nerve from a sinew.[18] On the other hand, the illustrator interprets what he sees to create a picture that communicates a concept. The illustrator can discriminate between important items and the nonessential items in the picture and make the important items stand out. Often what is left out of the picture is of great consequence in emphasizing the remaining parts of the picture so that the message is clearly and unambiguously presented.

Third, the illustration is a record of scientific observation, preserved for posterity. It can depict great discoveries and pass information from one generation to the next. "Medical progress has been a step by step process in which men in one part of the world have added blocks of knowledge upon foundations which may have been laid down by men in another part of the world, or of another generation, even another era, possibly speaking a different language. . . . It is interesting to note that many of the great investigators and pioneers in the past, people like Varolio, Eustachii, Spigelius, Scarpa, Bartholin, and of course Leonardo and Vesalius, and many[,] many others, found it desirable, even necessary to resort to illustrations to express their ideas. And based on those early drawings, often amplified, modified, expanded upon, much of our current-day knowledge of anatomy, physiology and clinical medicine has been built."[19]

ᴏᴵᴏᴏᴵᴏᴏᴵᴏ

Before beginning a project, Frank studied and planned and studied and planned some more. He always said that the hardest part of making a picture was planning it. He would decide what topics the series of pictures would encompass. He had to consider whether it would be color or black-and-white. He needed to know if it would be a poster or appear in a publication—a textbook, a scientific article, or a popular magazine. The audience would to a large extent govern the amount of detail in the picture and how he presented a subject. Once he felt confident that he knew and understood what would be in the picture, it was then straightforward to put it on paper.

The pictures told a story. "The important thing is what you are trying to say in the picture," he noted.

> I am not sure I know what technique means unless it implies a directness in setting down one's ideas, or a facility in making the medium depict what is in one's mind. Before one can have technique, one must have an idea, something to depict . . . the essential point of the picture. . . . I do not mean to belittle technical competence. It is important. But it is only the "handwriting" used to express an idea or concept. . . .
>
> When I undertake to illustrate a subject, I first study it intensively. I cannot paint a picture unless I first know what I am trying to paint. I read the literature [and] seek out an expert in the field who can guide me in my study of it. I visit hospitals and laboratories [and when] I have a grasp of it I go back to my studio and plan how to portray this concept. . . . I seldom make sketches on the spot. Indeed, I prefer a little lapse of time between my studies and the actual painting because in that way my mind automatically filters out the inconsequential and I am able to focus on the essentials.[20]

Frank needed to understand the anatomy, pathology, embryology, physiology, and all the subtleties of what he was illustrating before he could feel confident about what pictures he was making. He always wanted to show the fundamental nature of a condition, not just its existence,[21] and to do that he had to know what was essential to the understanding of the condition and what was not.[22]

In 1940, the Fellows of the New York Academy of Medicine, a most distinguished group of physicians and researchers, had elected Frank to fellowship in the academy.[23] They have one of the largest medical libraries in the world, and Frank spent many hours there researching subject matter and studying the pertinent literature. He was an excellent student who would not settle for a rudimentary knowledge of the material. He met with the top specialists in each field he was illustrating, and he listened to them and asked them questions. When he left the meetings and left the library and left the studio, he would still be thinking about his work and planning his pictures, his eyes glazed over, looking with his mind's eye at the picture he planned to create. Only when he thoroughly understood the subject and the message of the illustration would Frank make a picture.

A great part of Frank Netter's genius was how he planned a picture to convey the message. First, he would decide on the point of view, the vantage point. Would the viewer see the subject from the front or from the rear, or from above, or from the side, or exactly what angle? Next, of particular importance for illustrations of dissection, he would decide the plane. How deep should the illustration go? He was a superb anatomist, and that knowledge of anatomy—what lies in what plane, what is shown from what angle—was crucial to making such decisions intelligently. Last, he decided the focus of the picture. Is the whole body shown, or only part of the body? How much will identify the region, and will extraneous areas obscure the message? What is the message of the illustration? He always came back to the message.

Keeping in mind the big picture—the message of the illustration—he would begin to lay out the sketch. He would start to doodle and work it out in his mind, adding more and more detail to the pencil sketch until he felt he had it right. Then Frank would take or send the sketch to the specialist. Sometimes he would write a note in the margin to the effect of "I am not sure about such and such; please clarify" or "Please let me know if you agree with how I have represented this." Much of the discussion that went on between the consultant and Frank concerned the wording in the legends, so by the time the picture was painted, the decisions as to the wording and terminology were already made. They might go back and forth for clarity and correctness and applicability for several iterations. Finally, when both Frank and the specialist were satisfied with the sketch, Frank would take up his brushes and make the finished picture.

Much of Frank's work was research—90%, he said, and 10% painting. But when he was in his studio, he was constantly drawing and painting. He traveled all over the United States and the world to meet with subject-matter experts, and on his return he always had presents in his suitcase for his children. He delighted in their delight.

For models, Frank used his family or a neighbor, anyone who happened to be there, and they were usually more than happy to oblige. He used Cornelia and Jim and Mary. Often he used himself. He asked the model to hold the pencil as if it were a hypodermic syringe, for example, and he would take a photograph of that. Or he asked the model to stick out his tongue and look sick, and he would photograph him in that pose. Then he would use the photograph to guide him in making the picture. Sometimes he would ask the model to come to the studio so that he could take the photos. In his studio he had some lights on stands and a camera set up on a tripod. Or he would bring a small camera outside and take pictures of his models in the daylight. Many of the family photos he commandeered for his pictures too, and in the final picture, the model was always recognizable.

CHAPTER 9

DIVERSE INTERESTS

THROUGHOUT THE 1940S, AND continuing into the early 1950s, several pharmaceutical companies competed for Frank's time, each competitor offering contracts with varying terms and prices for his art. Frank made pictures of a section of a mosquito for Winthrop Chemical Company, of a cat for Doho Chemical Corporation; and for the headache medicine Bromo-Seltzer, he made a picture of a busy switchboard operator inside a man's head. But his chief patrons were Ciba, Armour Laboratories, and Pfizer.

Mary read each contract he received, and if she had any reservation about a specific point in one of them, she discussed her concerns with Frank and his brother, George, who acted as his legal counsel. She often encouraged Frank to push for more in those contracts. In 1943, Frank signed a partnership agreement with Mary that paid "special attention to the field of medical illustration and related fields with respect to investments."[1] Mary had come from a background different from Frank's New York City upbringing, yet she was his peer, his classmate, a doctor as he was, and his business partner.

⚜⚜⚜⚜

Forrest Laboratories, Inc. was a small pharmaceutical company based in New York[2] that owned trademarks for an antihypertensive drug,[3] a laxative preparation,[4] and a fungicidal ointment.[5] In about 1942, Frank and Mary acquired Forrest, changing the name to Forrest, Inc. It was not a big operation. Aside from Mary, who was president of the corporation, Walter Susslin was the only other employee. He had been vice president at Forrest

Laboratories and stayed on in that role after Frank and Mary bought the company.

Under the new ownership, Forrest continued to grow the product line, adding a treatment for anemia[6] in 1943, a hemorrhoidal suppository preparation[7] in 1945, and a children's aspirin[8] in 1949. It contracted out the manufacture of medicinal preparations and received the products in bulk at the Forrest offices. Mary and Walter then repackaged the drugs, counting and bottling the pills, and packing cartons for shipping to pharmacies all over the country.

The two biggest sellers were the antihypertensive drug Theocalbital and the Serts suppository. Frank made some anatomical pictures for Forrest to distribute as advertising material to doctors. For the antihypertensive drug, he prepared a series of anatomical plates illustrating the pathology of hypertension in the coronary arteries and the kidney. For Serts he made a series of plates on the anal canal and sphincters. These were small folders showing his pictures and unobtrusive advertising copy, with product information limited to the back cover. Forrest offered the folders to the medical profession as educational material.

⌀⊹⊙⊹⊙⊹⌀

After World War II, before the mass migration to the suburbs began in earnest, Frank and Mary began looking for a home on Long Island. Small farms producing crops of potatoes and cabbages predominated down the middle of the fish-shaped island, between the expanse of white-sand ocean beaches along the island's south shore and the craggy fingers of land reaching out into Long Island Sound on the north shore. The North Shore, the Gold Coast, had been developed during the Gilded Age, and there magnificent estates, opulent mansions with elaborate gardens, were homes of the wealthiest Americans, from the Astors to the Vanderbilts. By 1945, the lifestyle with a cadre of resident servants was long gone, and many of those grand houses were vacant and for sale.

Over the 59th Street Bridge the Netters went, to look for a home in what Mary called "the country." They drove east until they had gone little more than an hour from New York City, coming to the tiny settlement of East Norwich and the Incorporated Village of Muttontown, named for the sheep that had grazed in the meadows there in the 1600s. Not much more than an intersection of a couple of two-lane roads, East Norwich had a post office, a Methodist church, and an elementary school. Commerce consisted of a general store, a stationery store, and the upscale Rothman's Inn restaurant.

On the outskirts of East Norwich, on Northern Boulevard, there was a luxurious manor home for sale. Its masonry-pillared iron gates opened to the long tree-lined drive leading to the mansion's grand portico, with 10 imposing Corinthian columns. Here was a Georgian mansion on a grand scale, 14,000 square feet of living area, 30 or more rooms, 11 baths, and 7 fireplaces, on 70 acres of land modeled after the fashion of an English country estate. Originally called Blythewood, the mansion was built in 1913 by architect Henry Otis Chapman. Lewis & Valentine Co. did the stunning site planning, and later landscape architects Innocenti & Webel laid out the gardens. The resulting grounds were a delight, with a swimming pool, rose garden, and tennis court. Outbuildings included a garage with chauffeur's quarters, a caretaker's cottage, a dairy barn, and horse stables. Bordering Old Brookville, the property was bounded on the west by the glamorous Chimneys estate of Howard C. Brokaw. Jock Whitney owned the estate across the road.[9] The Marjorie Merriweather Post estate, which would become the home of the C.W. Post Campus of Long Island University, was just out the driveway and a few miles down on the left.

Continuing their search near the historic hamlet of Oyster Bay, they looked at another estate in the incorporated Village of Cove Neck, an exclusive residential area that is the site of Sagamore Hill, Teddy Roosevelt's home. The land there juts out into Long Island Sound and separates Oyster Bay Harbor from Cold Spring Harbor, so named for the cool freshwater springs that bubble up beneath the salt water. The breakwater along the side of Cove Neck Road has since been raised, but back then, storm waves broke high over the road and a driver had to time it just right to catch the wave on its retreat, gunning the engine to dash through before the next wave broke over the low-lying area of road.

Tennis Court Road runs east up to heavily wooded property set high on the hill. The estate there had a stable, a greenhouse, and a caretaker's cottage, but the main house was never built. The drive ran down to the waterfront on the other side of the neck, and on the rocky beach was a boathouse large enough to dock a sizeable yacht inside it, but the building was in a state of terrible disrepair.

Further out on Long Island, Route 25A goes past a fish hatchery and, behind it, the picturesque St. John's Episcopal Church, its white steeple reflecting in the pond beyond. Off to the left across the harbor is Cove Neck on the west side, and on the east is the quaint hamlet of Cold Spring Harbor, where the whaling industry once thrived. For 25 minutes more, Frank and Mary drove along the narrow road that winds through the Village of Lloyd Harbor and over the causeway to Lloyd Neck.

At the end of a drive that meandered beside a pasture, and situated high on a bluff overlooking Long Island Sound was the most majestic mansion, abandoned, half hidden behind dense foliage. When it was built circa 1900, the builders spared no expense. They used the finest marbles and woods, and employed skilled artisans to create the moldings and carvings. The property included acreage, mature specimen trees, formal gardens gone to seed, woodlands, staff quarters, a caretaker's cottage, and other outbuildings. Wild ailanthus trees and other volunteers sprouting between the flagstones had overtaken the terrace at the rear of the mansion. The landscape shrubbery, once carefully nurtured but then for years neglected, had become overgrown. But it was the spectacular panoramic views of the waterfront and deepwater dock that enchanted.

The Netters purchased the Muttontown mansion as well as both the Cove Neck and Lloyd Neck properties. Frank said that was crazy, but Mary argued, "We do not have to be like everybody else."[10] Nevertheless, they agreed to sell the 80th Street house in New York City, and set up housekeeping in the Muttontown mansion. They soon sold that magnificent jewel of elegance and design in Lloyd Neck. The Cove Neck property, on the other hand, had great potential for development. In 1949, Mary drew up the plans to subdivide it and sell off the lots.[11] The stables became one parcel, the greenhouse another, the boathouse another, and several more became two-acre or four-acre building sites, with a portion of the rocky beach on Cold Spring Harbor reserved for collective use by the residents. Mary's sister Renie, with her husband and son, had recently relocated to Long Island, and they took two acres and the caretaker's cottage.

𐰦𐰦𐰦

In the years that followed World War II, television captured the eyes and pocketbooks of America. Following its demonstration at RCA's Window to the World exhibit at the 1939 New York World's Fair, commercial broadcast television caught on quickly. *Kraft Television Theatre*, *Meet the Press*, and *The Howdy Doody Show* all premiered in 1947, and baseball fans crowded around 9-inch screens to watch the first broadcast of the World Series—the New York Yankees battling the Brooklyn Dodgers to win four games to three. In 1948 and 1949 sales of television sets rose at a phenomenal rate, as did sales of products advertised on the shows. Viewers remembered the sponsors and bought their products. Television was good for business. So impressed was Mary by the phenomenal way television could reach vast audiences that she came up with an idea for a weekly half-hour television show called *The Doctor Draws a Picture*, starring Frank Netter. In a social setting, Mary wrote in the proposal for the show, doctors often find themselves asked about "'the headaches my sister-in-law gets,' or about 'my wife's backaches' or about 'my neuritis,' etc. Wherever the physician goes, he is greeted by a barrage of medical questions. It is . . . information, not pills"[12] the public wants.

The plot and story line of the show was that in everyday situations, the doctor encounters people who ask him medical questions.

The doctor was Frank, and he would explain the problem and draw a picture to clarify the medical condition in terms that a layperson could understand. In each episode there would be a different character in a different setting, and a different health concern. The character asking the question might be a doorman or a bank vice president, a taxi driver or a waiter, just someone the doctor met in the course of an ordinary day. The doctor would explain the problem simply and with the aid of the pictures he would draw. There was to be entertainment value, some amusing twist, but the main interest would be in the health topic, and viewers could write in to request leaflets on the topic of the week.

At Mary's urging, Frank entered into a business agreement in 1949 regarding introductory promotion of the program. Expenses were to be shared equally among Frank; Peter Lasker at radio station WLW in Dayton, Ohio; and Norman (Bud) Weisman, an attorney with Iddings, Jeffrey, Weissman, and Rogers, in Dayton.[13]

Mary worked with writer Bill Devlin to develop a script for a TV pilot on sinus infections. They also prepared synopses of five additional programs and a list of seven more topics, such as heart trouble or backaches, "to round out a thirteen-week schedule."[14] Frank's signature is on the cover letter of the package of his background information and biographical materials, including photographs of the *Transparent Woman*, copies of the Ciba publications, and a copy of Mary's book, *Beauty Plus*, more than enough material for Bud and Peter to use in making a marketing presentation.[15] The effort was apparently successful, because WLW, a television channel in Cincinnati on the Crosley Broadcasting Network and the first NBC television affiliate, agreed to look for a sponsor for the show.[16] At the end of May, Mary typed another letter from Frank that urged clarification and a written agreement on the financial arrangements.[17]

At 7 AM on Tuesday, August 7, 1951, Frank and Mary arrived in Dayton on the Spirit of St. Louis Pennsylvania Railroad passenger train.[18] The next day, Frank made a TV pilot in which he played a doctor who walked out of a city apartment building, where he met the doorman, who complained about his sinus headache and asked the doctor a series of questions—what causes it, what to do for it. Frank then drew a picture in chalk on the door of the building explaining the condition, to the satisfaction of the doorman. In the end, the doctor went off in a taxi and the doorman got in trouble with the building manager for the graffiti left on the door, which added some comic relief to the plot.

By late August, the production people at WLW television had favorably critiqued the pilot. Although it still needed cutting and rework, they were preparing a sales brochure to attract a sponsor.[19] After the program directors reedited the film, they concluded that the show had tremendous possibilities but needed a polished performance and more movement. They recommended using a professional actor to play the doctor, and using Frank just for closeups for the artwork. WLW was lining up two pharmaceutical houses as potential sponsors.[20]

Replacing Frank with an actor promoted the concept of medical illustration, but not the renown of Frank Netter. Yet if he were relieved of the acting, he could handle six to eight 15-minute shows in just a day's time, which would leave him free to pursue other projects. No sponsor was forthcoming, however, and after three years and several thousand dollars, the television show amounted to nothing more that a TV pilot.

ᴥᴥᴥᴥᴥᴥ

Giles Cory—everyone called him Cory—had a small antique shop on Third Avenue where he reigned from a wheelchair. Cory befriended Mary and taught her a great deal about furniture. She had by then abandoned her medical practice and stopped writing her newspaper column altogether, although *Beauty Plus* was in its third printing and being quoted by Alicia Hart, a nationally syndicated columnist.[21] Mary loved the antique business. She attended sales at the New York furniture auctions, and sold furniture out of Cory's shop. When she decided to trade full time on her knowledge of French furniture, she and Frank formed a partnership for a business known as the Gold Dolphin Antiques. And her business thrived.

By 1950 the Gold Dolphin moved to a building—actually three buildings—under the Third Avenue El on the corner of 54th Street, in New York's antique furniture district. The main entrance to the retail shop was on 54th Street, and there were display windows on both 54th Street and Third Avenue. On the main floor was the retail store. There was a shop in the back and on the second floor, and stock on the upper floors.

The logo for the shop was a cherub riding on the back of a dolphin, a cute little thing, gold, of course, to match the store name and play on the widespread use of gilt in French period decor. Mary placed advertisements for the Gold Dolphin in *Town & Country* and other fashionable magazines and set up elegant booths at the antique shows. As the shop developed a reputation for having chic pieces of furniture, it attracted an exclusive clientele. Mary also did a big business renting furniture as scenery and props for television productions and stage sets.

The Gold Dolphin was hugely profitable and had eight full-time employees, including painters, a cabinetmaker, a carver, and an upholsterer, who could repair, refinish, restore, and refurbish a piece of furniture and make it look beautiful. Julian, the carver, was a real artisan. If a piece of furniture had a broken piece of carving, Julian could repair it and make it look perfect.

Mary was in charge of the day-to-day operations of both Forrest and the Gold Dolphin. At home she managed the paperwork and did any typing Frank needed. She was juggling running the drug company, the furniture business, and a large household. On weekends, while Frank continued to work in his studio, Mary read or played solitaire in the living room.

She had a pitiful day-to-day wardrobe and was not much interested in clothes. She just did not take the time to shop. At one time, she did not have a dress suitable to wear to go shopping for a dress in the fashionable Fifth Avenue stores. She joked about having to go buy a dress to wear to go buy a dress. When she did go clothes shopping, she would come home with two or three outfits from Bergdorf Goodman and six pairs of Delman shoes, shoeboxes stacked three high and tied with twine. And although she put on weight, becoming not obese but decidedly overweight, Mary was still a beautiful woman.

During the late 1940s, the business partnership shared by Frank and Mary grew larger and more diverse. By 1951, they had established the Netmar Corporation as a holding company for their property and assorted interests. In particular, Netmar owned considerable real estate, including the three buildings on the corner of Third Avenue and 54th Street in New York where the Gold Dolphin antique store was, some other investment properties they owned in New York, a commercial building on South Street in Oyster Bay where Forrest was, and the Muttontown estate on Long Island.

Photo: Mary Netter, c. 1948.

CHAPTER 10

FOLLY FARM

THE MUTTONTOWN MANSION WAS a grand house. It was silly that they, of all people, this son of immigrants and this daughter of the Confederacy, should own such a grand estate. Folly Farm was the name they gave it.

Folly Farm, *Frank H. Netter, engraving, probably for a Christmas card, c. 1950.*

Mary bought furniture at auction and used the resources of the Gold Dolphin antique shop to furnish the house in a grand style. The heavy front door opened to a relatively small white-paneled vestibule, from which another door opened to the enormous front hall, a striking introduction to the grandeur and immense scale of the home. On the white marble floor lay a French Aubusson rug, its scrollwork accenting the architectural details of the hall's rich moldings. Beyond twin grand staircases, glass French doors offered a view of the rear terrace.

To the left of the front hall, a double door opened to the palatial living room. A carved plaster ceiling 14′ above the parquet floor, another Aubusson rug, even larger than the one in the hall, and pickled paneling enhanced the 60′ wide room. The focal point was a pair of oversized, deep-seated, purple velvet Chesterfield sofas facing each other before the fireplace. In an ornate sculpted frame over the fireplace was the picture Frank had painted of the three older children, Cornelia, Frankie, and Jimmy. At the New York auction houses, Mary bought used books by the pallet load to fill the built-in bookcases, 6′ wide and running floor to ceiling, one in each of the four corners of the room. A concert grand Steinway, its tone rich and complex, sat to the right of the door. Diagonally across the cavernous room from the piano were a game table and chairs for card playing. On the tabletop, Frank painted a trompe l'oeil scattering of playing cards so realistic that frequently players tried to pick them up. Beyond the living room was a sunroom, which overlooked another terrace and the swimming pool.

At the opposite end of the front hall from the living room, another double door led to the massive formal dining room. An Aubusson rug wove a delicate floral garland of soft dusky pink English roses around the room. Over the table a brass chandelier hung from the carved plaster ceiling, and along three of the paneled walls, sideboards burst with silver serveware that Mary had bought by the barrelful at auction.

The adjacent breakfast room looked out over the rear terrace. Mary furnished it as a sitting room, marrying unusual chinoiserie antiques with French furniture. It had blue walls and was appropriately called the blue room. Over the fireplace, she hung a portrait of Jim painted by Keith Shaw Williams, whom Frank knew from the Salmagundi Club. The room had a light, airy feel and was especially magnificent in spring when the apple tree outside the window bloomed, accenting the masses of rhododendrons surrounding the terrace. But for all its glamour, it was the most casual of the rooms in the main part of the house, perhaps because of its more manageable size, and it served as the family gathering place.

Twin grand staircases in the front hall led upstairs to the master bedroom suite—two bedrooms, two bathrooms, and a dressing room—and to five additional bedrooms, each with en suite bath and walk-in closet. The bedrooms, Mary furnished functionally, albeit with a few French antiques from the Gold Dolphin. Oddly, in each bedroom she placed the bed on the wall sideways to the door instead of opposite it. In the master suite, she put a large bed with an Art Deco black patent leather headboard in one room, and in the other, a king-size bed with an ornately carved headboard upholstered in tufted raw silk in the pale rose pink she favored— his-and-hers bedrooms.

The service wing of the house was built to accommodate numerous live-in servants. The butler's pantry, itself the size of a modern kitchen, sat among the blue room, the dining room, and the cook's enormous kitchen. A multipurpose room—originally the servants' dining room—lay beyond, as well as the service entrance where the back stairs led to servants' bedrooms.

The service drive, 200 yards to the east of the main drive and parallel to it, was, like the main drive, lined with linden trees. It led in from Route 25A for a quarter mile, then forked left, past the garage with chauffeur's apartment—although the Netters did not employ a chauffeur—and up to the back service entrance of the mansion. The right fork led back clear through to Remsen Lane, past the caretaker's house, the dairy barn, the stables, pigsty, and chicken and turkey coops, with livestock—Black Angus cattle, sheep, pigs, horses, chickens, and turkeys. There were orchards of apples, pears, and cherries; a grape arbor; and fields of flowers, asparagus, and rhubarb, all allowed to go fallow beside a bank of enormous abandoned glass greenhouses.

Folly Farm was miles from the village, and if anyone had to go anywhere, they went by car. Mary's sister Renie came to work at Folly Farm and was a big help with buying groceries and chauffeuring the younger children to school, the dentist, and the like. Francine liked to spend Saturday night at her aunt's cottage in Cove Neck and go to church with Renie and her family at Christ

Episcopal Church in Oyster Bay. Mary would pick Francine up after church, but Mary herself never went to church.

While the Netters did not employ live-in servants at Folly Farm, they had help. Mary was not in the kitchen cooking or doing anything like that. Two women came in every day to do the household chores. Dora White was of Scandinavian descent and had come as a bride to Long Island from Duluth, Minnesota. Mrs. White wore simple dresses and tied her long strawberry blond hair into a bun at the nape of her neck. Teresa "Tessie" Sabrese was of Italian heritage, and her olive skin and black permed hair contrasted with Mrs. White's light coloring. Every day, their husbands brought these women from their own homes up the service drive to Folly Farm. They cooked the meals, did the laundry, and cared for the Netter children. At the end of the day, the husbands came to pick up their wives and take them home to their own children.

As there was no live-in help, the bedrooms in the servants' wing—nine on the second floor and more on the third—primarily served as storerooms for Forrest and the Gold Dolphin, with one exception. In the far back of the house, in what had been one of

Photo: Folly Farm entrance, 2008, courtesy of Zachary Lemle and www.oldlongisland.com.

the maids' rooms that overlooked the back service entrance to the mansion, one room was set up as an office.

To help maintain the financial records and business correspondence, Mary hired a secretary, Vera Burrows Stetson. She was a prim and trim woman who wore high-necked dresses and sensible shoes, and tied her graying hair back in a chignon, presenting a stern facade. She came and went by the back service drive, kept to herself, managed the books, and typed letters for Frank.

ᏒᏇᎧᏇᎧᏇᎧ

It seemed that Frank was always in his large studio on the third floor of the mansion. He would eat an early morning breakfast—black coffee, cereal, and fruit—and be upstairs in the studio by 7:00. At noon, he might emerge and go down to East Norwich to buy a newspaper and cigars, and pick up the mail at the post office. He had a sandwich and a cup of coffee for lunch, eating alone in the dining room, reading the *Daily News* and looking at the cartoons—his friend Otto Soglow's *The Little King*, Al Capp's *Li'l Abner*, and Frank's personal favorite, Chester Gould's *Dick Tracy*—and then returned to the studio. He worked there in paint-splattered khaki shirt and pants, while a dark five o'clock shadow of a beard began to appear on his face.

Francine loved to go to the studio to see him make pictures. He set out art supplies on the table for her to paint or draw and to use in experimenting with various media. When he gave her pastels, she pressed too hard and the chalk broke. So he showed her how to pass the stick of color gently over the paper. He was a big proponent of India ink, perhaps since his days working on school publications, and gave her some India ink and a brush and paper and told her to draw whatever she wanted, which was usually a ballet dancer or perhaps flowers. She did not like the ink because it got on her hands and clothes, and would not wash off. When he first let her try watercolors she would scrub the brush into the paper, so he showed her how to use the brush: how to mix colors, how to twirl the brush on the palette, how to wash on the color with just the tip of the brush, and how to achieve different effects. He taught her how to clean the brushes, carefully smoothing them back into shape. And all the time, she would tell him about her day. He must have enjoyed her company, because he always seemed glad to see her whenever she came to the studio.

At about 5:00, he showered and shaved, and came downstairs to meet Mary for cocktails in the blue room. She would laugh a hearty laugh and smile a broad smile and teach the children to play parlor games. Then Mrs. White would call the children to dinner in the kitchen. Frank and Mary had their dinner later in the dining room, after which Frank most often went back up to the studio and worked on his pictures far into the night.

❧❧❧❧❧

Late on summer afternoons, after working all day at his drawing board, Frank would come down from his studio, change his

Photo: *Frank Netter with his daughter, Francine, in front of the mansion, c. 1948.*

clothes, and go out to the pool to take a swim before dinner. He was a good swimmer and would swim laps up and down the length of the pool. He had a smooth stroke and great form, and he taught his children to swim in that pool. He let them feel how the water held them up, showed them how to kick from the hips, legs straight, and taught them to cup their hands and rotate their arms. "He made it fun," remembered Francine, "but he was serious about it too and insisted I practice my stroke."[1]

Saturday mornings, Frank joined Cornelia, Jim, and Francine for horseback riding lessons at the stables in Syosset. The four of them would ride around the ring at a walk, trot, and canter, and would jump over gates. Jim became an accomplished horseman, and won numerous blue, red, and yellow ribbons at the Long Island horse shows. Many times, Frank went to watch him ride in shows at the exclusive Piping Rock Club in nearby Locust Valley.

On one of the early days at Folly Farm, the cattle somehow got loose and overran both Folly Farm and the neighboring Brokaw estate. Mary called the Old Brookville police for a cattle roundup, and Frank, Cornelia, and Jim mounted the horses to go after the cattle—not on the cowboys' quarter horses but on saddle-bred horses trained for show jumping and fox hunting. Police cars and show horses chased Black Angus cattle across the manicured lawns and through the gardens of those elegant North Shore estates. After that embarrassing episode, the Netters decided that

Photo: Frank Netter in his riding habit, c. 1949.

farming was not for them, and they sold all the farm animals and the horses.

The only domestic animals that remained at Folly Farm were a couple of cats and a black standard poodle who was too big for a friend's New York City apartment. Frank had brought her home to the country on a hot summer day. Thinking it fitting for a poodle to have a French name, he named her Chouchou, a French term of endearment. She was a successor to a miniature poodle named Pierre that they had owned previously. Frank apparently liked the breed. No froufrou dog was Chouchou. She was a good-natured dog, calm and gentle. Her black wavy hair was clipped short in a sporting clip, with just a cap of longer hair on the top of her head and a pompom on the end of her tail. Frank took her to obedience school every week to teach her to heel and sit and stay and come on command. She had a difficult time learning, got nervous, and wet the floor right there in the school, much to his chagrin. Frank tried breeding her and paid some handsome stud fees for some handsome poodles. When the puppies came too soon, Frank and Mrs. White worked to save them, Frank tying the cords and Mrs. White assisting, but the puppies died and Chouchou mourned.

ᏩᏉᏉᏫᏉᏉᏩ

There were many guests at Folly Farm. Freddie Freed, Frank and Mary's professor in obstetrics from NYU, occasionally came with his paramour, Mae Bookmiller—Bookie, they called her—to visit the Netters.[2] Bookie was about the same age as Frank and Mary. She was an obstetrical nurse at Bellevue who wrote an authoritative textbook on obstetrics, published in 1949,[3] for which Frank made the drawings.

Max Som, Frank's best and dearest friend since their days together in medical school, visited often on weekends in the summertime, when life centered around the swimming pool. He drove out from New York on Saturday with his wife and his son, Peter, and his little dachshund, and they spent the night. Max always brought huge sirloin steaks to put on the charcoal grill, or else he brought live lobsters, enough for everybody.

If he could get up a game, Max played tennis on the clay court out beyond the swimming pool. Frank might work until midafternoon, but then he would join Mary and their guests. They would

Photo: Frank Netter and Max Som by the swimming pool at Folly Farm, c. 1950.

swim in the pool and sit in the sun having drinks and laughing. For the cookout in the evening on the tree-shaded terrace off the blue room, Mrs. White prepared everything except the steaks. Max grilled those over the coals, dousing any flare-up with his scotch and soda.

After dinner, the two couples would sit at the game table in the living room and play hearts. They would drink Haig & Haig scotch late into the night, laughing and joking, and reminiscing about being in medical school, about how hard the professors made them work, and telling stories about what some of their former classmates were doing.

The Netter brothers were very close, and George and Gertie and their children came to Folly Farm for holidays and in the summer too. They came every year for Thanksgiving. Richard Netter often came with his family, as did Mary's sister Renie, with her husband and son. Everyone liked to come to Folly Farm.

❧❧❧❧❧

While Frank and Mary were passionately drawn to each other, they also had some dreadful fights. The children, lying in their beds at night, could hear their parents yelling at each other behind the closed doors of the master bedroom suite. Mary could really rile Frank; with just a word, she could reach down into his soul and set him into a rage.

Late in the evening toward the end of one summer, when he was about 42 years old, Frank and Mary got into a fight in the front hall at Folly Farm. They were hollering and screaming at each other. Frank was boiling over. His face was red, and he was sputtering. He ran out the front door and off to the right, toward the grass. Jimmy and Francine were standing right there and saw it all. Go with your father! Go with your father! Mary told Jimmy. Make sure he is okay.

Jimmy was just a 10-year-old kid, but he went out there, and he soon came running back into the house to his mother. Jimmy had found Frank lying on the ground, and he was not okay. Mary got in the car, with Jimmy in the front seat and Francine in the back, and ever so slowly she drove on the grass, creeping along in the dark, Jimmy peering out into the darkness and looking for Frank lying on the grass. Where was he? She did not want to run over him. They

Photo: *Frank and Mary Netter, costume party, Society of Illustrators, c. 1950.*

found him finally and got him into the car and into the house, into the living room and onto a purple sofa. Mary called a local doctor, who came to the house—doctors still made house calls then. He gave Frank some medicine and said that he had had a mild heart attack. Frank recovered at Folly Farm and soon returned to his normal activities.

Frank and Mary continued to get dressed up and go in to New York to the parties held by the Society of Illustrators. Frank was a good dancer too. He knew all the ballroom steps—the fox-trot, the waltz, the Latin rumba, and the Charleston from the Roaring Twenties. He could lead and guide a partner around the floor, which was popular with the ladies.

The Illustrators had a yearly New Year's Eve party, to which everyone wore costumes, some quite elaborate. For the turn of the decade, New Year's Eve 1949, Mary spent two days sewing their costumes, creating outfits considered risqué for those conservative times. She wore a black brassiere, black panty girdle with garters, and black fishnet stockings. She sewed red satin rosebuds over the nipples of the bra, and a red heart over the crotch of the girdle. Over that, she gathered some black tulle into a see-through skirt. Frank dressed in a union suit, over which he wore his evening dress tailcoat, a black bow tie, a red sash diagonally across his chest, his top hat, and black dress shoes. He parted his hair in the middle, as usual, but instead of combing his long top locks back, he combed them down to the sides, and he added a large fake black handlebar mustache. Looking like two cartoon characters, they got in the car and drove off from Folly Farm to the party in New York, taking the prize for those costumes.

ơⱷⱺⱷⱺⱷⱺ

By 1950, through advertising, antique shows, and word of mouth, Mary had built up the Gold Dolphin's reputation for fine French antiques and glamorous interior decoration. She drove in to New

York every day to oversee the store. It was not a particularly easy drive, about an hour each way in traffic.

During school vacations, Cornelia and Jim both worked at the Gold Dolphin. Jim helped with moving the furniture, while Cornelia learned about selling to customers or painting furniture in the shop in back of the store. She mixed a little white paint in a paper cup, just stirred it up in a used coffee cup, which still had Mary's lipstick stain on the rim. The coffee left in that cup gave the paint a beautiful color that achieved just the right antique patina.

Frank would go to the city occasionally to meet with a consultant or to do research at the Academy of Medicine. Or if Sadler's Wells Ballet[4] was performing in New York, he would take Francine to see Margot Fonteyn dance at the old Metropolitan Opera House.[5] Whenever he was in the city he went by the Gold Dolphin to see Mary. One time a junk man with a pushcart came up Third Avenue hawking his wares. He had some old pictures he was selling, and Frank stopped to look at some of the frames. One old frame, maybe an antique, interested him, and only then did he look at the picture inside it. It was an old painting, a classic piece, small, 27″ × 20″, but there was something about it that reminded him of a work by Velázquez, a copy, perhaps, or even a sketch by the master himself, and he bought it.

After some subsequent research, Frank became convinced that his painting was a preliminary study by Diego Velázquez for his masterpiece, *Las Hilanderas* (*The Spinners*), hanging in the Prado Museum in Madrid. "There are many factors which convince me that the picture is from Velázquez's own hand," Frank wrote. "There is the masterful brush work. The composition . . . deviates somewhat from that of the final painting as though he were experimenting. It is brushed in loosely and quickly as he would when playing with the composition. The painting is on rough coarse canvas such as that which Velázquez habitually employed."[6] Thus began Frank's quest to determine the provenance of his painting.

⟡⟡⟡⟡⟡

Frank suffered habitually from sinus infections, and when the pressure was too great, he would go to see his friend Max Som at his otolaryngology office on East 60th Street[7] just off Lexington Avenue, which was within walking distance of the Gold Dolphin. Max had some very sick patients who came to see him, but he always made time to wash out Frank's sinuses with warm saline to relieve the sinus pressure.[8]

Frank had a tremendous network of professional contacts, and Max was a great resource in those days. Frank often asked him to recommend a specialist at Mount Sinai or Beth Israel, as a consultant for his pictures. Joe Gaines, whom Frank knew from his student days at Mount Sinai, was another resource. He had his office on the ground floor of his townhouse on East 80th Street,[9] just steps from the town home Frank and Mary had owned. Dr. Gaines was a distinguished gentleman, gentle yet stern, the epitome of gynecological authority.

Sometimes a family member or friend needed help with a medical problem and turned to Frank and Mary for guidance. When Mary's youngest sister, Evelyn, got sick, she came to stay at Folly Farm, and Frank and Mary made appointments for her to see the best specialists in New York, although as doctors they both knew that it did not look good. She had Hodgkin's disease at a time when treatment for that was scientifically premature.[10] During the summer of 1950, all of the McFadyens came to see Evelyn and stayed at Folly Farm. Mary put beds for them in the bedrooms in the servants' wing. Her sister Katie and her family drove up from Greensboro, and as they approached New York, a great forest fire in Canada sent down a foreboding pall of smoke to cover the city.[11] Evelyn died that autumn.

CHAPTER 11

THE LIFE OF A DOCTOR

CIBA HAD ITS ORIGINS in 1858 as a chemical company manufacturing synthetic dyes, in Basel, Switzerland. By 1900 the company had expanded into pharmaceuticals and gained an international commercial presence; and from the second decade of the twentieth century, it had manufacturing facilities not only in Switzerland but also in England, Italy, Russia, and Germany. When Frank first began making pictures for Ciba in the 1930s, their offices in New York City were in a loft building on Greenwich Street, but they soon moved to larger quarters in Summit, New Jersey.

After the series of die-cut flyers proved popular with the doctors, Ciba sponsored the publication of a series of color portfolios of Frank's pictures on various anatomical subjects. Between 1941 and 1947, they published 14 separate portfolios, each containing from 6 to 34 medical illustrations and showing the anatomy, pathology, and physiology of a different structure of the body. One he did on the endocrine physiology of the female and others on the pathology of various organs—the heart, the lungs, the stomach, the testicles and prostate, the esophagus, the nose and sinuses, the duodenum, small intestine, large intestine, and the breast. Three portfolios in the series incorporated those pictures on war injuries that Frank had made when he was in the army consulting with Dr. Michael DeBakey.[1]

Those portfolios were enormously popular, and Ciba could not keep up with the demand for reprints. The advertising manager at Ciba, Paul Roder, got the idea that Ciba should publish a compilation of the plates from those portfolios in a hardcover volume, 191 of Frank's full-color illustrations accompanied by concise explanatory texts. The book came out in 1948, and as a service to the medical profession, Ciba sold it at cost of printing, mailed postage-paid on receipt, for \$6.50. It measured 9½″ × 12½″, was bound in indigo buckram, and carried the title *The Ciba Collection of Medical Illustrations: A Compilation of Pathological and Anatomical Paintings Prepared by Frank H. Netter, MD*. The demand for that book was so great that within months it went to a second printing.[2]

ↃᛜᚯↃᛜᚯↃ

Ciba Symposia[3] was a monthly pamphlet published between 1939 and 1951 that addressed subjects "from the fields of anthropology, ethmology [*sic; recte* ethnology], medical history, education, art and the like. Avoiding the heat of debate and omitting techniques of commerce," Ciba stated, its aim being "that *Ciba Symposia* bring enjoyable and constructive diversion to the physician whose interest is our primary concern."[4] Thus, the articles were meant to entertain. Some pictures Frank made for advertising purposes appeared on pages of that publication. The first mention of Frank Netter in *Ciba Symposia* was an article in the March 1947 issue on medical exhibits.[5] It referred to Frank's *Transparent Woman*, saying, "A dramatic feature [of the Golden Gate Exposition] and 'first showing' was the Hormone Lady, designed and executed by physician–artist, Frank Netter."

The topic of the May–June 1949 issue of *Ciba Symposia* was medical illustration. It had three articles, chronicling medical art through the ages, from the ancient to the current. The first article, by Loren C. MacKinney, "Medical Illustration, Ancient and Medieval," surveyed early medical representations, including depictions found in tombs and on fragments of pottery from ancient Egypt, Greece, and Babylon, and some early manuscript paintings from Byzantium, Europe, and Persia. On the last page of that article, there was an advertisement for *The Ciba Collection of Medical Illustrations*.

The second article, "Illustration in Printed Medical Books," by Carl Purington Rollins, presented an overview of printing, specifically the printing of medical illustrations, beginning with early woodcuts—including the sixteenth-century work of the great Belgian anatomist Andreas Vesalius, in his *De Humani Corporis Fabrica*[6]—progressing to metal engraving and the detailed work of Scottish obstetrician William Hunter, then to lithography, and photography and halftone printing used by Ciba.

Frank authored the third article in that issue. It was about the current state of medical illustration, and described his own work and how he went about making pictures. In "A Medical Illustrator at Work," Frank emphasized the message of an illustration rather than technique of the illustrator. The true art, he said, is in having a clear concept of what the picture will communicate.

ᘓᘉᘓᘉᘓᘉᘓ

Clinical Symposia was another of Ciba's periodicals but with an entirely different focus, despite the confusing similarity in name, size, and format to those of *Ciba Symposia*. Begun in 1948, *Clinical Symposia* presented in booklet form "clinical subjects from the forefront of medical progress."[7] Various authors contributed monographs describing their research or clinical experience, and Frank worked with the authors to coordinate illustrations with the text, but his pictures were always the highlight of those publications, which Ciba gave away to doctors and students to promote the Ciba Company. Beginning in the first issue, Frank illustrated a series of anatomical plates on the nervous system, the brain and spinal column, the autonomic nervous system, and neuroanatomy. He met with some of the leading physicians of the time—Dr. Abraham Kaplan, clinical professor of neurosurgery at New York Polyclinic[8] and student of Dr. Harvey W. Cushing[9]; Dr. Gerhardt von Bonin, professor of anatomy at the University of Illinois at Chicago; and Dr. Albert Kuntz, professor of anatomy at Saint Louis University—and learned from them the latest thinking on these subjects, while they provided the descriptive text.

At that time Frank was still making pictures for some of the Ciba ads—he made an unsigned drawing of an infant, using his son

Jonathan as the model. Another picture, which he signed "F. Netter," was of a man and boy fishing from a rowboat floating amid the reeds on a pond. But *Clinical Symposia* was never intended to promote a particular Ciba product. Product advertisements were few and incidental to the topics discussed in the monographs. *Clinical Symposia* served as an educational tool for the practicing physician. Frank's pictures illustrating the newest findings and clinical techniques were responsible for much of the success of the publication.[10]

Ciba also published a small book in hardcover in 1949 with no product advertising. It was a purely academic monograph on saddle block anesthesia,[11] 52 pages with 12 full-color plates by Frank Netter and edited by Dr. J. Harold Walton at Ciba.

☙❧☙❧☙

Mary's nephew Ralph Mills came north in 1948 to attend photography school in New York City. Mary invited him to stay at Folly Farm, as there were more than enough bedrooms and baths in the mansion as well as space for privacy. The proximity to New York City made for an hour commute to school, and he rode into the city with Mary when she went to the Gold Dolphin. At Folly Farm, Ralph set up a darkroom in one of the small rooms adjacent to the studio on the top floor. The room was already equipped with a sink, which facilitated film processing.

Ralph was a tall, robust, agreeable young man, with Southern manners and sober ways. He took photographs of the Netter children—an amusing one of Jim, wide-eyed and reading adventure comic books, and another of Jonathan, who was just a baby, toddling across the lawn, grasping his favorite soft toy in one hand and a rhododendron flower in the other. Ralph took pictures of the grounds at Folly Farm, and when Mary's brother Aubrey came to visit, Ralph took a picture of him sitting with Frank on one of the purple sofas in front of the fireplace in the living room.

He would seclude himself for hours in his darkroom on the third floor and finally emerge with the prints. Ralph in his darkroom

Photo: Aubrey McFadyen and Frank Netter sitting on one of the purple sofas in the living room at Folly Farm, c. 1947. Note Netter's painting The Netter Children *hanging over the fireplace. Photo by Ralph Mills, courtesy of Kathryn Mills*

and Frank in his studio spent many hours making pictures there on the top floor of the mansion. Frank often worked from photographs of models, and he asked Ralph to take some photographs for that purpose. Ralph took photographs such as the one of Jonathan that Frank used to make a picture for Ciba for an ad for their Vioform Cream, which appeared in *Clinical Symposia*.[12]

ↂↂↂↂ

During World War II, Armour Laboratories became the major supplier of human albumin for the US military. In 1946, Armour published a booklet on the biliary system,[13] with eight full-color plates of Frank's pictures, and he made pictures for several of Armour's one-page ads. Mary modeled for some of those Armour ads. He also made a picture from a photo of Francine as a baby in a high chair, and several pictures of Cornelia for various of the Armour ads, making her look sick in one and healthy in another. He took a photo of Cornelia sitting with Francine on his bed and leaning against the black patent-leather headboard, and made the pictures from that.

Armour asked Frank to create *The Life of a Doctor*, a series of 12 pictures depicting a doctor practicing his craft in the New York of the 1930s and '40s. He made pictures of medical students in three instances: in *Osteology Cram*, studying late into the night for their first exam; in *Anatomy Lab*, dissecting a cadaver; and in *Fourth-Year Obstetrics*, delivering a baby in a tenement. *Class Reunion* is probably after a photograph taken at an actual reunion. In the middle of that picture there is a beautiful woman doctor who resembles Mary in face and pose. The patient in *Gynecology Examining Room* also appears to be modeled after Mary. The young doctors, the interns in *Ambulance Call* and *Catastrophe*, he painted after photos of himself as the model.

Ralph and Frank took photographs of each other for Frank to use as models in painting some of these pictures. In *Catastrophe*, the fireman carrying the child was painted from a photograph that Frank took of Ralph wearing an overcoat. *Country Night Call* has two figures in it. For the doctor, Ralph was the model. Frank took a photograph of him on the steps to the portico of the mansion. For the model of the man in the doorway waving, Ralph took a photograph of Frank posing in the doorway to the studio. The doctor's car in the painting, actually just a painting of only part of a car, Frank took from a photo that Ralph took of Frank's own car. The house in that picture was taken from a photograph Ralph took of the caretaker's cottage on the Folly Farm estate. For the finishing flourish, Frank painted Ralph's name, "R. Mills," on the mailbox in front of the house in that painting.

In those pictures Frank captured the people in a most remarkable way: the tearful woman in tattered clothing bending over the injured man on the gurney, in *Emergency Room*; the array of people waiting to see the doctor in *The Clinic*—some weary, some bandaged, some bored, and the worried mother cradling an infant and a little girl straining for a glimpse of the baby. They were real people and real events, from his own experiences, experiences shared by most doctors in the first half of the twentieth century. Armour printed the pictures on 11″ × 14″ stock and gave them away to doctors as promotional material. They were popular, as the doctors could identify with the events depicted. Unlike his medical illustrations, for which he signed away the copyright, Frank retained ownership of both the copyright and the original paintings and hung the original paintings of *The Life of a Doctor* in his studio.

Also for Armour, Frank made a series of 16 portrait paintings of scientists and researchers who had made significant contributions to the field of endocrinology. The series was titled *Portraits of Pioneers in Endocrinology*. From photographs, Frank painted the portraits of Dr. Oscar Riddle, who isolated prolactin; Dr. Robert James Graves, after whom Graves' disease was named; Dr. Thomas Addison, from whom Addison's disease takes its name; Drs. George H. Whipple and George R. Minot, who discovered that a diet of calf's liver or beef liver is effective in combating anemia; Sir Frederick Banting, who worked to isolate insulin; and the great surgeon Dr. Harvey W. Cushing, among others. Frank signed each picture "F. Netter, MD." Armour reproduced the portraits as a portfolio of 9″ × 9″ prints.

ᦟᦟᦟᦟᦟᦟ

Fleur Cowles was the wife of Mike Cowles, the newspaper heir and publisher of *Look* magazine, and in 1950 she started *Flair* magazine. The first issue of *Flair* featured an article on Frank and his work.[14] It showed a photo of Frank at the library at the Academy of Medicine and described him as "the most brilliant medical illustrator of our time." In the photo he sat at a desk with a stack of books in front of him, pencil in hand poised over a sketchpad. He wore a burnished gold or tan sport coat, with a black shirt, a black tie with white polka dots, and a black pocket square. With his shiny black hair parted in the middle and combed back, as always, he made quite a dashing figure. Some of his medical illustrations appeared on the next page of the article, followed by more photos of him at home in his studio and in an operating room. *Flair* was celebrated for its fine design and editorial production, which came at a greater financial cost than it could sustain, and the magazine folded the following year.

Frank also had orders for less technical illustrations for use in articles targeting the general public. *Life* magazine[15] ran an article on polio in 1949 for which Frank prepared some simplified pictures of the spine and nerves. Two years later, in 1951, *Collier's Weekly* magazine ran an article on polio,[16] also with illustrations Frank made. Before a vaccine was available, polio blighted the summer months, striking without warning, paralyzing or killing. Albert Sabin, Frank and Mary's medical school classmate, was working on developing a polio vaccine,[17] but every summer season without the vaccine meant another polio epidemic.

ᐒᐤᐒᐤᐒ

Pfizer was founded in Brooklyn, New York, before the Civil War. In the first part of the twentieth century it was a leader in the production of citric acid and vitamin C, and by 1945 it was the leading producer of penicillin. In 1950, Pfizer launched its Terramycin brand of tetracycline.

The *Pfizer Series of Anatomical and Pathological Transparencies*[18] was a series of six small booklets that Frank made in the early 1950s for Pfizer Antibiotic Division. Each booklet presented a different anatomy or pathology: pulmonary tuberculosis; the lung; the abdomen; the pregnant uterus; the adrenals and kidneys; and the head and neck. The pictures were printed on clear acetate and thus were transparent, so each page represented a layer of anatomy that was peeled away as the page was turned. The right side of the booklet showed through the pages from the outside into the layers of anatomy, and the left side, as the pages were turned, showed the layers looking out from the cross-section, with each layer highlighting certain features of the anatomy and pathology. The result was a unique three-dimensional effect.

ᘐᕉᘐᕉᘐᕉ

Dr. Ernst Oppenheimer was the chief pharmacologist at the Ciba Pharmaceutical Company. He had been trained in medicine and pharmacology in Europe, from where he had emigrated before the war. He was widely respected and recognized as a man devoted to science. To him, truth was paramount, and he tolerated nothing less than excellence.

Oppenheimer insisted on seeing every picture Frank did for Ciba, and he reviewed each of them in great detail. They would sit together, and Dr. Oppenheimer, with his German accent and his pipe constantly at hand, would make suggestions. He could appear gruff and judgmental, and Frank later recounted how he painfully endured these critique sessions. The criticisms irritated him no end, and Frank would argue back at Oppenheimer, explaining why it had to be done that way.[19] Nevertheless, the pictures got done. In time, Frank came to realize that Dr. Oppenheimer—Oppy, as he called him—was driven by the pursuit of scientific knowledge. He possessed a real enthusiasm for the work. And Frank came to view Oppy's critical remarks not only as wise counsel but also as encouragement and admiration for the work.

In 1952, Dr. Oppenheimer retired from his position as vice president for research. He looked forward to a peaceful life, without the stress that comes with being a high-powered executive. On a visit to San Francisco, the Oppenheimers decided they wanted to retire in that area. They found a home high on an idyllic wooded hillside north of the city in Mill Valley, with a lovely view of the valley below.

Then Paul Roder got the idea for Ciba to sponsor a series of atlases depicting the anatomy and pathology of the human organism, devoting a separate volume to each system of the human body. When Ciba asked Frank to do it, he estimated it would take 10 years to complete the atlases, and for that time Roder wanted Frank's full attention to the project. The contract was drawn up, and George Netter, as Frank's attorney, negotiated the details. It was for 10 years, during which Frank would agree to devote himself exclusively to the project, and Ciba would pay him a premium not to make pictures for any other pharmaceutical company. Frank would continue to make illustrations for *Clinical Symposia* while creating the atlases.[20]

In 1952, Frank signed the contract with Ciba for the production of illustrations for the atlases. Like the 1948 volume, this series of atlases was to be called *The Ciba Collection of Medical Illustrations*. With that agreement, Ciba became Frank's sole patron. Frank gained the ongoing financial support he required to keep making pictures, and in return Ciba would earn a reputation for service to the medical community.

Dr. Oppenheimer agreed to come out of retirement to work with Ciba on the new project and become the editor of *The Ciba Collection*, directing production of the volumes from his mountainside home. The two of them, Frank and Oppy, laid out a plan for 8 to 10 volumes, listing the systems that the project would illustrate, although they recognized that some systems might require more than one tome. Much of the communication between them was by mail. Once in a while, Frank went to see Oppy in Mill Valley. They sat on the terrace at the Oppenheimer home overlooking the valley, two souls enthused by the project before them. "Between us, then," wrote Frank, "there was a sort of communion, a common interest never spoken but clearly understood."[21]

The first in the series of atlases was *Nervous System*,[22] which appeared in 1953. It used many of the plates that Frank had prepared previously for articles in *Clinical Symposia*. In the 33 issues of *Clinical Symposia* that Ciba had released by 1952, 22 of the articles featured Frank's illustrations on topics of the anatomy and pathology of the brain and spinal column and the autonomic nervous system.[23] The distinguished collaborators who had prepared the text to accompany each plate in those issues—Drs. Abraham Kaplan,[24] Gerhardt von Bonin,[25] and Albert Kuntz[26]—are credited in *Nervous System.*

The plan was for this volume to serve the practicing physician in identifying the neurologic aspects in all fields of medicine. Relevance to clinical application was the primary goal, so it was indexed for reference. Dr. John F. Fulton wrote in the foreword that Frank's being a doctor imparted superb clarity and instructive value to the plates. Alfred W. Custer at Ciba prepared a brief biography of Frank for the volume and therein made the erroneous statement that Frank was born in Brooklyn, an error perpetuated for decades. The book was in the same large format as the 1948 volume, and Ciba sold it to the medical profession at cost. The green buckram cover had a black square on the front on which was printed the book's title and Frank's name in gold block letters, so that doctors and students began calling the series the green books. Within two years, both first and second printings of *Nervous System* had sold out.[27]

The book was such a success that in the spring of 1953 Ciba sent Frank and Mary to Europe for him to meet the executives at Ciba headquarters in Basel. It was a big deal to go to Europe in the early 1950s. To prepare, the Netters studied French from phonograph records, but they did not learn much. Mary, always afraid of flying, insisted they travel on separate airplanes, but she had no concerns about their riding together in the car to Idlewild Airport. One flew on Pan Am, and the other on TWA, stopping to refuel in Nova Scotia. After sitting 16 hours on the plane, the propellers whirling and four engines humming in their ears, they landed at Le Bourget in Paris. "Imagine me!" he exclaimed. "Me! Frank Netter! Here on the Champs-Élysées!"[28] It was an exciting adventure, a two-week tour, from Paris to Basel, where Frank met with the people at Ciba, then to Venice and on to see Mary's brother Doodle, by then a major general stationed in Trieste,[29] then to Rome, where before returning to New York Frank bought a silk suit, a deep-mustard-colored one in the new continental cut.

᠗ᡧᡬᡫᡦᡬᡧᡖ

Reproductive System[30] was the next volume of *The Ciba Collection* to be published. There were 233 plates in the volume, of which 144 Ciba had published previously in *Clinical Symposia* or the Ciba portfolios. Dr. Joe Gaines and Dr. Isidor C. Rubin were both at Mount Sinai and had prepared *Clinical Symposia* articles, and the plates from those were reused in *Reproductive System*. Dr. Samuel Vest at the University of Virginia had written *Clinical Symposia* articles from which Ciba reused 63 plates, but he collaborated again with Frank on 14 new plates made for the volume. Ciba was also able to reuse some plates from the series of portfolios Frank had done in the 1940s, with the addition of new text by Dr. Charles F. Geschickter, at Georgetown University Medical School, and Dr. Robert A. Hingson, at Western Reserve School of Medicine.[31]

Frank made only 89 new plates specifically for the volume, and the authors, leaders in their field, added the text. Dr. Somers H. Sturgis at Harvard Medical School consulted on six new plates for the volume,[32] and he asked Dr. George W. Mitchell, Jr. to write some of the text on the anatomy of the female genital tract and on diseases of the vagina.[33] Dr. Mitchell was young then, in his thirties and just starting out, and he met Frank for the first time in Boston and subsequently went to Long Island, stayed overnight at Folly Farm and worked with Frank there. "I was impressed with the estate," Dr. Mitchell recalled, "the acres of rhododendron that were in bloom at the time, the stately rooms, and the dining table that looked like it could seat 50 people. 'Not quite that many,' his wife [Mary] said, 'but if you see any of the furniture you like, it is all for sale.'"[34]

Dr. Mitchell found Frank to be kind and thoughtful, interested in others, and willing to talk about himself, about his early life during the Great Depression and about being able to make a living with his pictures. "He was a superb anatomist," Dr. Mitchell remembered. "I sometimes thought that he knew more about it than I did myself. He was a tremendous study, but easygoing. His art had a flair to it and was very attractive."[35]

Dr. Oppenheimer worked with Frank to develop a plate on gonadal relationships.[36] It is an interesting plate, illustrating both the male and female hormone flows from the pituitary, showing in one picture the male on the left and the female on the right, thereby emphasizing the similarities and differences of gender. Dr. John Rock at Harvard Medical School wrote the foreword to the volume.

Harold Davison was the representative from the Embassy Photo Engraving Company, the company Ciba used for reproducing Frank's pictures. Harold made several trips to Folly Farm to pick up the artwork from Frank, each time returning with the original art and the letterpress proofs. He and Frank examined the proofs, comparing them to the original art, and reviewed the reproduction quality of each picture before Colorpress began the printing process.

The first printing of *Reproductive System* appeared in 1954. As did the *Nervous System* volume, it served as a clinical reference and presented both the normal and the diseased. Many more consultants contributed to this volume than to the previous one, but inconsistencies and duplications were avoided with detailed planning and by the proofreaders at Ciba who pored over the text. The purpose of the book was to present the medical facts—anatomy, embryology, physiology of the male and female reproductive systems. The scope did not include pictures of obstetrics or the detail of how to do the surgical procedures, only the concept that the procedures could be done. Thus, it served the purpose of the general practitioner and not so much that of the specialist.

In general, the books and articles that Ciba published were beautifully done and made a large contribution to the distribution of medical knowledge. The atlases had no advertising copy whatsoever, and *Clinical Symposia* carried minimal advertising for Ciba pharmaceuticals. Ciba gave the authors copies of the books, and as subsequent books came out, sent them those as well. If there were slides, Ciba sent sets of those to the authors, which they generally found helpful in their teaching.

CHAPTER 12

PALM BEACH

AT HER ANTIQUE SHOP, Mary came in contact with some interesting people. Among her clientele were old-money gentility and deposed Old World royalty, as well as the many decorators and theater people with whom she did business. Her friends included Princess Marta and the Archduke Franz Josef of Austria, and Marguerite Cassini, the Italian countess, who had two famous sons, Oleg, the fashion designer, and Igor, who wrote the *Cholly Knickerbocker* society column for the *New York Journal-American*.[1] The Countess, as Mary called her, had lived in Russia for many years when her father had worked for the tsar, and she had married Russian diplomat Alexander Loiewski. Countess Cassini introduced Mary to some of the exiled Russian nobility who had taken up residence in New York, and Mary cultivated those friendships, as it was perhaps good for the Gold Dolphin to have her name known in those circles. She also liked the idea of cavorting with so-called royalty and took an interest in learning to speak Russian; but as with learning French, she never progressed past being able to speak a few words.

One of the people Mary met through Countess Cassini was Elizabeth Seversky. Although not royalty, Elizabeth had a certain allure, a charisma that Mary liked immediately. Elizabeth was a woman of stunning glamour who had developed a method of elongating her eyelashes using ordinary cotton and cake mascara. She had a little dog, a miniature pinscher whom she named Gigolo, and she put little Gigolo in her purse and traveled out to Folly Farm with him. So enchanting was Elizabeth with those eyelashes and that little dog that she convinced Mary to buy the patent for the eyelash formula.

In late 1953, Mary and Cornelia traipsed off to Palm Beach with Elizabeth, Mary exploring whether that enclave of the rich offered opportunities for the Gold Dolphin, and Elizabeth prospecting for a husband. They visited the ritzy shops and looked at real estate, examining the decor in the houses that were being offered for sale.

Just a few blocks south of fashionable Worth Avenue, halfway between the elegant Breakers Hotel in the center of town and Mar-a-Lago, Marjorie Merriweather Post's fabulous palace to the south, they found a sorely neglected oceanfront home.[2] Ever-present breezes off the Atlantic Ocean cooled the two-story Moorish-Mediterranean-style mansion, and salt spray assaulted the building and clouded the windows. The house was in need of major updating and was just the thing for a Gold Dolphin makeover. Mary bought the house on the spot, and the three women moved right in without linens or the barest necessities. Elizabeth came to the rescue, arriving at the house with Gigolo in her purse and an entourage trailing behind her, carrying sheets and towels and toiletries. She had batted those eyelashes at the manager of the Colony Hotel, and he loaned her whatever niceties the ladies might want or need. Mary and Cornelia set about taking measurements and making plans for the renovation and decoration of the house, planning its transformation into the loveliest of homes.

The gardens needed only grooming, and hiring a gardener quickly solved that, but the house needed major work. Off came the red barrel-tile roof; on went cool, flat white tiles. Up came the buckling rubber-tile floors; down went smooth terrazzo poured in long diamond patterns. In came a new kitchen and baths. Onto the living room walls went French-style paneling, the signature of Mary's designs, but the pecky cypress paneling remained in the spacious two-story entry hall. Together, Mary and Cornelia laid out the floor plans for furniture Mary would ship down from New York while Cornelia, who had gained interior decorating experience working at the Gold Dolphin, would stay in Florida to supervise the workmen and oversee the installation. As Mary had done at Folly Farm, she put each of the beds sideways to the door, instead of opposite it.

ᘛᘚᘛᘚᘛᘚ

The renovations on the Palm Beach house were nearly completed by mid-September 1954. Frank packed up his studio, and he and the children[3] walked out of Folly Farm, leaving that grand mansion with only Vera Stetson working in the back office, and went to live in Palm Beach. Mary stayed in New York, living in a house she had bought on East 57th Street,[4] managing the Gold Dolphin and overseeing the selection of furniture for the Palm Beach residence. She would come to Florida later.

Palm Beach was a sleepy little town in the off-season, when shops closed and maintenance crews literally removed stoplights from their posts and replaced them with stop signs. The season ran from mid-October through April, with the high season running January through March.

Eastern Air Lines, headquartered in Miami, monopolized air travel along the East Coast. Once or twice a week, the airline offered a direct flight between New York and West Palm Beach, but more frequently Eastern's fleet of Lockheed Constellation and Douglas DC-7 piston-driven propeller planes made the run between Idlewild or LaGuardia Airport and Miami in somewhat over four hours, and passengers to West Palm Beach changed to the smaller DC-3 for the bumpy ride to the West Palm Beach airport. Down the steps to the tarmac they came, Frank, Jim walking next to him, Francine and Jonathan trailing behind like baby ducks following their mother. The West Palm Beach airport, giving no hint of the modern facility it would become, was then just a one-room ticket counter, resembling a rural train station, with the baggage claim area outside. Cornelia met them at the airport and took them in the car over the bridge to Palm Beach, down the wide Royal Palm Way esplanade to the ocean, then on South Ocean Boulevard just a few blocks to their new home.

The Palm Beach house was not nearly as large as Folly Farm but nevertheless was an elegant mansion in its own right. The front entrance was not ornate, opening into the large two-story entry hall paneled in pecky cypress. Straight ahead was the sun-drenched loggia, three Palladian windows on the left facing the ocean, on the right three arched entries to the dining room with three Palladian glass doors to a terrace and gardens. At the far end of the loggia was the stately living room, Palladian windows all around, and outside just beyond was the large salt-water swimming pool. The grand staircase in the entry hall led to the four bedrooms upstairs, the master suite overlooking the pool. Again, as at Folly Farm, there were no live-in servants, and on the north end of the top floor, in what had been the servants' wing, Frank set up his studio. Here, as at Folly Farm, Frank maintained an open-door policy in his studio, where the children were welcome to come and watch him work and talk about their day.

In that sleepy town, the younger Netter children had more freedom than they had previously known. They had the ocean at their doorstep and a pool in the yard, and they settled into their school routines at Palm Beach Private School. Frank bought a red MG-TD roadster—not a safe car, but not a fast car—and Jim could be seen driving down County Road and around Palm Beach in that MG. Francine rode her bicycle wherever she wanted to go on the island—to school, for shopping, to tennis lessons, or to visit a new friend. She joined the church choir at the Episcopal Church of Bethesda-by-the-Sea. Frank did not himself practice religion, but he encouraged Francine to maintain her relationship with the Episcopal Church. It was a home she would always have, he told her.

The Palm Beach Pier at the end of Worth Avenue—subsequently swept away in a series of storms in the 1960s[5]—was a favorite spot for Frank and Jonny to go in the evenings. The two of them took drop lines and a bucket of shrimp bait and spent many hours together fishing off the pier.

Weekdays, Frank went to town before breakfast to buy a cigar and the local newspaper at a small stationery store across from the ocean pier. On Sundays, he also bought a version of *The New York Times* that came from New York by airplane. He swam laps in the pool before dinner and took his meals with the children in the dining room. For supper on the cook's day off, he took the children over the bridge to a diner in West Palm Beach. Occasionally he took them to lunch at the Polo Club or the Colony Hotel. He did not have much of a social life but kept at his work.

From Palm Beach, he talked to Mary on the phone—when was she coming down, she could open a shop on Worth Avenue. Frank wrote letters to Mary begging her to come, saying that he continued to maintain a home for the children, and they wanted her there. Yes, she would come soon. She had to figure out when she could manage to get away from the Gold Dolphin, but it would be soon.

ᴑᴉᴑᴉᴑᴉᴑ

In 1954, Frank worked on a *Clinical Symposia* issue with Dr. Marvin Moser, who was in charge of vascular diseases at Walter Reed Army Medical Center. He was a hypertension expert and worked with Dr. Andrew G. Prandoni, an expert in peripheral vascular disease. Dr. Moser recalled:

> We were doing work on people with frostbite and people with vascular disease of all kinds, both due to inflammatory reactions with ulceration and with gangrene and all sorts of crazy things. We found that by injecting something in the artery instead of giving it by vein or by mouth you got a much better effect. Giving medication by arterial injection was not very common [then] because people were afraid of giving injections in arteries. Today, when you catheterize people, everyone goes into arteries. But in those days it was considered quite radical. We did 200 to 300 or more of these, and we showed dramatic improvement in ulcerations, preventing gangrene, and allowed for healing in people with pretty badly diseased limbs, from arteriosclerosis as well as from inflammatory vein diseases and arterial diseases. So that is where the illustrations came in.

We were working with Ciba because Ciba was the manu-
facturer of Priscoline, the drug we used. In those days they
never supported the research; they provided the material.
One of us contacted Ciba when we were about to report these
cases—and again there were about 250 of them—and [Ciba
got Frank] to illustrate it. He did a beautiful job, [showing] the
sites of the injections and some of the results we got. He was a
remarkable illustrator.[6]

∞∞∞∞

In the fall of 1954 Frank was beginning work on the third volume
of *The Ciba Collection of Medical Illustrations, Digestive System*. It was
the most ambitious project yet. One all-encompassing book on the
digestive system would have been so voluminous as to require a
lengthy production process and to be prohibitively expensive. For
that reason, Frank and Dr. Oppenheimer decided to publish the
volume in three tomes—Part I, *Upper Digestive Tract*; Part II, *Lower
Digestive Tract*; Part III, *Liver, Biliary Tract and Pancreas*—following
the traditional order in which the digestive system is normally
described. However, Frank worked first on making the pictures of
the large organs of digestion, and the first book published was Part III.[7]

One driving reason for choosing to work first on Part III, aside
from complying with incoming requests,[8] was that Frank had the
opportunity to work with Dr. Hans Popper, "the father of modern
hepatology,"[9] who was then at Cook County Hospital and Northwestern University Medical School in Chicago. It is clear from the
credits in the book that Dr. Popper contributed enormously to the
volume, serving as consultant on 107 of the 133 plates[10] and writing
a major portion of the text. Among his numerous publications, Dr.
Popper counted three *Clinical Symposia* issues—on jaundice,[11] on
hepatitis,[12] and on cirrhosis[13]—all with Frank's illustrations. Also,
at the time he started working on the *Ciba Collection* tome, Dr. Popper was just completing a major book[14] of his own about the structure and function of the liver.[15]

While the list of consultants is remarkably short—in all, just five consultants contributed,[16] and certainly Dr. Popper's contribution was enormous—it was supplemented by Frank's exhaustive review of the literature. The bibliography is extensive, having no fewer than 371 entries. Dr. Popper and the other consultants sent him some of the reference materials, but Frank's chief complaint about living in Palm Beach was that he had no access to a large medical library, as he had in New York at the Academy of Medicine. He either had to go to New York or ask the librarian to send him the books and journals. His second complaint was that when he did go to the medical library or to see consultants, travel to and from Palm Beach was difficult, as it was then somewhat remote. Nevertheless, Frank enjoyed Florida life in that elegant house on South Ocean Boulevard. The climate suited him, and he found some relief from the incessant sinus headaches he had suffered in New York.

⚜⚜⚜

From September until Christmas, Mary stayed in New York. Frank asked her to come to Florida, but she did not. Mary was afraid of flying, and delaying might have been her way of avoiding getting on an airplane. She finally did come to Florida, and having nothing suitable to wear, she went to Worth Avenue and bought two dresses—a blue Alençon lace sundress and a pale pink linen sheath—and shoes to go with each.

Those evenings, Mary and Frank sat in the living room and had cocktails before dinner. Mary was interested in the house and its decor, and what furniture to put where, and how should this or that be done. He expressed an interest in her plans for decorating, but it was just a visit, and then she abandoned him once more and went back to New York. It was about then that she met Sonny.

Winfield "Sonny" Aronberg was a theatrical attorney and a bachelor. For more than 10 years he had been Eugene O'Neill's attorney. He and O'Neill used to pal around, go to the racetrack together, go drinking in the jazz clubs, things like that.[17] Sonny saw

O'Neill through some tough alimony negotiations, the suicide of his eldest son, and the estrangement of two children. Only months before O'Neill died in November 1953, Sonny was dismissed as his attorney, ostensibly at the insistence of O'Neill's third wife, Carlotta. Sonny must have met Mary shortly afterward.

Sonny was a great joke teller; he always had a joke and a little spark in his eye. He was sort of a caricature of a sports columnist, a little bit of an ex-boxer in him. He had a lot of dash, but he dressed a bit shabbily, with jackets that did not hang properly, the pockets of his coat pushed down on the sides, and the crease in his pants a thing of the past. He had a large hooknose and thin gray hair. He stood about 6′ tall, although he had rounded shoulders and an old man's physique. But something in his personality must have been attractive to Mary. He took her to the horse races at Belmont and to the boxing matches at Madison Square Garden, and he taught her to whistle through her teeth. It was a world she had never seen, and it perhaps intrigued her.

ᘒᕲᘒᕲᘒᕲᘒ

It was one of those balmy February afternoons in Palm Beach, and Frank took time to go to the barber. For years, he kept his black wavy hair in the same style, long on the top, parted in the middle, and combed neatly back. He was not gone long, and on his return Francine's friend Dora Dixon met him at the door. The girls had been looking at the goldfish pond on the back terrace when Francine tripped and fell over the edge of the terrace 4 or 5′ to the landing below. Francine was now lying down in her bedroom with abdominal pain. He went to her room and examined her. "I think you have ruptured your spleen," Frank said more to himself than to her, because certainly the little girl in lying on the bed in her pink-and-white room did not understand what that was.

Palm Beach in those days was a sleepy winter resort, where the doctors saw few trauma cases, certainly not of the magnitude and variety Frank had seen at Bellevue and beyond. He called a local surgeon who came to the house, and after examining Francine offered to take out her appendix. Aghast, Frank stood at his daughter's bedside, the diagnosis clear in his mind that she was hemorrhaging internally. Desperate to get her the surgery to stop the bleeding, he chartered a plane to take Francine to New York that afternoon. He called his friend and colleague Sam Klein, who was a fine surgeon and had trained many interns and residents at The Mount Sinai Hospital in New York. Frank told Sam that he was bringing Francine to New York and to be prepared to operate. No, don't do that, Sam said. Get an ambulance. Take her to Miami Beach, to Mount Sinai Medical Center, where there is a very good young surgeon who trained under me. His name is Rudolph Drosd. So Frank took Francine to Miami Beach in a sleek and comfortable ambulance, different from the top-heavy boxy affairs he had ridden as an intern. Frank rode in the front with the driver for the 75-mile trip, daylight turning to dark, the lights on the highway shining on Francine's face in the back of the ambulance and Frank telling her to close her eyes and lie still.

At Mount Sinai Medical Center in Miami Beach, Francine seemed to spontaneously recover. Leaving Cornelia with instructions to take Francine home from the hospital, Frank went to New York. But when Francine then collapsed onto the hospital floor, there was no doubt that her spleen was ruptured and she was hemorrhaging. Dr. Drosd prepared to operate to remove her spleen, but the hospital staff had a terrible time getting permission for the surgery, he recalled,[18] as they were unable to locate her parents. But with Cornelia's help the staff tracked them down in New York and got permission. Frank and Mary took the next flight to Miami, but by the time they arrived at the hospital, Francine was out of surgery and in recovery. That was the last time she saw her parents together as a couple. When Francine left the hospital,[19] it was Mary's sister Renie who came to help the child readjust to life at home in Palm Beach. Mary was by then back in New York.

It was the beginning of May 1955 when Francine had recovered sufficiently for Frank to take her to lunch at the Polo Club. It was the Saturday of the Kentucky Derby, and after they were seated in the dining room, the club's events director, a pretty young woman, came to the table and invited Frank to join the party in the bar area to watch the race on television. "He was gone from the table only a few minutes," Francine remembered. "From the other room, I heard the raucous laughter of the men and women, and it seemed to me that the handsome and successful doctor–artist did not go unnoticed by the Palm Beach society ladies. He could have had a lively social life if he had so chosen, but he stayed pretty much to himself. He worked day and night, took a swim before dinner, and dined with his children."[20]

CHAPTER 13

BACK TO FOLLY FARM

THE ENSUING DIVORCE WAS bitter. It was ugly. It dragged on for nearly two years, with a lot of haggling over property and arrangements for the children; and it was mentioned in Igor Cassini's *Cholly Knickerbocker* newspaper column.

By late summer 1955, Frank and Mary agreed that she would take the Palm Beach house and that he would live at Folly Farm with the children. Frank packed up his studio in Palm Beach, and in August he and his children went back to New York, back to Folly Farm. They had all changed during that year in Florida. Frank had settled in to a quiet routine, and the children had grown more mature and independent, coming and going on their own. They found Folly Farm to be a sad, forsaken place. It had sat vacant for the past year.

Mary, who had taken up with Sonny Aronberg, stayed in New York City at the 57th Street house. In mid-October, in a letter addressed to Mary at the Gold Dolphin, her sister Katie wrote, "Think this over carefully—you've got a lot to lose . . . I can't visualize you leaving Frank for someone else . . . what has he got?"[1]

At the end of October, Frank went to Chicago to see Hans Popper in consultation for his work on the *Digestive System* Part III volume. On October 31, Frank surprised Katie, Mary's sister in North Carolina, with a phone call from Chicago. Mary had been there with him, he said, but had gone back to New York, and he wanted to know if Katie had heard from her. Katie tried to encourage him, and told him that she wished things could be worked out, that he and Mary were so right for each other, and that Mary had been such a help to him. No, he told Katie, Mary had not helped him.

Katie took the train to New York that week and met Mary at the Gold Dolphin on Thursday, November 4. She went there only to see Mary, not Renie or anyone else. You should go back to Frank, she told Mary. Your children need you.[2]

On her return trip, Katie stopped in Washington to see their brother Aubrey. He was distressed to learn of the rift between Frank and Mary, and that evening he penned a four-page letter to Mary. You and Frank helped each other in your successes, he wrote. You are a team, and you risk losing it all. It will wreck your family, and you will lose your friends. And the children, think of the children. "Whatever the differences between you, I can imagine none which an honest apology or concession should not bridge. And I plead that both of you not go into criminations and recriminations that will make mending of your differences difficult."[3]

"I was also enormously fond of Mary." Richard Netter said. "And it was a sad part of my life when they were divorced. She was a brilliant student, brilliant. And she was so competitive with the world, you know, to be the best doctor. When Frank surpassed her in his medical achievements, then she quit. She could not catch him. But she was quite a gal."[4]

⚜︎⚜︎⚜︎

When Frank returned to Folly Farm after the year in Florida, he bought a big boat of a car, a 1955 Chrysler Imperial in a deep mustard gold color, with tail fins, wrap-around windshield, and cream-colored leather upholstery. Special license plates with a prominent "MD" identified the car as belonging to a doctor. When doctors still made house calls, police extended a courtesy to drivers of cars with MD plates, allowing them to park in certain restricted parking zones.

For an appointment in New York Frank dressed in his Italian suit—by chance the same mustard gold color as his car. He wore a custom-made black shirt—he had all his shirts custom-made—and a white silk necktie, the same color as the Chrysler's leather upholstery. He drove into the city and parked on the street. After his meeting he returned to the car and as he fumbled with his keys a policeman approached him. The ensuing conversation went along these lines:

"What are you doing?" the policeman asked.

"I am getting in my car."

"This your car?"

"Yes. This is my car."

"You a doctor?" said the officer, looking at the MD plates.

"Yes. I am a doctor." Frank had the car door open now.

"You don't look like a doctor."

"No? What do I look like?"

"A gangster."

Frank liked to tell that story. He thought it was funny. He had lots of stories, true stories and silly joke stories. Whenever he spoke to an audience about his illustrations, he liked to begin by telling a funny story. He had one story he called the Uncle Pincus story, and another story about a British barrister, which he concluded with a moral as to the value of properly illustrated documents.

On January 11, 1956, Frank gave a lecture to the New York Academy of Medicine before the Section on Historical and Cultural Medicine.[5] His was one of three papers for a program on art and medicine,[6] and it was subsequently published as "Medical Illustration, Its History, Significance and Practice," in the May 1957 issue of the *Bulletin of the New York Academy of Medicine*.[7] In it, Frank elaborated on the function of medical illustrations and how they have aided the advancement of knowledge and the progress of surgery. He told of Leonardo da Vinci's study of anatomy; of Andreas Vesalius's published medical illustrations; and of the work in the eighteenth century of Scottish obstetrician William Hunter and his brother, surgeon John Hunter. Frank then described how "the development of medical illustration went hand in hand with improvement in the [printing] reproductive process"[8]—lithography, photoengraving, halftone screening, and the four-color process. Modern illustrators he mentioned were Max Brödel at Johns Hopkins and Tom Jones at the University of Illinois at Chicago. He told of his own career, how he got started, about the

Transparent Woman, The Life of a Doctor, his work in the army, and *The Ciba Collection.* He explained how he made a medical illustration, beginning with the study and work with a consultant; then making the sketch and deciding on the vantage point, the plane of dissection, and the focus of the picture; and finishing with the painting.

ଚ❧ଚ୶ଚ❧ଚ

For *Clinical Symposia,* Frank collaborated with many of the world's outstanding physicians. He made these contacts through various means—some Frank knew or were referred by colleagues or other collaborators, some the Ciba staff met at one or another medical convention, and others sent unsolicited proposals to Ciba. By whatever means the topics were chosen and authors selected, Frank made the pictures and the consultants wrote the articles about their pioneering research and clinical breakthroughs.

One of the authors was Dr. Michael DeBakey at Baylor University, whom Frank knew from their days together in the army. Between 1950 and 1953, Dr. DeBakey developed a method to use Dacron grafts to replace a diseased portion of the aorta.[9] Frank went down to Texas, and he and Mike DeBakey sat for hours talking about just one aspect of the procedure, and about how they were going to organize the article. Mike gave Frank a draft of what he was going to say in the article, and together they worked out what illustrations Frank was going to make. Frank first wanted to understand everything. He visited in the operating room, so as "to grasp it fully, to see it, to understand it thoroughly as if he were the surgeon," recalled Dr. DeBakey. "It became more than just a picture for him. He wanted to reflect the concept."[10] Frank then began to sketch the illustrations. When they were satisfied with the sketches, Frank took them back to his studio to paint the pictures and Mike wrote the final draft, making sure that what he wrote was effectively what Frank had drawn. Dr. DeBakey described their collaboration this way:

He was a very interesting person to be with. I never heard him say a serious criticism or characterization of anybody. I am sure he had some tough people to deal with, but he never complained, you know. He was a relatively happy person. I enjoyed so much being with him. It was so easy to work with Frank. He was just comfortable anywhere, polite, you know. Of course, that's because he was a fine character, just a fine person, a real gentleman.[11]

The *Clinical Symposia* article they did together showed the surgical procedures in reverse order from the chronology of their development in practice. The first aneurysm operation that Dr. DeBakey and his team developed was for the abdominal aorta. After the success of that procedure, they attempted to repair an aneurysm of the thoracic aorta. When they succeeded with that too, they operated on the ascending aorta, and then the aortic arch. As they succeeded with each operation, they operated higher and higher, moving up the aorta, finally developing the procedure for the arch resection. But in the article, Dr. DeBakey began with a description of the surgery of the aortic arch and worked down the aorta to the thorax and then the abdomen. Frank illustrated the article, "Surgery of the Aorta,"[12] which was published in *Clinical Symposia* in 1956.

ᏇᏇᏇᏇᏇ

No sooner had Frank completed pictures of hepatitis for an issue of *Clinical Symposia*[13] authored by Dr. Hans Popper than he himself came down with the disease. The jaundice was unmistakable, even with his olive skin, and in early 1956 he was hospitalized in New York, where the prescribed treatment was bed rest and a low-fat diet.

After his discharge, he went home from the hospital with instructions to rest and not to work. He was confined to his bedroom, although sometimes for a change of scene he snuck downstairs to the living room to rest on a purple sofa. He did not much care for watching television, other than the news. He read a few uninteresting mystery novels. Wearing his bathrobe, he took his meals—bland, as they were devoid of fat—in the large dining room. As he sat at his place at the head of the table, bored to death, the large expanse of the table before him, he got the idea to paint a garland of cabbage roses around the top of the dining-room table to match the floral pattern in the Aubusson rug on the floor. If he was not allowed to work, at least he would not be bored.

Up to his studio he went, and with his pencils and pad of tracing paper back down to the dining room he came. Over the next few days, still wearing his bathrobe, he made several sketches of the garland that he then transferred to the tabletop, interconnecting them to fit together around the table. He then retrieved his oil paints from the studio and began applying paint to the tabletop. It was a lovely sight, the painted roses he created beautifully echoing the garland in the Aubusson. The three table leaves, however, presented a problem, a real tedium, because when one or more of the leaves was added, the pattern still had to match and flow together on both sides of each leaf. But he persisted, and after many days it was done. Making medical pictures was no more difficult than getting that garland matched across those table leaves, so back to his studio to his medical pictures he went.

⚬╉⚬⚬╉⚬⚬╉⚬

The divorce settlement agreement that Frank and Mary signed in June 1956 consisted of 50 pages.[14] Mary sold the Palm Beach house and kept the New York townhouse where she lived, as well as Forrest and its patents. She also kept Elizabeth Seversky's eyelash-elongation patent, although nothing ever came of it. In exchange, Frank took both Folly Farm and the 54th Street buildings housing the Gold Dolphin, which went out of business. Frank did not pay alimony. He paid Mary an amount each year for 10 years, whether or not she remarried. Sonny might have suggested that arrangement to her. He had previously argued against alimony for an agreement signed by Eugene O'Neill.[15] Mary might have agreed to it because she was planning to marry Sonny. If she remarried, alimony would stop.

Custody arrangements for the minor children, Francine and Jonathan, were that they continue to reside with Frank and spend holidays and the summer with Mary. Francine remembered being shuttled from Folly Farm to 57th Street for their first visit on Christmas Day in 1955, when the divorce was still pending. They spent several days in New York, during which time Mary and Sonny took them to the American Museum of Natural History, ice skating in the old Madison Square Garden,[16] and then down to Chinatown to eat. In the morning Mary and Countess Cassini tried to braid Francine's long hair, but they could not quite manage the hairstyle. "At the end of the visit," Francine remembered, "Daddy came to the 57th Street house and rang the bell. I was standing right there when my mother opened the door, and when she saw him she threw her arms around his neck and cried, 'Oh, Frank!' He just stood there, stiff with his arms down at his sides, and turned his head away. Then we left."[17]

It was February the next time they visited their mother. At the end of the visit, when the doorbell rang, Mary opened the door to find a uniformed chauffeur. The driver gave Mary a note, handwritten on stationery from the elegant Hyde Park Hotel[18] on Madison Avenue: "Mary—This will authorize the bearer, a Carey Limousine chauffeur, to pick up the children and deliver them to me. Frank."[19]

She recognized his handwriting, of course, and put her children—9 and 10 years old—in the back of the limousine and sent them out into the dark city. The driver brought them to the hotel, where Frank and a pretty, dark-haired, somewhat plump middle-aged woman and another couple were having dinner in the restaurant.

At the children's Easter-time visit to Mary, a driver again called for them. He brought them to a nice apartment building and led them upstairs to the door of an apartment. The dark-haired woman answered the door. Frank was standing behind her and welcomed his children into the small living room. Francine remembered:

> It was a pretty room. A pink-and-red floral chintz overstuffed couch was the main piece of furniture, and alongside was a skirted lamp table covered with figurines and knickknacks. I remember sitting on a wooden bench near the door while they went to another room for a minute. I could hear them talking—her saying, "Come on, Frank," and him, "No, not with the children here"—and then he came and took us home. I was a little girl and very naïve, having been raised in the seclusion of Folly Farm, but as I think back on it, he must have been very lonely, working alone in the studio day and night, taking his meals by himself in that big empty palace of a house on Long Island, and wanting some companionship. The breakup of his marriage was a big loss for him. He was dating that woman, but I never saw her again, and I do not think he saw her much after that night.[20]

From 1954 through 1956 was a time of great personal turmoil for him, yet Frank made the pictures for some 25 issues of *Clinical Symposia*, in addition to those for Part III, Volume 3, *Digestive System*, which was published in 1957.[21] Amazing progress had been made in the medical knowledge during that time, and before the tome went to press, Frank had to revise some pictures he had made in 1954 during the early work on the book. In the introduction, which Frank wrote in early 1956, he said, "The unstinting efforts and gracious devotion to the project of Mrs. Vera Stetson, assistant to Dr. Netter, contributed much to ease and expedite the task."[22]

CHAPTER 14

VERA

MARY VERA BURROWS WAS born on July 26, 1901, in a sweltering New York City tenement on West 40th Street and 9th Avenue.[1] It was only a few blocks from where Frank would be born five years later, but a different neighborhood entirely. Here was Hell's Kitchen, with its slaughterhouses and railroad yards, an area fraught with crime and corruption, home to notorious gangs as well as to poor and working-class Irish Americans.

Vera's mother, Henrietta McKinley, had come to the United States from Ireland in 1876 at the age of three. She married at 15 and was just 16 years old when Beatrice, the first child, was born.[2] Vera was the fifth of six children that Henrietta had by the age of 31. Their father, Harry Burrows, worked at various jobs—laundryman,[3] collector,[4] and, eventually, insurance adjuster.[5] But before Vera reached her fifth birthday, Harry had abandoned the family.[6] And Henrietta moved with her children from Hell's Kitchen. By 1930, Henrietta, with the help of her children, had bought a small house in Ozone Park, Queens. She lived there with Vera and another daughter, the youngest child. Vera was then 28 and working as a secretary in a bank.[7]

Little is known about Vera's first marriage except that in 1933 she was divorced in Chicago from a man by the name of John Bruns,[8] and there appear to have been no children from that marriage. Vera's second marriage was to James D. Stetson, who worked as a broker in New York.[9] He was ten years her senior, was twice married previously, with two grown children. Vera had one son by that marriage, John Pate Stetson, born in December 1936.[10] James's family apparently did not approve of the union, and when he died in early 1953[11] his brother spirited the body away to be buried in the family plot in Asheville, North Carolina. Afterward his family had little to do with Vera or the boy.[12]

Thereafter, Vera and her son, John, lived with her widowed sister, Beatrice, on Perry Avenue in Bayville, Long Island,[13] in a house left to the sisters by their aunt. Bayville was a quiet, middle-class community overlooking Long Island Sound, situated between the more opulent North Shore communities of Mill Neck and Locust Valley. Lace curtains hung on the windows of the small white clapboard house the women shared. Vera and John occupied tidy but bland, colorless rooms in the main part of the house, while Beatrice lived in a cheerful, light-filled room added on to the rear of the house where she sat and chain-smoked cigarettes. In June the garden just outside her door overflowed with blooms of salmon pink roses. By the mid-1950s, the sisters' closest kin were a brother, George, and his wife, Gladys, in California; a niece; and several nephews.

☙❧☙❧☙❧

Vera was coming and going to work by the back door at Folly Farm and kept to herself in her small office in the servants' wing. When Frank was to be divorced, she saw her opportunity. She bobbed and blonded her hair, had her teeth fixed, and bought stylish new clothes. She patted on face powder she bought at B. Altman department store, darkened her brows with a brow pencil, and swiped a bit of shadow on her lids and pink lipstick on her lips. She was never without pink polish on her nails. She clipped on earrings and cinched her waist with a belt. Now, in this new persona, Vera personally made a tray and took lunch upstairs to Frank in his studio. There they sat, the two of them at his small conference table, eating lunch together.

She would go home from her job at Folly Farm, and Frank would come to pick her up at her house for a date. He took Vera to dinner and dancing. They enrolled in a dance class to learn all the ballroom dances and practiced their steps on the marble floor of the pool room at Folly Farm. She praised him and laughed at his jokes, and he gave her an emerald cocktail ring.

Frank and Vera married on December 30, 1956. The wedding was a Protestant ceremony at the home of Vera's friends William and Kay MacDonald, in Manhasset. Beatrice was matron of honor, and Frank's brother, George, was best man. Afterward, they threw a party for about 100 guests, with dinner and dancing at the Brookville Country Club. An announcement in the following day's *New York Times* reported the wedding.[14]

The newlyweds honeymooned in Europe, traveling for two weeks to England, through France to Switzerland, Italy, Spain, and Portugal. The trip allowed Frank time to meet with consultants for the next volume of *The Ciba Collection*, Part I of *Digestive System*. In Manchester, England, Frank met with Professor George A.G. Mitchell[15] to discuss the anatomy and innervation of the esophagus and stomach. In Basel, Frank stopped to meet with Dr. Rudolph Nissen[16] and Professor Gerhard Wolf-Heidegger[17] to discuss the anatomy and diseases of the stomach.

Frank and Vera went to Italy, where they bought a Murano glass chandelier, and then to Spain. In Madrid, Frank visited the Museo Nacional del Prado to see, among other great paintings, Velázquez's massive[18] *Las Hilanderas*. Completed in 1657, it depicts the fable of Arachne, the greatest weaver in ancient Greece, who in her vanity challenged the goddess Athena to a weaving contest. In the foreground of the painting, Arachne and Athena sit spinning, and in the background is a display of the completed tapestries. Arachne of course loses the contest, and Athena turns her into a spider, doomed to spin forever. It is this great masterpiece for which Frank had what he believed to be a preliminary sketch.

At the Prado, Frank met with painter Fernando Álvarez de Sotomayor y Zaragoza, curator at the museum, and showed him a snapshot of his small painting. Señor Sotomayor was most interested and told Frank that Velázquez was known to have made such preliminary studies. He asked Frank to send him a better photograph, which Frank promised to do as soon as he returned home. But before Frank could send it, he learned that Señor Sotomayor had died, so for the time being at least, Frank's efforts to authenticate his painting were stalled.[19]

⟡⟡⟡⟡⟡⟡⟡

Vera could do much more for Frank as his wife than as his secretary. She arranged his social calendar. She hosted parties. She accompanied him on business trips. She had Frank make charitable contributions to various organizations, which led to invitations to social functions, debutante balls, and charity dinners. She joined the committee to plan a dinner dance to benefit the Long Island Little Orchestra Society.[20] She cultivated new friendships among society matrons, and she planned luncheons to entertain the doctors with whom Frank collaborated. Theirs was a traditional marriage. He provided the means, and she provided the social activities. She typed his letters, managed his calendar, and ran the household, which freed him to concentrate on his work. Vera had her origins in New York City, as did Frank, but she was not his peer. She was his complement.

It was not long after Frank and Vera had returned from Europe, early in 1957, when Francine came home from school, went up the grand staircase, and turned to go to the studio. Vera was just coming out and stood in front of the door, blocking the way. You children don't bother him, she told Francine. He has to work. Go away now. The studio door, always open in the past, Vera now closed behind her.

At Folly Farm, there were other changes. Frank subdivided 50 acres at the back of the estate and offered the land for sale.[21] "The price went to $2500 an acre," he recollected years later when land was selling for 200 times that, "and at the time I thought it would never go any higher."[22] He sold the back acreage, the garage, the stable, the barn, and the caretaker's cottage. The back service drive became Linden Lane, a private road named for the stately trees lining both sides. The mansion still sat on 15 acres, with a tennis court, swimming pool, rose garden, and the long, unobstructed front drive.[23]

After working all day making pictures in his studio, Frank shaved and cleaned up and came down to the blue room for cocktails with Vera before the family dined together at a table set up in the butler's pantry. Frank made Vera a gift of a champagne miniature poodle he named Jolie, and that well-behaved little dog fit herself into their everyday routine. Vera often smiled but did not laugh much, and she frowned at off-color jokes. It was a genteel life, without the great passion that Frank had shared with the mother of his children.

ᛰᚤᛰᚤᛰᚤᛰ

Frank was 50 years old and in his prime as an artist. His pictures from that time are some of the most beautiful of his career. In collaboration with Ernst W. Lampe at Columbia University, Frank made exquisite pictures of the hand for a *Clinical Symposia* article[24] that appeared in 1957. That article became a classic on the anatomy and surgery of the hand.

Also in 1957, Ciba published a *Clinical Symposia* article by Dr. Frank J. Ayd, Jr. with psychiatric portraits.[25] Those pictures capture the essence of the appearance of people with various neuroses—the depressed man in his disheveled clothes and mismatched socks, one red, one blue; the anxious woman sitting forward in her chair wringing her hands; the prim and rigid obsessive woman; the overly confident deluded man leaning back in his chair, legs crossed; the nervous woman, her stockings falling down and her clothes in need of repair.

Frank did two *Clinical Symposia* issues with superb anatomist Dr. John Franklin Huber, one on the anatomy of the mouth[26] and another on the anatomy of the pharynx,[27] both of which appeared in 1958. Frank visited Dr. Huber several times at Temple University, and that collaboration resulted in some of the finest anatomical pictures of Frank's career. The pictures of the mouth and pharynx are classic representations of the blood supply and of the nerves of that area.[28] The picture of the interior of the pharynx[29] is a clear and precise illustration of the anatomy, but the symmetry and color also evoke a certain artistic modernism and abstract aesthetic.

Medicine was advancing rapidly, faster than Frank could paint, prolific as he was. Almost as soon as the first edition of the *Nervous System*[30] volume appeared in 1953, Frank knew he would need to update it, but his schedule did not permit going back to that volume. He worked with W.R. Ingram to prepare a *Clinical Symposia* issue on the hypothalamus,[31] published in 1956. That publication was appended to the third and later printings[32] of the *Nervous System* volume as a supplement.[33]

In the 1950s, the surgeon-in-chief at Children's Hospital of Philadelphia was Dr. C. Everett Koop. He was operating on infants with "congenital defects incompatible with life, but nevertheless amenable to surgical correction," Dr. Koop explained. "These are things like kids born without a rectum or with intestinal obstruction, or their abdominal organs up in the chest, or a connection between their esophagus and windpipe and so forth. And at the time that we did it, this surgery was considered to be as esoteric as anything you could do in medicine."[34]

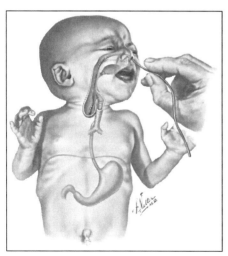

"Emergency Surgery of the Newborn," Frank H. Netter, Clinical Symposia *volume 11, number 2, 1959, cover, courtesy of Elsevier.*

Frank worked with Dr. Koop in 1958 to prepare an article for a *Clinical Symposia* issue[35] detailing some of the surgical procedures. They met a couple of times in New York and talked over what they were going to do, and then Frank wanted to go to Philadelphia to observe the surgeries. The man who was to become United States Surgeon General recalled:

> These patients were sometimes few and far and between. Sometimes none for three months, and then they came in three in the same week. The baby might be born in a place like Wilkes-Barre, Pennsylvania, and the doctor there would refer the baby to me. Sometimes they were middle-of-the-night emergencies. The case might not have gotten to Children's Hospital until around ten o'clock at night. Then the team did a workup, and we started operating at 12:00 in the morning, and operated all night. When I knew I was going to do an operation, I telephoned him [Frank] to let him know and he'd come down. He spent maybe four days in our operating room and in addition we spent four half days going over the pictures and being sure that they were what we wanted to show.
>
> What came out of it was a good summary of that newborn surgery. I remember going over it and looking at every detail. What a thrill it was the first time I held that [issue] in my hand, to realize that the pediatric profession now would have proof positive in the hands of an observer that these are things that could be done and that you could save lives! Up until that time, the whole outlook for newborn surgery was very, very depressing. Many of those babies were just put in the corner of the nursery to die. The state of pediatric surgery in this country was abysmal—very high mortalities, anesthesia was terrible. A small band of us were pioneers in the field and turned that around, and Frank Netter was part of that. That very graphic little book made it clear to pediatricians that those babies could be sent to a pediatric surgeon and could be salvaged. The publication of that little

Symposia, which went to most of the doctors in the land, was one of the best ways we could let the medical profession know that times had changed and you could have a very sick newborn with a surgical problem that would kill him, but it could be corrected.

I was a very young man then, and I thought Frank Netter was up with the gods. I was very flattered. I was sewing an intestine that was about as big as a piece of wet spaghetti. It is very hard to see that in a photograph. But in his drawings, you know, he made them stand out. Frank reduced very complex anatomical problems to things that seemed to the observer to be relatively simple. Now, that doesn't mean it is simple for the surgeon, but it was simple to understand for the people who refer patients to surgeons. In a sense, they are the people you want to reach when you have a new field, because surgeons are the last in the line of referrals.

People who are artistic often have different temperaments than people in medicine. They come off either as being very flamboyant or very overpowering. But Frank was not like that. He was a gentleman. There are teachers and then there are teachers of teachers and that is what Frank Netter was, he was a teacher of teachers. And that is a spot reserved for very few people in our profession.[36]

⚬⟡⚬⟡⚬⟡⚬

In 1958, Ernst Oppenheimer reached his seventieth birthday, and Frank painted some silly cartoons sure to please his dear friend and editor. *The Stages of Oppenheimer* had three caricatures of Oppy, laid out in comic-strip format. The first, "The Budding Scientist," showed a baby with Oppy's face smoking a cigar, sitting in a high chair with a microscope perched on the tray. In "The Terror of Summit," Oppy is dressing down an employee who is cowering on the floor behind the desk. In the third panel, "Philosopher and Connoisseur," Oppy is relaxing on his patio in Mountain View,

California, looking over a Frank Netter picture of a lovely nude, while from the doorway Mrs. Oppenheimer is calling, "Ernst, come wash the dishes!"

Frank sketched while on the phone to his stockbroker. He doodled in the margins of the sketches for his illustrations, or on the phone book or anything nearby. "I had to be careful," remembered Francine, "or I would have had his little pictures all over my homework." Every year he made a picture for a Christmas card with caricatures of himself and Vera, and he had 100 or so copies printed on card stock to send to friends and family. One year, he made one of the stately entrance to Folly Farm. Another year he did a silly one, of Vera and himself, ice packs on their heads, looking disheveled and exhausted from holiday preparations.

He was always holding a pencil in his right hand, and with his left hand, if he was not holding a cigar, he was twirling a forelock of his hair around his left index finger. He tried several times to stop smoking. During one attempt in the mid-1950s, he ate a dried apricot every time he wanted a cigar. He ate so many of them that he felt sick to his stomach and went back to smoking cigars instead. Sometimes he would take a cigarette, if there were no cigars, but he would only take a few puffs and put it out. He did not like cigarettes at all.

⚶⚶⚶⚶

Digestive System Part I[37] was published in 1959. Frank signed each plate, but out of expediency or style preference, he began leaving the backgrounds unpainted. As was his usual practice, Frank used Vera or his children as well as himself[38] as models. In the *Digestive System* Part I volume, for example, Frank made a picture from a photograph of Jim sticking out his tongue.[39] Vera was the model for many of the pictures in that book and is clearly recognizable.[40] Some of the most stunning pictures of the volume are the 29 anatomical pictures of the mouth and throat that Frank made with Dr. Huber.[41]

Max Som, Frank's dearest friend, had earned a well-deserved reputation as a brilliant surgeon of the head and neck. Patients from all over the world flocked to him—very sick patients facing laryngectomy and hoping he could save their voice box. Max contributed to 33 plates[42] in the volume in the sections on the anatomy and diseases of the esophagus and diseases of the pharynx.

For the section on physiology, Frank worked with Dr. William H. Bachrach,[43] at the University of Southern California School of Medicine. "Physiology," Frank wrote in the introduction, "implies motion, and to present this in static pictures was a task which I approached with some trepidation."[44] He flew out to California with Vera in 1957 and again in 1958 to consult with Dr. Bachrach on 26 plates on hunger and appetite, the digestive process, and diagnostic aids.[45]

It was with *Digestive System* Part I that Frank began his association with renowned anatomist Professor George A.G. Mitchell at the University of Manchester, in England, an association that would last for 26 years and encompass more than 100 separate text entries to accompany anatomical plates.[46] When in England on his honeymoon with Vera, Frank had spent three days with Professor Mitchell discussing the subject in detail and made the pictures after he came home. Professor Mitchell subsequently had occasion to come from England to New York and see Frank in his studio. Frank spread out the pictures, and Professor Mitchell looked at them and was stunned. "Oh, no, you have made some errors here." Together they looked it up in Professor Mitchell's text and found that the pictures were as described. "When I see the subject presented graphically in this way," Professor Mitchell told Frank, "I have a different concept of it."[47]

"The making of pictures is a stern discipline," Frank explained. "One may 'write around' a subject where one is not quite sure of the details, but with brush in hand before the drawing board, one must be precise and realistic. The white paper before artist demands the truth, and it will not tolerate blank areas or gaps in continuity."[48]

CHAPTER 15

THE EAST SIDE

BY 1960, FRANK HAD sold Folly Farm and bought a large townhouse on 65th Street[1] off Madison Avenue, in New York's plush "Silk Stocking District." He and Vera hired an interior decorator to do over the entire house. In the dining room, at the rear beside the garden, the decorator draped fabric from ceiling to floor to resemble a tent. On the second-floor landing between the living room and the library, Frank painted a trompe l'oeil niche holding a bust of Marie Antoinette. In a gilt frame over the living room mantle was a portrait of Vera he had painted in oils. It was a good likeness of her; she was posed seated on a Louis XVI chair. Everything in that house was elegant, glamorous, using French furniture Mary had brought to Folly Farm from the Gold Dolphin.

The fifth floor, the top floor, was where Frank set up his studio. He had a place for his drawing board beside the north-facing window, his taboret, and his skeleton. Consultants could come to work with him there and would see the 12 *Life of a Doctor* paintings hanging on the walls of his studio.

Every day, Frank would go down to the kitchen for his breakfast—a cup of black coffee, cereal, some fruit or juice—and then he took the small elevator to the fifth floor, where he made pictures. During nice weather, he often rented a car and took Vera for a drive to Sands Point to play golf and get out in the fresh air for a little exercise.

As she had done at Folly Farm, Vera continued to arrange Frank's social calendar. She served on committees for the Debutante Cotillion, and they went to the Waldorf, the Plaza, or the St. Regis, to the charity balls and dinner parties, he in his tuxedo—or even white tie and tails on occasion—and she in copies of designer gowns her dressmaker made. She moved in that social milieu as if she had been born to it.

ᘒᘙᘒᘙᘒ

From 1959 to 1961, Frank was busy making pictures for *Digestive System*, Part II, *Lower Digestive Tract*.[2] He worked again with some of those who had collaborated on Part I, *Upper Digestive Tract*: Professor George A.G. Mitchell,[3] in Manchester, England; anatomist Dr. Nicholas A. Michels,[4] at Jefferson Medical College; Professor Gerhard Wolf-Heidegger,[5] at the University of Basel, Switzerland; and Dr. William Bachrach,[6] in California. Frank also worked again with Dr. John Huber at Temple University and made some beautiful pictures of the anatomy of the abdomen.[7] Frank traveled to meet these consultants or they came to see him, and they would teach him what they were doing.

At this time too, Frank began his long association with Dr. Edmund S. Crelin, at Yale University, whose meticulous work and counsel in the field of embryology contributed much to *Digestive System*, Part II.[8] Frank was also making pictures for various issues of *Clinical Symposia*, and Ciba used many of his pictures both in the *Ciba Collection* books and in *Clinical Symposia*.[9] Accordingly, Frank did a *Clinical Symposia* article with Dr. Crelin in 1961 on the development of the gastrointestinal tract.[10]

In *Digestive System*, Part II, Frank also used some of the plates from the *Clinical Symposia*[11] issue he previously had worked on with Dr. Koop.[12] And in the section of the volume on abdominal injuries,[13] Frank included the pictures he had created in 1945 in consultation with Dr. DeBakey for the early educational material sponsored by Ciba.[14] When he had made those older pictures, Frank had used a plainer, more streamlined signature, with less flourish than his later signature. In time, his "F. Netter, MD" signature, with the tiny flag on the top of the N, came to be recognized by physicians and health-care professionals worldwide. Subtle but distinct variations in the signature from one plate to the next indicate that he painted each one. It was the artist's signature, the final flourish to each picture.

For Frank's plates on diseases of the gastrointestinal tract,[15] he and Vera traveled to Brazil, where Frank consulted with distinguished doctors at the University of São Paulo: José Fernandes Pontes, Virgilio Carvalho Pinto, Daher E. Cutait, Mitja Polak, and Jose Thiago Pontes. In an effort coordinated by Dr. Polak, the team of five physicians was responsible for contributing to most of the plates in the section on diseases of the lower digestive tract. The Brazilians were cordial hosts and entertained Frank and Vera socially during their stay. Brazil is the origin of some superb gemstones, so while there, Frank bought a deep-blue aquamarine, which he brought home to Francine for her birthday.

Sam Klein, that fine surgeon at The Mount Sinai Hospital, had been friends with Frank for nearly 30 years, since their time together on the outpatient staff in the early 1930s. In 1960, Sam was the acting director of the Department of Surgery at Mount Sinai, a position he held for about a year and a half until the next chief arrived. Dr. Arthur H. Aufses, Jr. worked closely with Dr. Klein, and Sam asked Arthur if he would help him work with Frank to write three small articles on the abdomen for the *Digestive System*[16] volume. Together they wrote the sections on the acute abdomen, alimentary tract obstruction, and vascular occlusion, to accompany four plates in that volume.[17]

Drs. Aufses and Klein met with Frank several times, both at Mount Sinai and at Frank's studio on 65th Street. "Sam and I wrote this stuff," Dr. Aufses recalled. "In those days, we used to take a lot more time writing every paragraph than probably most of us do today. And I remember it came out and was very well received. I personally was tremendously impressed the way you would tell Frank about something and all of a sudden there it was on a piece of paper in pencil. The next time we saw it, there was the finished thing. He was remarkable. It was fascinating to watch, to see the way he worked."[18]

In planning the *Digestive System*, Part II, Frank and Oppy decided to include a section on hernias, even though the condition is not considered part of the digestive system but involves the abdominal wall. They turned to Dr. Alfred Iason, who had worked with Frank on an issue of *Clinical Symposia* on hernias.[19] He was the author of a well-known textbook[20] for which Dr. Ben Pansky previously had contributed text and illustrations. Dr. Pansky was a young professor of anatomy at New York Medical College, and he considered it a great honor, he said, when Dr. Iason asked him to help with the book.

Dr. Pansky went a number of times to meet Frank in his studio on 65th Street. He loved to draw and was interested to see where Frank worked and to see some of the original illustrations. Frank put him right at ease as they discussed the layout of the illustrations and their content,[21] and encouraged him to continue drawing. Thus inspired, Dr. Pansky subsequently wrote and illustrated two anatomy textbooks of his own.[22]

As with all his publications, Frank and his consultants were faced with deciding how deeply into the topics they would have to go to convey clearly and concisely the essential points without omitting important details. They succeeded in succinctly describing the subjects, at least in part because the consultants were simultaneously knowledgeable clinicians and experienced teachers. The *Digestive System*, Part II, was published in 1962. The anatomical pictures in Sections IX and X, including the ones Frank did with Drs. Huber and Mitchell, are some of his finest, showing with clarity the anatomy and relations of the various components. Some of those illustrations are complicated by numerous lead lines, which might have given students some difficulty, noted Dr. Pansky, but that was the only criticism anyone had.[23]

ᏬᏬᏬᏬᏬ

Ernst Oppenheimer and Frank had originally estimated that it would take 10 years to complete the series of atlases on the entire anatomy and pathology of the human body. They soon realized they had grossly underestimated the task, so in 1960 Ciba renewed the contract for another 10 years. George Netter, acting again as Frank's attorney, negotiated the terms, and he insisted that the contract state that Frank had "established a reputation as the foremost medical illustrator in the United States," which was true.

In 1960 also, Dr. Oppenheimer's carcinoma of the lung was diagnosed, no doubt aggravated by years of his pipe smoking. After radiation treatments, the cancer was in remission as they began planning the next volume, *Endocrine System*.[24] Frank with his cigar and Oppy, still with his pipe, busily laid out the sections, choosing the topics and carefully picking the experts they would invite to consult.

Dr. Peter H. Forsham had known Dr. Oppenheimer for many years. The two had met at the Peter Bent Brigham Hospital[25] in Boston, before Dr. Forsham relocated to California to head the Metabolic Research Unit at the University of California School of Medicine, San Francisco.[26] In fact, it was Dr. Forsham who encouraged Dr. Oppenheimer to choose Marin County for retirement. From his home in Mill Valley, Oppy would drive down to San Francisco on Friday afternoons to join in the discussions with Dr. Forsham and his staff at the Metabolic Research Unit. For *Endocrine System*, Dr. Forsham contributed to several sections, consulting for 21 plates[27] on the adrenal glands, the gonads, and metabolism. And at Dr. Oppenheimer's suggestion, Dr. Forsham assumed the role of guest editor for this volume.

It is not surprising, then, that many of the consultants on this volume were drawn from the University of California School of Medicine, San Francisco.[28] Frank made several trips to California between 1961 and 1963 to see them and to learn from them. Dr. Felix O. Kolb was the associate director of the Metabolic Research Unit there, and Dr. Oppenheimer asked him to work on some plates for *Endocrine System*. When Frank went out to San Francisco, he stayed at the Sir Francis Drake Hotel, and Dr. Kolb met him there at the hotel a few times. Frank did the sketches, and they talked about the subject, the parathyroid or osteoporosis. Sometimes they talked about how Frank got started doing medical illustration—that he was practicing medicine during the Depression when the pharmaceutical companies began asking for his pictures. Frank and Dr. Kolb spent several hours together at each session, and then Frank went home, worked up the pictures, and sent the sketches back to Dr. Kolb for review. They did 17 plates on metabolic bone diseases[29] for *Endocrine System*—Dr. Kolb doing the text and Frank, the pictures. "He was very friendly," remembered Dr. Kolb. "I admired how he did all this beautiful stuff. He was so knowledgeable in what he was doing."[30]

Between 1962 and 1964, Frank worked with 30 consultants for *Endocrine System*.[31] The entire section on the pancreas, 31 plates,[32] he did in consultation with Dr. Rachmiel Levine, well known for his discovery of the role of insulin in glucose metabolism. Dr. Donald S. Fredrickson, at the National Heart Institute, who subsequently became director of the National Institutes of Health, wrote the text for five plates on metabolism.[33] Frank worked again with colleagues Dr. Crelin, at Yale, on the embryology[34] and Professor Mitchell, in England, on the innervation of the adrenal glands.[35] A couple of times, Frank took the two-hour train ride from Grand Central Terminal to New Haven to consult with Dr. Aaron Lerner at Yale for the two plates on the pineal gland.[36] Dr. Lerner picked him up at the train station,[37] and they spent a few hours together. Then Frank took the train back to New York.

Dr. Robert E. Olson was doing research at Saint Louis University, writing papers about public health and nutrition, when Frank called him up and asked him to work on problems of lipids and atherosclerosis and obesity. "Hormones play a big role in obesity and in coronary artery disease," Dr. Olson explained. "In the risk for heart disease, for example, males are much more susceptible than females to coronary artery disease."[38] They talked on the phone and sent sketches back and forth in the mail and never met face-to-face, but the outcome was four plates[39] that dealt with atherosclerosis, weight control, obesity, and the difficulty of controlling it; and seven plates[40] on vitamin deficiencies. "He was as much an educator as he was an artist," said Dr. Olson of Frank. "He exemplified the teaching of medicine with illustration."[41]

Dr. Calvin Ezrin was a junior investigator at the University of Toronto in Canada and had defined "the functional structure of the pituitary gland, the master gland of the body, and how the pituitary gland affected health and disease," he explained. "Up to that time it had not been really analyzed as to its various components."[42] Dr. Ezrin was neither an anatomist nor a pathologist but had a medical practice and had done the research as part of the qualifications for a specialty in internal medicine. The research had brought him to the attention of Dr. Oppenheimer, who contacted him about working on *Endocrine System*.

Dr. Ezrin met Frank for the first time in Toronto when they got together to decide which pictures Frank would make. They discussed actual patient presentations in addition to the biochemistry and structure of the gland. Frank accompanied Dr. Ezrin on rounds at the hospital, saw the patients, and took photographs of them. They went over to the University of Toronto's Department of Art as Applied to Medicine,[43] where Frank spoke to the students and faculty there. That was thrilling for them, as they held Frank in high esteem; and because Dr. Ezrin was the one who had brought Frank there, his status at the university was greatly enhanced. "He had lunch at my home," recalled Dr. Ezrin, "and he had his cigar, but my wife didn't like it, so he didn't light it. He was kind of a down-to-earth guy with no pomposity at all. It was very comfortable to be with him—this star coming to visit me."[44]

Frank made some handsome pictures of the anatomy of the pituitary,[45] the blood supply of the pituitary, and an exceedingly clear diagram of the hormone flows.[46] They did 34 plates[47] altogether, constituting a major section of the volume. When he saw the finished pictures Frank had made, Dr. Ezrin recognized some of his patients, the ones Frank had photographed, and in one, he saw Frank's face—not a self-portrait, but he had used himself as a model.[48] "I was a junior [faculty member], and he gave me confidence that I had some worth," recalled Dr. Ezrin.

> When you do something like that for the first time, you wonder just how important it is. He made me aware that it was very important. He gave me confidence to keep asking questions of medicine and disease and so on. We talked a lot about personal things too. I told him that I felt uneasy about posing as an expert in this field of the pituitary, when I really was not that immersed in it for so many years. But he said not to give it up. I should go along with the pituitary cell work in a separate channel and also continue to do my work with patients. And that is really what happened. By the time I left Canada in 1976, that pituitary work had developed into the reference center for the world, for pituitary tumors. I owe him a lot.[49]

That is how Frank worked, with big shots and junior researchers alike. He was always grateful for their time and respectful of their work and knowledge. He would go to see them, they would come to see him, or they would communicate by telephone and through the mail. He reviewed the literature they recommended, the papers of the experts, of the consultants; and then he asked them to teach him the subject. Once he understood it, he would commit his understanding of the concept to paper. His ability as an artist was exceptional, and he made beautiful renderings not just with his hands but with his mind. He would see patients on the wards, maybe take their photographs, but when he went into the operating room, he rarely brought a camera or sketchpad with him. He remembered what he saw. In making the picture, he filtered out the insignificant details, interpreted what he had seen, kept the big effect, and captured the concept. He focused on the message of the picture, sometimes approaching it from an unusual vantage point to illuminate the subject. He always depicted the human side, living patients with real feelings and emotions. "These are not machines we are treating," Frank said many times. "They are real live human beings."[50]

❀❀❀❀❀

Ciba published four issues of *Clinical Symposia* in 1963. They used the plates that Frank prepared for *Endocrine System*, which was still in preparation, and the authors adapted the text from that volume to fit the *Clinical Symposia* format.[51] Volume 4, *Endocrine System*,[52] was published subsequently, in 1965. Unfortunately, Ernst Oppenheimer did not live to see either those *Clinical Symposia* issues or *Endocrine System*. He battled the cancer for two years and died in 1962. While Dr. Oppenheimer had worked on the planning and selection of many of the contributors, it was Dr. Forsham who saw the project to completion.

The *Endocrine System* book was dedicated to Dr. Oppenheimer. Dr. Kolb had taken a photograph of Dr. Oppenheimer, which appeared on the dedication page. "Oppy was a great guy," Dr. Kolb said. "He used to always smoke his pipe. He was German born, and he came over and eventually became medical director of Ciba. He lived here very close to us in Mill Valley, and eventually he died of lung cancer. He kept smoking his pipe, and perhaps it would have happened anyhow. But he was actually the person at Ciba responsible for [production of] the atlases. It really was a wonderful thing for the medical profession to have this."[53]

Dr. Oppenheimer had served as mentor, and his passing was an immense loss to Frank, both professionally and emotionally. In the book's dedication, Frank wrote:

> Some of the best times in both our lives were those when I would go to visit him, and we would sit on his terrace in the warm California sun, reviewing the pictures and discussing problems. On those occasions I could feel his enthusiasm for the whole project, and I am sure that he sensed the same devotion in me. Between us, then, there was a sort of communion, a common interest never spoken but clearly understood. . . . When his death came, a great and important influence [went] out of my life.[54]

Dr. Oppenheimer had worked on the *Ciba Collection* volumes from their inception. Losing him midstream, so to speak, was part of the challenge to go on with the project and at the same time part of the impetus to complete the work. But Ciba continued to trust Frank to lead the effort, as evidenced by their giving him free rein to continue with subsequent volumes. From then on, it was solely up to Frank to decide content, to make the outline of the books, and to select collaborators. The Ciba team assisted, but their role dealt more with the publishing than with content.

ᎧᏗᎧᏗᏗᏗᎧᏗᎧ

In the summer of 1965, Frank and Vera moved to smaller but stunning quarters in a penthouse apartment on Beekman Place, by the East River, in the Manhattan neighborhood known as Turtle Bay. The main entry opened to the living room and dining area, furnished formally in French antiques. A spiral staircase led up one flight to an inviting, less formal sitting room and an outdoor terrace. The expanse of windows gave access to the spectacular view of the East River and the 59th Street Bridge. Frank and Vera took their cocktails there before dinner; and the lights across the river, those along the East River Drive below, and especially those on the bridge structure, lit up the night sky.

In a room off the entry area Frank set up his drawing board and his taboret, his skeleton, and his fluorescent lights. He had his library of books along one wall, a round table and chairs to one side, and a small lavatory where he washed his brushes. He hung the *Life of a Doctor* on two walls and had everything he needed, except north light. The building sat on the northwest corner of 50th Street and Beekman Place, and in this studio the window faced south.

For their Christmas card that year, Frank made a picture of the Beekman Place building decorated with wreaths and Christmas trees and showing Frank and Vera standing on the penthouse terrace, with their little dog, Jolie, waving to Santa, who was flying overhead in his sleigh.

Merry Christmas from Beekman Place, Frank H. Netter, ink and gouache on illustration board, 1965.

"Osteology Cram"

This and the facing page: illustrations from Frank H. Netter, Life of a Doctor, *gouache on board, c. 1950, courtesy of Ehrman Medical Library Archives, New York University School of Medicine.*

"Ambulance Call"

"Clinic Waiting Room"

"Country Night Call"

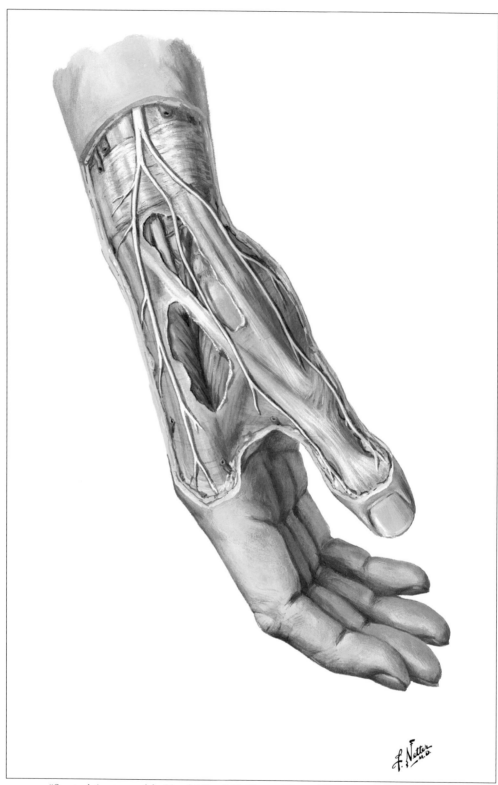

"Surgical Anatomy of the Hand," Frank H. Netter, Clinical Symposia *volume 9, number 2, 1957, figure 20, courtesy of Elsevier.*

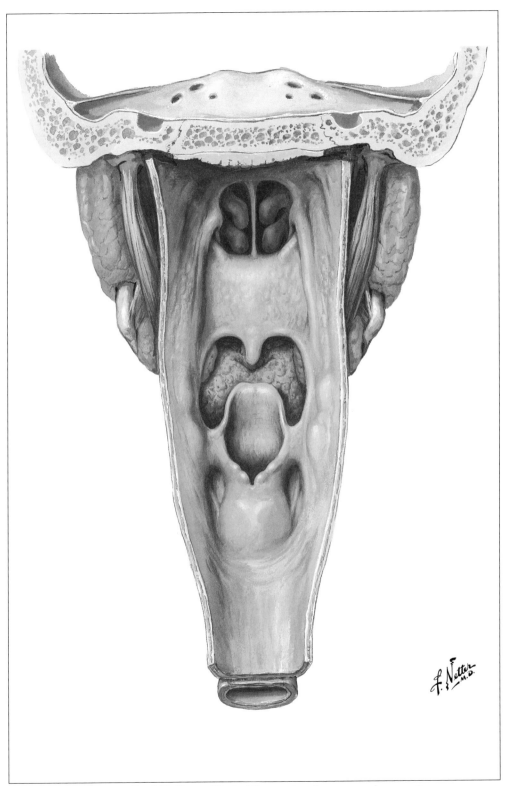

"Anatomy of the Pharynx," Frank H. Netter, Clinical Symposia *volume 10, number 4, 1958,*
plate II, courtesy of Elsevier.

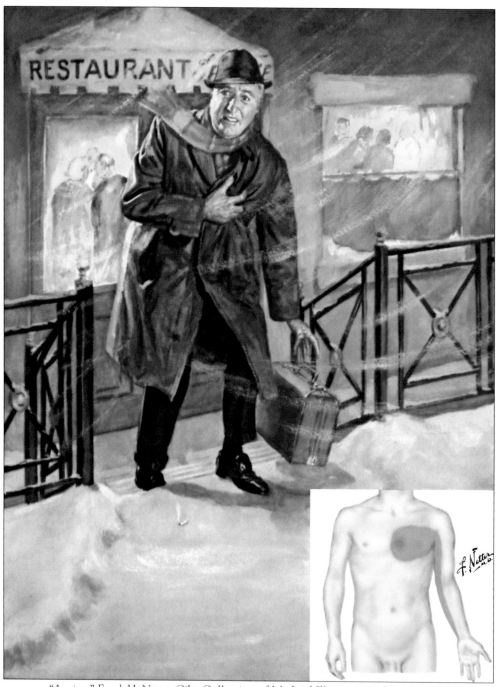

"Angina," Frank H. Netter, Ciba Collection of Medical Illustrations, Heart, 1969, *Section V, plate 57, courtesy of Elsevier.*

CHAPTER 16

HEART

DR. FREDERICK F. YONKMAN was the 63-year-old vice president of research at Ciba Pharmaceuticals and in that capacity had known Dr. Oppenheimer. He now stepped into the role as editor of *The Ciba Collection* and with Frank began planning the next volume, *Heart*.[1] Beginning in about 1965, outside consultants worked with them on the early planning: Dr. Hans Popper, who had moved to Mount Sinai in New York; Dr. Irvine Page, the director of research at Cleveland Clinic and recipient of the prestigious Lasker Award; and Dr. George Wakerlin, medical director of the American Heart Association.[2] It was Dr. Page, as editor of Modern Medicine Publications, who in a letter informed Frank that he was to receive the 1966 Modern Medicine Award for Distinguished Achievement.[3] Professor G.A.G. Mitchell again consulted, contributing to the plates on innervation for the *Heart* book.[4] This was now the fourth volume on which he had consulted. He would go on to contribute to the anatomy sections of all the remaining volumes.

Among those at Mount Sinai whom Dr. Popper recruited to work on the book was Dr. Bernard Wolf, chairman of radiology. He had been at Mount Sinai since his days as a resident there in 1939,[5] and Frank had known him a long time. They had worked together previously on three plates in *Digestive System*, Part I,[6] and now Dr. Wolf consulted with Frank on seven plates on the anatomy of the heart.[7] He asked Dr. Murray G. Baron, a junior member of the department, to provide angiocardiograms that he made using three pieces of celluloid taken on different planes and put together to create an unusual three-dimensional effect, and they were in the volume alongside Frank's pictures.

Dr. Robert S. Litwak, also at Mount Sinai, consulted on pacemaker implantation,[8] and Frank went in the operating room with him and his associates at least a dozen times, observing various procedures not only for pacemaker implantation but also for surgery of the valves—aortic valve replacement, mitral valve replacement, tricuspid valve replacement—and of the aorta. Frank's pictures encompassed cardiovascular physiology, anatomy, and cardiac pathology, as well as surgery and management.[9]

At the time Dr. John Abel was an assistant professor of cell biology and anatomy at New York Medical College who together with Dr. Johannes A.G. Rhodin of the same institution contributed to pictures of the myocardium.[10] Dr. Abel recalled working with Frank:

> I was immediately excited when we agreed to work together on the heart. To my surprise he wanted to come over to my office rather than having me come to his. I expected an aggressive, fast-talking entrepreneurial type, but instead this . . . unassuming gentleman came into my office and politely introduced himself.
>
> After rather brief introductions we set to work. Within the first ten minutes you knew you were in the presence of a true genius. He immediately grasped the details of cellular and molecular biology of the heart, as well as the process controlling its contraction cycle. What is more amazing, actually most amazing, was his ability to bring this information to life on paper before your very eyes. . . . Not only was he able to process and understand [the subject but he was also] able to visualize it immediately and present it in a lifelike form on paper. Amazing![11]

At the Cleveland Clinic, Dr. Page recruited a formidable team of researchers to work with Frank on 23 plates for the *Heart* book. Dr. Page had pioneered research describing the mechanism controlling blood pressure. Dr. Donald B. Effler had performed the world's first "stopped heart" surgical repair in 1956. Dr. Mason Sones, Jr. was the first to perform coronary arteriography, which for years was the only resource for visualizing arteries in the heart in vivo.

"In my school days," said Dr. Abel Lazzarini Robertson, Jr., "I tried to grow human arterial cells in tissue culture and later in organ culture. I brought these techniques to my new lab at Cornell–New York Hospital, and later NYU. Irvine Page . . . invited me to join him in a new lab, and he made the arrangements for Dr. Netter to come to Cleveland and work with all of us."[12]

During the preparation of the *Heart* volume, Frank spent two weeks in Cleveland, usually meeting with the researchers before 8:00 AM. He had read most of their publications in advance; and during the day, while the researchers went about their routines, Frank would go to the Cleveland Clinic medical library, where he created sketches. In the afternoon he came back and met with them again, and they reviewed the sketches he had made during the day.

The plates on the surgical procedures for coronary artery disease[13] he did with Dr. Effler. He spent time with Dr. Sones reviewing arteriography.[14] He made plates on cardiovascular pathology[15]—arteriosclerotic heart disease, hypertension, and occlusive disease—and on hypertension.[16] With Dr. Robertson, he spent two days going back and forth over the cross-section of the coronary artery and cell function in the arterial wall.[17] Those figures became well known among cardiologists. "The illustrations are still very valuable," observed Dr. Robertson. "In almost 40 years of research subsequently, we have increased our knowledge, but the basic principles are in this volume."[18]

⊙⥿⊙⥿⊙⥿⊙

The consultant most involved in the preparation of the *Heart* volume was Dr. Lodewyk H.S. "Bob" Van Mierop, who recalled:

> The story is that in the early to mid-'60s I was in Albany, New York, with six surgeons there. At one point, [The] Mount

Sinai Hospital asked me if I would be interested in being a consultant with them and go there every month and attend a cardiovascular conference. There, I had a conversation with Dr. Hans Popper. He is the one who initially asked me if I would be willing to work with Frank on the *Heart* volume. I was delighted. It was great. Of course, I knew about Frank Netter. I had for a long time.

So, it was worked out. The problem was that I was in Albany and Frank was on Beekman Place in New York City, and it was a long way. To simplify matters as much as possible, I gave him specimens of heart with a description, and he could make his plates after those specimens. If I had been in New York City, it would have been easier. My visit was always rather brief, maybe about an hour, and then I had to go back to Albany.

Another way of doing it, we found out, instead of my going up and down to go over the plates, and having to make modifications, was I just made the drawings of the specimen or a concept, say with colored pencil, and then had Frank transfer that into his beautiful paintings. It avoided long discussions, modifying the pictures. For example, for the embryology section, there are no specimens, really. We had only microscopic slides, because the embryos are very tiny. So [as models] we used drawings of the developing heart that I made [previously] for a paper that I wrote for the American College of Cardiology.

Or in the case of the arteries and veins, which had not been published, I just made drawings in color pencil of the development of the arteries and the development of the veins, and gave them to Frank, and he made sketches. And on my next visit, we would go over them, and unless there was a major problem, nothing needed to be done very much.

We met every month for quite a while. It was a lengthy project. All the times I met with him were delightful. Frank was a remarkable, unusual person. So was Vera, incidentally. He had his workroom, his atelier, which was interesting in itself. The main item there, other than the drawing board, was an old overstuffed chair, splattered with paint of various colors. The whole place smelled of Frank's cigar smoke.

I was surprised to see that Frank did all his work by himself. A lot of people, after they found out that I was working with him on these plates, asked me how many assistants he had. I told them he doesn't have a single one. He does it all by himself. He told me that he could do one plate in a day, which is remarkable. But one thing he never did, even though I asked him, was show me how he did it.

So I'll never forget that room on Beekman Place. He had a little dog also. But the atmosphere was very special. We would talk business, but it often deteriorated to talking about other things as well. One thing that he gave me, which I appreciated a great deal, was some prints of paintings he had made when he was a resident [*Life of a Doctor*].

His plates were exquisite. The thing that helped a lot, even in talking to him, was that he was an MD himself. If you just have an illustrator, they are usually pretty sophisticated, but it makes a difference if the illustrator is a doctor, like Frank. It made things a lot simpler. He could have been a stuck-up artist, but he wasn't at all. He never gave the impression that he enjoyed being famous. He just did a job.[19]

They did 62 pictures[20] together for the volume, consisting of plates in section I on anatomy, including the classic cross-section of the heart;[21] the entirety of section II, on embryology; and all of section IV, on congenital anomalies. In a unique approach to the pictures in these latter sections, Frank color-coded certain tissues to identify and contrast them against a grayscale framework, making it easy to distinguish the details. Ciba also published a *Clinical Symposia* issue on the anatomy of the heart,[22] derived from the work Frank and Bob Van Mierop did together for the *Heart* atlas.

∞∞∞∞∞

Perhaps more familiar to the lay public than any of the other consultants working on the book was Dr. Paul Dudley White, at Harvard, who came to prominence as physician to President Dwight D. Eisenhower. Dr. White authored the section on angina pectoris, so aptly illustrated by Frank's picture[23] of a man having a heart attack—that well-known picture of a somewhat heavyset man leaving a restaurant, going out into a cold snowy night, climbing the steps to the sidewalk, dropping both the briefcase he had been carrying and the cigarette he had been smoking, and grabbing his chest, his face contorted in pain and fear. All of the precipitating factors—heavy meal, exertion, cold, smoking—are there in that one picture.

It must have been after Frank's visit to Dr. Travis Winsor at the University of Southern California for some work[24] on the *Heart* book that in 1966 Frank and Vera flew to Mexico City, where Frank met with Dr. Ignacio Chávez Rivera, at the Instituto Nacional de Cardiología de México in Mexico City to discuss heart physiology.[25] Pictures in Vera's photo album show that they also traveled to Acapulco for a few days of relaxation, as well as to Athens, Greece. Drs. Thomas A. Doxiadis and Christos Stathatos were at the Evangelismos Medical Center there and consulted with Frank on two plates[26] describing parasitic diseases in the *Heart* book. Since the parasite *Echinococcus* attacks the kidney as well as the heart, Frank took advantage of his time with Dr. Doxiadis to work with him on a plate[27] on the topic to be included in the subsequent volume, *Kidney*.

In addition, Frank found time in 1966 to paint a portrait of Max L. Friedman, benefactor and secretary of the board of overseers of Albert Einstein College of Medicine. That school was just 10 years old at the time, yet it was as esteemed as its namesake. The commission Frank received for the portrait he promptly donated back to the medical school.[28]

ᐇᐇᐇᐇᐇ

Dr. C. Walton Lillehei had pioneered open heart surgery in the early 1950s at the University of Minnesota. Frank made the trip out to Minnesota and met with members of Dr. Lillehei's team.[29] One was Dr. Jesse E. Edwards, who worked on rheumatic and acquired heart disease. After their initial meeting in Minnesota, where they reviewed the outline and Frank made a few sketches, Dr. Edwards sent Frank some reference material, photographs and the like. Frank then revised the outline and the schedule of illustrations, and they went back and forth through the mail, Dr. Yonkman at Ciba sending copies of Frank's pictures to Dr. Edwards for review, and Dr. Edwards making suggestions, preparing the legends and the accompanying text, and providing the micrographs that appeared with illustrations.[30] Initially, they planned for 13 or 14 plates but wound up doing 20 plates[31]—11 on rheumatic heart disease and 9 more on inflammation of the endocardium, the aorta, and valves.

Dr. Maurice B. Visscher, also at the University of Minnesota, was the chairman of the physiology department and one of the most prominent cardiac physiologists in the world. In 1967 he asked one of the professors there, Dr. Marvin B. Bacaner, to coauthor the text for four plates[32] on the physiology of the heart and circulation. Dr. Bacaner went to New York three times to see Frank. He would stay at one of the small hotels in Turtle Bay and walk to Frank's apartment with that wonderful view of the river. They would sit for hours in Frank's studio, Dr. Bacaner explaining the concepts and Frank making sketches. Occasionally they went to lunch at a nearby French restaurant where Frank knew the staff and would order special items not on the menu, and there they talked about their medical training and about The Mount Sinai Hospital, where incidentally Dr. Bacaner had done his residency, and about how Frank had made pictures to pay his way through school.

But "the thing that impressed me the most," Dr. Bacaner recalled, "is how committed he was to the accuracy of the concept and how hard he worked to illustrate it, to put the concept into pictures, where you could grasp it easily. That section on the heart is the most accurate and advanced concept of heart performance."[33]

⟡⟡⟡⟡⟡

The world's first human heart transplant caused a worldwide sensation. In early December 1967 Dr. Christiaan Barnard, working in South Africa, used the technique developed by Dr. Norman E. Shumway at Stanford University in California. It was controversial and raised ethical and legal questions as to the definition of death. But on January 6, 1968, Dr. Shumway performed a heart transplant at Stanford. Although Frank was nearly done with pictures for the *Heart* volume, he considered the transplant procedure so important that he wanted to add it to the forthcoming volume, and immediately flew out to California to learn about it from Dr. Shumway.

The procedure was innovative yet forthright. The right and left atria of the heart are incised, leaving the venous connections to the upper chambers of the heart in place. The superior and inferior vena cava remain in the right atria, and the pulmonary veins, in the left atria. Because only the atria and the two great arteries require suturing, and not the six great veins, time in surgery is reduced, offering a significant advantage in securing the donor heart in the recipient's chest and starting it to function in the patient. But the patient Frank saw was a very sick man. Mike Kasperak had suffered for years from a damaged heart, which had caused his other organ systems to fail. The justification for the transplant, of course, was his imminent death. Kasperak lived 14 days with the transplanted heart. The primary problem with early transplantation was tissue rejection, which was not solved until more than a decade later when the immunosuppressant drug cyclosporine was used to prevent rejection of transplants.[34]

Frank did four plates on heart transplantation, which were tucked in at the end of the *Heart* volume.[35] The pictures of the transplant operation turned out "absolutely beautiful," recalled Dr. Shumway. "He was a kind and gentle man, and it was indeed a pleasure to work with him. Our little procedure certainly did not challenge his artistic capacity, but the pictures were almost three-dimensional."[36]

◌⟡◌⟡◌⟡◌

He painted "1968" below his signature on his second portrait of Vera. He painted it from a snapshot of her, taken at a party at Beekman Place. She is standing in the entry area to the apartment, with her hand resting gently on the breakfront, an urn of flowers behind her. It is a pretty picture, with deep yellows and teal greens accenting the pearls at her neck and embroidered in her dress, and she is smiling with her mouth, her eyes, her whole posture. He had the painting set in a French-style frame of gold leaf and hung it in the formal living room with the French antiques.

◌⟡◌⟡◌⟡◌

Between 1964 and 1969, Ciba published 21 issues of *Clinical Symposia*. Of those, 6 incorporated illustrations and text appearing subsequently in *Heart*.[37] Ciba had a staff of editors and proofreaders for the *Ciba Collection* atlases, and a separate staff for *Clinical Symposia*, the editor of which was Dr. J. Howard Walton. Each group worked with Frank, and while they shared Netter plates for the publications, they did not share staff.

Heart was published in 1969. Vera wrote a genial piece about the artist for the volume. It was a lighthearted but accurate description of him and was included with a photo of Frank. Dr. Lillehei wrote the foreword, noting the recent advances in cardiology. It had been little more than a decade since the heart–lung machine came into use, enabling the development of advanced surgical techniques—open heart surgery and even transplantation—to successfully manage conditions previously deemed hopeless.

Keeping abreast of those advances was the challenge for Frank. The *Heart* volume was larger and more detailed than any of the previous ones. As Frank wrote in the introduction, "New facts were being discovered, new concepts evolved, new methods and technics developed. I had difficulty keeping abreast of them with my studies as well as with my pencil and brush. . . . I am aware that, even as this book goes to press, the pace of progress is accelerating."[38] While major advances have occurred and increasingly complex repairs are done, the pictures Frank made for the *Heart* volume reflect the beginning of what has become a remarkable specialty.

To announce the release of the *Heart* book, Ciba hosted a big celebration in Chicago. An exhibit of selected pieces of Frank Netter's original art opened on April 20, 1969, at the Conrad Hilton Hotel. Two days later Ciba hosted a reception at the Sheraton-Blackstone Hotel. They invited the press and dignitaries, and all 49 experts who had served as consultants on the book. Frank of course was there to thank the Ciba staff and all the consultants. He wrote in his notes:

> One of the pleasures of my work is getting to know and collaborate with men—my so-called consultants—all over the world who are in the forefront of medical progress. But I must say that my collaboration with Dr. Van Mierop was the most pleasurable of all for a variety of reasons. First of all, he is such a swell fellow personally. Secondly, I have never met anyone who had such a profound grasp not only of his subject but of the whole gamut of medical knowledge. He is not only a pediatrician but a cardiologist, an anatomist, a physiologist, an embryologist, an investigator. . . . In addition he has a unique ability to simplify a subject and to explain it. And to top it off, he is a damned good artist himself.[39]

In appreciation, Ciba sent each of the consultants a complete set of *The Ciba Collection of Medical Illustrations*.[40] As was the practice, Ciba supplemented that with the new volumes when they came to be published—every collaborator on every volume received all the books in the collection. The American Medical Writers Association honored Frank with the 1969 Harold Swanberg Distinguished Service Award for his work on the *Heart* book.

CHAPTER 17

CIBA-GEIGY

THREE COMPANIES HEADQUARTERED IN Basel—Ciba, J.R. Geigy, and Sandoz—made up the entire Swiss chemical industry. They competed with each other in sales of pharmaceuticals, dyes, and agricultural products.

Geigy was founded in 1758 and was the oldest chemical and dye company in Basel. In the 1930s the company ventured into insecticides—Geigy researcher Paul Müller discovered DDT, for which he was awarded the 1948 Nobel Prize for Physiology or Medicine. Their first major pharmaceutical drug was an antirheumatic, introduced in 1949. Over the course of the next decade and a half, Geigy was successful in launching antidepressants, diuretics, and antiepileptics.

In 1970, Ciba merged with Geigy, thus creating the Ciba-Geigy Corporation. The Ciba Pharmaceutical Company, publisher of *The Ciba Collection of Medical Illustrations* and of *Clinical Symposia*, became a division of Ciba-Geigy. Work continued at the Ciba Pharmaceuticals facility in New Jersey, as did production of the Ciba publications. Frank kept making pictures for Ciba Pharmaceuticals and everybody in medicine knew his work.

ఠ౿ఠ౿ఠ౿

How Dr. Earle B. Weiss came to work with Frank is a curious story. Dr. Weiss was just beginning his career and was a junior staff member in the pulmonary unit at Boston City Hospital. He remembered:

> It was 1968 or 1969, and I came back from a holiday, and my secretary said, "You got a message from Ciba in Summit, New Jersey. You subscribed to the 500,000th copy of *The Ciba*

Collection," which was the *Heart*, "and they want you to come to New Jersey and meet Dr. Netter, receive the book and have lunch with him."

So off I went. We had a charming time. He was very engaging and a very interesting person. Dr. Yonkman, the medical editor, was there. The three of us had lunch together. During the course of the conversation I mentioned, "Dr. Netter, you have never done anything on asthma."

He looked at me and he said, "Well, don't you think it is about time?" That is what he said to me.[1]

And that was the start of a thorough monograph on asthma in *Clinical Symposia*. They began a correspondence, and Dr. Weiss prepared the manuscript. Frank read it and prepared preliminary drawings based on the text. Dr. Weiss meanwhile moved to St. Vincent Hospital in Worcester, Massachusetts, where he had an extensive laboratory facility. Twice, between 1971 and 1973, Frank flew up from New York for the day. He met with Dr. Weiss in his office for two or three hours, went through the facility, looked at the instruments used for making lung-function measurements, and met the technicians and the patients. Dr. Weiss recalled:

He had a way of capturing it all with a glance. I gave him the text and I gave him my knowledge, and the rest he put together. He was extremely careful and very detailed. It was obvious what he was doing was preparing the definitive monograph on asthma that was appropriately and really beautifully illustrated. And in order to do that, he had to get everything right. He spent a lot of time and had a lot of piercing questions and was careful so that each plate made an important point. For the asthma monograph, he summarized all the physiology, the important anatomy, and then all the treatment modalities. The net result of that, and it was true of all the other things he did, was that this became a major resource for educators and for students. In a few pages of illustrated text, you got the essence of the subject.

I never indicated what the illustrations would be. He came to me with the illustrations. He came with a roll of tissue paper. These rolls had all the preliminary sketches, and we would sit and go over each one. And he would say, "Do you like that or do you not like that? Or is this wrong or is there a problem?" And I remember him frequently saying, "Well, this one is no good, so let's throw it away." So on the floor of my office in Worcester, there was this pile of tissue paper, [about] which he said, "Okay, we can throw all that stuff away now." After he left, I did not throw it away. I subsequently met him and told him the story that I had saved it all, and he laughed. I still have them. They are unsigned, but the thing about them that is beautiful is that they match the plates in my monograph.

It was an amazing experience. I see [in retrospect] how much influence Dr. Netter really had in medical education. I do not know anybody in the past several hundred years who has done anything like this. There weren't many physicians selected to work with him, and I consider it a great honor.[2]

Dr. Weiss's article on bronchial asthma[3] appeared in 1975. *Clinical Symposia* issues generally ran about 30 pages and contained 12 to 14 plates, and although some were slightly longer, the bronchial asthma article was by far the longest article, published in a double issue, volume 27, numbers 1 and 2 together, 72 pages containing 36 plates. Frank's cover illustration was of a young girl in respiratory distress, gasping for breath, grasping the clothes at her neck, perspiration running down her terrified face. She was to become well known among pulmonary physicians.

᠅᠅᠅᠅᠅

"Bronchial Asthma," Clinical Symposia *volume 27, numbers 1–2, 1975, cover, courtesy of Elsevier.*

In 1968, work began in earnest on volume 6, *Kidneys, Ureters, and Urinary Bladder.*[4] Dr. E. Lovell Becker at Cornell University Medical College was president of the National Kidney Foundation. He and Dr. Jacob Churg, a renowned researcher at Mount Sinai, served as associate editors, and each consulted on several plates in the volume.[5]

Forty-five experts consulted on *Kidneys, Ureters, and Urinary Bladder.* Dr. Johannes A.G. Rhodin—who previously consulted on three plates[6] for *Heart*—and his colleague at New York Medical College Dr. Louis Bergmann served as subeditors for the section on anatomy and embryology.[7] Frank again worked with Professor G.A.G. Mitchell for three plates on innervation, which were included in the anatomy section.[8] Dr. Robert Kark was a well known nephrologist at Rush–Presbyterian–St. Luke's Medical Center in Chicago. He worked on the section on diagnostic techniques[9] and served as subeditor of that section. In 1969 he asked Drs. Suresh Patel and Richard E. Buenger to provide text and radiographs. Even in his native India Dr. Patel had known of Frank's work, and he felt lucky that he was asked to participate.[10] Dr. John P. Merrill, at Harvard in 1954, had performed the first kidney transplant, and he worked with Frank on four beautiful plates on kidney transplantation.[11] Frank also did two plates with his friend Dr. Michael DeBakey on renal revascularization—renal artery bypass and resection of a renal artery aneurysm.[12] These were researchers in the vanguard, and Frank's illustrations were of the latest medical findings. Again, a number of contributors to *Kidneys, Ureters, and Urinary Bladder* also prepared issues of *Clinical Symposia*[13] on renal failure, kidney disease, and related topics.

Work on the volume was well underway in 1971 when Dr. Robert K. Shapter came to Ciba as editor and filled the void left by the death of Ernst Oppenheimer. Dr. Yonkman, who had filled the position in the interim, was well past retirement age when he turned over the reins to Dr. Shapter. Production of *The Ciba Collection* and *Clinical Symposia* had been under the umbrella of the marketing organization, but Dr. Shapter established a separate department, the Medical Education Department, at Ciba.

Dr. Shapter was Canadian, and his father was a printer–publisher in Canada, so he knew a great deal about publishing. He was a dynamic person, energetic and full of ideas.[14] He took in-house the purchasing of all of the supplies, including buying the paper on which the books were printed. He dealt directly with the paper mills, instead of going through a middleman, and saved a great deal of money by doing that. The paper for *The Ciba Collection* was 70-pound stock manufactured to a certain tint. The linen for the cover came from Ireland.

Kidneys, Ureters, and Urinary Bladder was the first of the *Ciba Collection* books to be printed by offset instead of letterpress. The advantages of offset printing were that it generally produced a sharper image than letterpress yet was more economical. It had been originally planned as a letterpress production, and Embassy Photo Engraving Company had prepared letterpress engravings of some of the early artwork, but their work was phased out. Case-Hoyt Corporation did the offset conversions and printing. With the advent of the newer technology, gone were the days where Frank reviewed and checked proofs. Case-Hoyt pressmen now monitored print quality throughout the print run. Dr. Shapter also oversaw the transition to computer-controlled photocomposition. Jack Cesareo was the graphic artist who prepared the illustration typography, which he did for many years going forward. There is also a definite difference from the older volumes in the look and feel of the paper. The new stock on which the book was printed was whiter, with a nonglare flat finish.

At about this time too, Ciba developed the *F. Netter, MD* logo in an effort to brand the Netter art. It was a stylization of Frank's signature, a good likeness of the artist's signature that had come to be recognized by doctors worldwide. The Medical Education Department had the logo printed up on clear tape, and they tacked it onto every picture that went to publication. If the picture had been signed, the signature was obliterated and the logo was used instead. Use of the logo supplanted individual variations that appeared in an original signature.

The challenge for Frank was the convergence of kidney function with other systems. "I could not consider . . . nephrology as an isolated study," Frank wrote in the introduction, "because kidney function is intimately related to function of other organ systems and to bodily function in general. The circulatory, endocrine, and metabolic systems are particularly involved."[15] It was therefore necessary for Frank to approach kidney function in relation to pertinent topics in those other fields, "such topics as hypertension, renin, angiotensin, aldosterone, other cortical hormones, inborn metabolic errors, immunologic factors, homeostasis, and water and electrolyte balance."[16]

Ciba-Geigy published *Kidneys, Ureters, and Urinary Bladder* in 1973. Dr. Becker wrote the foreword. In recognition of Frank's work on that volume, the National Kidney Foundation awarded him its Distinguished Service Award for 1973,

"F. Netter, MD" logo, courtesy of Elsevier.

and the Art Directors Club of New Jersey bestowed its Award for Excellence.

ᦂᦂᦂᦂ

The Christmas card Frank created in about 1971 was a cartoon showing on the left side a tiny igloo, some Inuit walking around, and a barber pole signifying the North Pole, and on the right a tropical island with palm trees, a beach, and people swimming. In the middle of the picture, Santa in his sleigh is going north and an airplane is flying south. Standing on the wing of the plane are the three of them—Frank, Vera, and their little dog, Jolie, waving to Santa in passing. With just a few squiggles, he captured the scene and told the whole story. They were moving south, back to his beloved Palm Beach.

South of town on Hypoluxo Island, in the middle of the Intracoastal Waterway, which is called Lake Worth at that juncture, they purchased a lovely site to build a home. Point Manalapan was a gated community being developed on the former estate of Consuelo Vanderbilt Balsan and her husband, Lieutenant Colonel Jacques Balsan. The magnificent main house and gardens of the Balsan estate were put to use as the Manalapan Club, a private club for residents. Frank and Vera began working with an architect to design a home that would be both elegant for entertaining and casual for everyday living, and accommodate a large studio at the north end to capture the steady north light.

In New York, they gave up their beautiful Beekman Place apartment and took a pied-à-terre in the Hampshire House, on Central Park South. That small apartment had a living room, bedroom, and small kitchen. It had sleek modern furniture—two Barcelona chairs, a chocolate suede sofa with clean straight lines, Parsons table, and four chairs for dining. Only a French crystal chandelier and a marble statue of a reclining nude on a pedestal at the far end of the room remained, while all the other French antiques went to Florida.

There was also a small room near the back service elevator that Frank made into a makeshift studio. It was hardly a studio at all, for he had not so much as a drawing board. He brought in tracing paper and pencils, and set up a card table on which to make sketches. The light was from a small window facing south and a swing-arm fluorescent. When he came to New York to go to the Academy of Medicine, or to see doctors at the great New York hospitals, he had a place to spread out his sketches undisturbed in that back room, but he created the finished art in Florida.

Dr. Charles Horton recalled going to the Netters' apartment at the Hampshire House. He was a surgeon at Eastern Virginia Medical School who worked with Frank on a *Clinical Symposia*[17] issue on the developmental anomaly in males called hypospadias that impairs urination unless surgically corrected. When he was in New York at a conference in 1972 giving a talk on the topic, he visited Frank afterward:

> I went to his studio near Central Park. He and his wife lived in an apartment up high. The doorman let me in, and Mrs. Netter offered me a cup of tea, and that was nice. We got to know each other a little bit. Then we walked over to the side room, and in front of the window there was a card table and a little viewer for 35 mm slides. And that was his studio. We went over 40 or 50 slides, and I was telling him what they were.
>
> And then I had another meeting with him at his house in Florida. He was a very kind host there. I stayed at his house. I never did know his wife well. We were just in a business relationship. . . . I did what he asked me to do—answer the questions about the illustrations, check what he had done to see if there was anything we wanted changed, but there were very few problems with it.[18]

CHAPTER 18

CHINA

O N APRIL 6, 1971, the US table tennis team was in Japan for the 31st World Table Tennis Championship, when team members received a surprise invitation from their Chinese counterparts to visit China. On April 10, for the first time since the Communist government came to power in 1949, a group of 20 Americans—table tennis players and journalists—entered China, and this Ping-Pong diplomacy paved the way for renewed diplomatic relations between the United States and China.

In July 1971, after the table tennis team's historic visit, James Reston, a correspondent for *The New York Times*, traveled to China to interview Premier Chou En-Lai. Unfortunately, Reston had an attack of acute appendicitis and was admitted to the Anti-Imperialist Hospital in Beijing, where Dr. Wu Wei-jan removed Reston's appendix. The following day, a doctor of acupuncture, Li Chang-yuan, was called to relieve the gas pressure in the patient's abdomen. He inserted three long needles into the elbow and calf, and lit pieces of an herb, which he waved around. On July 26, Frank read with great interest[1] James Reston's article, "Now, About My Operation in Peking,"[2] which appeared on the front page of *The New York Times* and described his experiences with acupuncture and how the medical care in China was intricately entwined with politics.

In September 1971, four US doctors visited China:[3] Drs. Victor Sidel of Montefiore Medical Center; Samuel Rosen, otolaryngologist at Mount Sinai; Paul Dudley White, from Harvard, who had consulted with Frank on *Heart*;[4] and E. Grey Dimond of the University of Missouri. In an article[5] in the December 6, 1971, issue of *JAMA*, Dr. Dimond reported his observations of acupuncture anesthesia in China. He had observed first-hand the analgesic value of acupuncture and suggested that the Western medical world evaluate the practice.

ᦂᦂᦂᦂᦂ

Frank was in the studio in late summer of 1972 when he received a phone call from a man who identified himself as being from the US State Department. He wanted to know if Frank would serve on a welcoming committee at a reception in Washington, D.C., for a delegation of the foremost physicians from China that was coming to the United States. "'I am thrilled and flattered at the idea.,'"[6] Frank recounted saying. "'But,' I asked, 'how does it happen that you chose me for this? We have so many great physicians, surgeons and research people and specialists. Why me?' His answer was that they thought that because of my illustrations I might be one of the few American doctors who were known in China. I said that I doubted that my pictures had penetrated the bamboo curtain, but nevertheless I hastened to accept this wonderful invitation."[7]

On October 12, 1972, the Chinese delegation of 11 medical specialists arrived in New York to begin a three-week tour of the United States, the first scientific delegation to visit since 1949. The delegation, including two women—both eminent obstetricians—and three acupuncturists, was headed by Dr. Wu Wei-jan. Dr. Wu was the vice-chairman of the Association of Surgery of the All-China Medical Association and was considered the foremost surgeon in China.[8] It was he who had performed the appendectomy on James Reston.

The State Department's reception for the delegation was in an elegant salon at the Smithsonian Institution, in Washington, D.C. Greeting the delegation along with Frank were Dr. John R. Hogness, president of the Institute of Medicine, in Washington; Dr. Wesley W. Hall, immediate past president of the American Medical Association; Dr. Carl A. Hoffman, current president of the American Medical Association; and Drs. Sidel, White, Rosen, and Dimond, the four doctors who had visited China in 1971.

Frank was on the receiving line, being introduced one by one to the members of the Chinese delegation as each visitor moved down the line of the welcoming committee. When Dr. Wu came to Frank, he took Frank's hand, held it firmly, and looked him in the eye. "Dr. Netter," Frank remembered Dr. Wu saying in fluent but accented English, "I have studied your pictures throughout my medical career, and it is a great thrill for me to actually meet you."[9]

Frank found Dr. Wu to be a "very fine and charming gentleman,"[10] dedicated to his craft, who never before had traveled outside of China, yet had taught himself English so as to be able to read the scientific literature. Frank and Vera accepted with great pleasure an invitation from Dr. Wu to join the delegation a few days later for dinner at the Chinese Mission to the United Nations in New York.[11] It was actually a banquet—no fewer than 16 courses. Each course consisted of small portions "served on exquisite china and glassware with many different wines—not at all communistic,"[12] Frank noted.

"On one occasion I told him about my interest in acupuncture," Frank wrote in his notes. "I mentioned that I had read [James Reston's] column [which] greatly stirred interest in acupuncture in this country. 'Yes,' he said, 'I operated on Mr. Reston, but not under acupuncture anesthesia. He had . . . acupuncture after the surgery for gas pains.'"

ᦟ᦮ᦟ᦮ᦟ᦮

Nearly a year after the Chinese doctors toured the United States, Frank was invited by the All-China Medical Association to visit China as part of a delegation of eight doctors. Frank wrote in his notes:

> I was thrilled to think that I was going to visit this great land of mystery as well as by the prospect of observing Chinese medicine first hand—especially acupuncture. I was fascinated by acupuncture because I knew of no scientific basis for such

a phenomenon. . . . Possibly we could learn much from this
ancient culture even tho [sic] cloaked in centuries of mysticism
and superstition.[13]

One of the doctors Frank knew in Palm Beach[14] was a talented thoracic surgeon who had been born in China, educated
in England, and trained at the best American hospitals. When
this doctor learned that Frank was going to China, he told him
about his brother, also educated in England, who was a doctor
in Shanghai. His nephew—the brother's son—was also a doctor
in China, but he had been sent by the government to a remote
part of Tibet in the Himalayas. They wanted the nephew to come
to the United States, at least for a visit or perhaps permanently.
This doctor in Palm Beach asked Frank if he would try to visit his
brother in China, to give him his personal greetings, and to let him
know that he would help bring his nephew to the United States.
He also had some small gifts for Frank to take to them and said
he would write to his brother and tell him to expect Frank's visit.
Anticipating that such a visit to the brother's family in Shanghai would be a pleasant and most interesting experience, Frank
agreed to it.

The people at Ciba were delighted at Frank's invitation to
China. For the occasion, they gave him 50 boxed sets of *The Ciba
Collection* to take with him as gifts for the Chinese doctors. Each
set consisted of the 8 volumes, including the latest book, *Kidneys,
Ureters, and Urinary Bladder*, with the dust jackets especially printed
in Chinese.

In early April 1974, along with seven other American doctors,
Frank boarded Swissair's inaugural flight to China. The delegation
left from John F. Kennedy International Airport in New York and
flew to Geneva, to Athens, to Bangkok, and then over the Himalayas to Beijing. While on that jet airplane, on a journey going
halfway around the world, Frank could not help but think of his
grandfather, Jacob Mordecai Netter, who had traveled to China

before 1860,[15] and how in some ways he was retracing his grandfather's footsteps, going east to China.

⟨ᴥ⟩ᴥ⟨ᴥ⟩

From the moment they arrived at the Beijing airport, it was apparent to Frank that the Chinese people had a deep dedication to their government. Everywhere, inside and out, there were enormous posters, pictures of the Communist leaders—Lenin, Marx, Engels, Stalin, and of course Mao Zedong. There was no product advertising, only signs promoting the Chinese system. "I was impressed by the tremendous public relations selling job,"[16] Frank recounted. Signs told of the power of the people and urged dedication to work—a story told in pictures of smiling Chinese workers all clutching their Little Red Books of the teachings of Mao Zedong.

Their tour proceeded in a structured, organized manner. The delegation visited factories, communes, hospitals, and schools. Always they were first escorted to a room where they were served tea. "It was just hot, very hot water with a few tea leaves in it," Frank explained.

> As you may know, cancer of the esophagus is very common in China, and I wonder if that is the result of all that hot tea. The head of the institution would welcome us, and the first words uttered were invariably, "According to the teaching of our great Chairman Mao." At times this was completely incongruous. For example, even when a doctor was giving a talk on some scientific subject, he would also start with the same words, "According to the teachings of our great Chairman Mao," although it is hard to see what the teachings of Chairman Mao could have had to do with gallbladder surgery or the repair of a fracture or treatment of arthritis.[17]

The Chinese were wonderful hosts, tending to the needs of their guests in every detail. They escorted the American doctors everywhere and gave the Americans no time to themselves to explore the sights. At every hospital they visited, Frank donated a set of the Ciba books, for which the medical staff was most grateful, and Frank was most grateful that his hosts took care of carrying around the 50 sets of 8 atlases per set.

Although hotel accommodations were spacious, there was no air conditioning. Instead, the bed was enclosed in mosquito netting. Frank had a private bath, but the water pressure was usually poor, and the water in the tub came in drips and the pipes banged. On the other hand, the personal service was wonderful. "The attendants lived and slept in an alcove in the hall and were ready to serve you 24 hours a day. They were particularly attentive to laundry service," he wrote, and "I had to be careful not to leave anything lying around or surely it would go to the laundry and come back beautifully done."[18]

The food was disappointing, not at all like what is served in Chinese restaurants in New York or San Francisco. In fact, one of Frank's jokes was that there was an excellent opportunity in China for someone to open a good Chinese restaurant there. Breakfast started with orange soda pop—not orange juice—followed by a starchy rice soup. "The other meals consisted of many courses in small portions. And although some were quite exotic [1000-year-old eggs and such, they were] not very appetizing."[19] One dish he found quite good was poached fish with lightly steamed vegetables.

In addition to hospitals and medical facilities, the American doctors visited temples, palaces, and historical sites of great beauty. To the north of Beijing, they walked atop the Great Wall. In the center of Beijing, they toured the magnificent Forbidden City, palace of the emperor for five centuries. They visited the emperor's summer palace and gardens, converted to a public park on the outskirts of Beijing. They went to the tombs of the Qing dynasty, the burial ground of five emperors, four empresses, five concubines, and one princess, and saw urns with precious stones, gold, statues, and other treasures from the glorious past of the ancient Chinese civilization.

They spent five weeks traveling from Beijing to Shanghai to Canton, visiting communes, factories, schools, and hospitals. "The poverty was obvious," Frank wrote in his notes. From his hotel window he saw a family of five living in a small hut with a bare earth floor, no plumbing, and only one small lightbulb for illumination. There was just one wicker bed and a wood stove for cooking and for heat.

There were no entitlements in China, no handouts. Everyone worked. He saw women doing work as equals of men, digging ditches and doing heavy lifting. "But the people seemed, I can't say happy, but contented. Their dedication to their work was apparent. We must remember how oppressed and exploited these people had been for centuries, and they were trying to lift themselves by their bootstraps. Apparently they had suffered particularly badly under the Japanese occupation before and during the war."[20]

ᘒ⬩⬩ᘒ⬩⬩ᘒ

The medical doctors Frank met in China were "devoted to their work, their studies, and their patients."[21] By decree, health care in China was required to use both Western medicine and traditional Chinese medicine. Mao Zedong had directed that health workers unite traditional and Western medical practices, and integrate health work with political doctrine.[22] At the time of Frank's visit, there was one physician for every 20,000 people, and the overwhelming need was to make health care available to the people, most of whom lived in the countryside. The slack was taken up by "barefoot doctors," who received just six months' training before going out to rural areas to deliver public health services. They relied heavily on traditional Chinese medicine—acupuncture and herbal medicine, the active principles of which were unknown—and referred difficult cases to the medical doctors at a commune or factory hospital, or at the provincial hospital.

With the emphasis on prevention, they were successful in reducing the incidence of infection and parasitic diseases. Through a program of education and sanitation, the incidence of parasitic schistosomiasis in China was dramatically reduced.[23] Drug addiction to opium had been eliminated and addicts eliminated often by harsh political means. There was no alcoholism, and the only alcohol Frank saw was wine served at the banquets that the American doctors attended. Venereal disease, they learned, had been virtually eliminated by a program of mass education.[24] Birth control was widely practiced in China. They used the birth control pill and the intrauterine device, and also sterilization. Frank liked to joke that there was another method that no one mentioned, although it was most effective: the clothing. Men and women wore the same nondescript, unbecoming clothes as they worked alongside each other. Women were not permitted to wear dresses and instead wore unattractive olive or navy pajamas. Frank, in his loud plaid suit and colorful shirts, must have cut quite a figure amid the conservatively dressed American doctors in their blue suits or blazers, and he stood in sharp contrast to the Chinese in their drab garments.

For 2000 years, acupuncture has been practiced in China to treat a wide range of disorders. Frank found it difficult to evaluate because many of the diseases they treated with acupuncture are self-limiting. Acupuncture anesthesia, on the other hand, was a new concept, something Frank was most interested to see. The American doctors were invited to observe surgical procedures done under acupuncture anesthesia. They were naturally skeptical, as acupuncture has no scientific explanation. But they went into the operating room and saw several operations. They saw the removal of an ovarian cyst. They saw a gastrectomy. "I saw even brain surgery," Frank said, and raising his hand to his head and patting his forehead, he described "excision of the pituitary by lifting a flap of the skull and removing the pituitary gland,"[25] all done under acupuncture anesthesia. The patient received 50 milligrams of Demerol,[26] and as Frank described it:

> The needles were inserted by the acupuncturist, most often at a point, called the "aigu," between thumb and forefinger or

in the ear and sometimes in the foot. They were stimulated by intermittent electrical currents instead of twisting as do the barefoot doctors. The patients did show signs of distress, as they were fully conscious, grasping the Little Red Book of Mao sayings, but the operations were done skillfully. The surgeon doing the gastrectomy wanted to do a vagotomy but couldn't because there was not enough relaxation.[27]

Another of the American doctors on the tour, Dr. William Longmire, Jr., professor of surgery at the University of California, Los Angeles, had also witnessed the surgery, and he had been skeptical, Frank recounted:

When we came out [of the operating room] I was dumbfounded. I could scarcely believe what I had seen. I asked Bill Longmire, "What do you think of acupuncture anesthesia now?" He replied that it was not very good anesthesia. "Bill," I said, "you missed the point. If a dog talks, you cannot blame it for speaking poor English. And that dog talked!" There was anesthesia. You cannot do those things without anesthesia. We do not know anything about this phenomenon. We should study it.[28]

ᲒᎩᎧᎩᎧᎩᎧ

The industrial city of Shanghai was the next stop on the doctors' tour. "We had been told not to do any tipping," Frank wrote in his notes. "But when we left Beijing, I could not resist leaving a little for the maids who had been so attentive. But when we got to Shanghai, there was an envelope for me at the desk containing the money I had left and a little note saying, 'You forgot this on your dresser.'"[29]

Amid their tours of factories and hospitals in Shanghai, Frank found time to keep the promise he had made to visit his friend's brother. He told the guide he wanted to contact the family and visit them, and the guide said he would telephone the family, as telephone service in China was limited. There was a central phone for each district and one person was designated to answer it and send for the desired party. After the guide contacted the family, he came back and told Frank that they would come to the hotel the next day. Frank had wanted to go visit them, but the guide arranged for the visit at the hotel.

The following day, the brother came to the hotel with his wife, and with the son and the son's wife. Frank ordered tea, and they exchanged gifts and talked, with the guide acting as interpreter. "I talked to my friend's brother but much to my surprise he seemed not to understand English,"[30] Frank said in his notes, and he recalled thinking that he must have misunderstood about this man having studied medicine in England, for otherwise he would surely speak English. The son spoke a little English and said he had traveled for about a week—2000 miles by train and bus—for the meeting with Frank. After about 15 minutes the family got up suddenly and left, which was surprising in view of the long trip the son had made to meet Frank.

ᘓᘐᘑᘐᘑᘐᘑ

The delegation was in Canton on May 1, for the annual May Day celebration. People were everywhere, some in traditional costumes. There were floats and dragons, and acrobats, and a table tennis exhibition. "Canton at the southern tip of China," Frank wrote, "seemed to me the most bustling and busiest and most interesting city we had visited."[31]

In Canton there was a huge building, not tall but covering a large area, which was the Chinese Trade Center. Every product that was "produced in China: clothing; silks; furniture; medical products; foods; machinery; farm equipment; electronic devices;"[32] everything was displayed in that building. Buyers sat at tables placing orders. The guide for the tour of the Trade Center was a young woman, a student at the foreign-language school who had been given that assignment for practical experience. "I asked her," Frank recalled, "what did she plan to do after she graduated. She looked at me in complete surprise. She said, 'What do *I* plan to do? It is not for me to choose or decide. I will do whatever and go wherever I am assigned.'"[33]

From Canton, the group of American doctors took an hour's train ride to the border, where they did the paperwork for the exit visa. Leaving their luggage to be sent afterward, they began their walk across the bridge to Hong Kong. Frank wrote in his notes:

> As I stood at the bridge and looked up, there was the Chinese flag. And there as I looked across the bridge, there was the British flag flying. I cannot tell you what a thrill I felt when I saw that flag. It was not the American flag, but still it said to me, "The Free World!" Suddenly I realized how much freedom meant. Suddenly I realized that for over a month I had been in a country of over 800 million people of a single mind with no dissenting voice, no individual thinking, where the government was supposed to do everything for you and could do anything to you.[34]

Frank crossed the bridge to Hong Kong, which was, as Jacob Mordecai Netter more than a century before had written in his journal, "securely under the flag of Britain."[35] In Hong Kong, Frank stayed two nights at the Peninsula Hotel—one of the most glamorous luxury hotels in the world—before taking a flight east across the Pacific, stopping in Hawaii and Los Angeles, and then across the North American continent to home. He had gone completely around the world, west to east, as had his grandfather, going to the land of the Chinese during a time of upheaval—Jacob Mordecai Netter during the Taiping Rebellion and Frank Netter during the repressive regime of the Cultural Revolution.

Back in Palm Beach, Frank called his friend, the doctor with the brother in China. Frank recalled:

> I told my friend about the visit, and he was surprised about the briefness of the visit and especially that his brother spoke

no English, because he was sure his brother spoke English as well as he or I since they had both been educated in England. He said the only explanation was that [his brother] was afraid to let the guide know he spoke English. They had been a well-to-do family in Shanghai [before the Communists] and accordingly were [now] regarded unfavorably. My friend visited me again a few weeks later and said that he had received a letter in which his brother said that the guide had told them that I was very sick and they should only stay but a few minutes—obviously a ruse to avoid too much contact.[36]

CHAPTER 19

POINT MANALAPAN

PALM BEACH HAD CHANGED a great deal from the time Frank lived on South Ocean Boulevard in the center of town. The island's surroundings had grown, and scrubland had been developed. Their house on Spoonbill Road was a long, low-slung ranch of concrete block and stucco construction. Wide roof overhangs blocked the rays of the Florida sun, and sleek walls of windows and sliding glass doors faced the lake on the eastern side of the island.

The front walkway led through a lush walled garden to the front entrance. From the domed ceiling of the marble-floored foyer hung the Murano glass chandelier the couple had purchased on their European honeymoon. Directly ahead was the formal living room, furnished with French antiques upholstered in cream-white damask and yellow silk satin. A mahogany Steinway grand piano sat on Louis XV curved legs before a wall of glass overlooking the lake. An Aubusson rug in deep rose, gold, and cream covered the floor; and over the fireplace, in its gold-leaf frame, hung the portrait awash in yellows and teals that Frank had painted of Vera in 1968.

On the side wall along with other smaller oil paintings Frank had collected, he hung the sketch of the Spinners, which he had bought years before from a junk man on the sidewalk in front of the Gold Dolphin and which Frank believed was a preliminary study by Velázquez. Frank was still researching its provenance; and in October 1971, at the suggestion of Joe Rothman at the International Foundation for Art Research, he telephoned and subsequently wrote to Professor José López-Rey at the New York University Institute of Fine Art. Professor López-Rey[1] was a renowned scholar and expert on the great Spanish artists Francisco Goya and Diego Velázquez, and Frank hoped he could authenticate the painting.

Unfortunately, Professor López-Rey's opinion is lost to history, as his reply might have been by telephone.

To the right of the foyer and through a set of double doors was the master bedroom suite, also with a wall of glass overlooking the water. And to the left of the foyer was a more casual living area, with furniture from the Beekman Place penthouse. The ceiling was painted black, something Frank had wanted, and that lent a contemporary feel to the room. Three walls were paneled in pickled pecky cypress, and a wall of glass fronted the lake.

From there, a hallway led to Frank's large studio on the northernmost end of the house. He had his drawing board arranged with the north-facing window on his left, his taboret at his right hand, and the skeleton hanging at the juncture of his taboret and drawing board. *The Life of a Doctor* decorated the walls, and on an easel in the corner sat his earlier oil portrait of Vera.

Photo: Frank Netter in his studio, Point Manalapan, Florida, c. 1975, courtesy of Novartis.

A screened lanai ran 110' along the rear of the house. In the balmy Florida weather the Netters took their meals at a dining table there, with ceiling fans spinning overhead and enhancing the breezes off the lake. On the wall over a deep seating arrangement was a sailfish, in iridescent blues, with its dorsal fin splayed wide. Frank had caught it during an offshore fishing excursion with some of the other men at Manalapan, and at their urging he had it mounted—something he later regretted when he received the taxidermist's bill. Just outside of the lanai was the swimming pool, smaller than either the pool at Folly Farm or the one at the South Ocean Boulevard house, but inviting nevertheless; on the far side of the pool, the lawn ended at the bulkhead on the edge of Lake Worth.

The neighbors at Point Manalapan were an amiable bunch. Many had retired from lucrative careers and were living the good life. They played golf or tennis during the day and enjoyed cocktails at one another's homes before dinner. Frank was a good golfer and won four hole-in-one trophies. In 1973, the Netters hosted a luau at their Point Manalapan house and invited all the neighbors to come in Hawaiian costume. The ladies came in grass skirts or colorful dresses and wore leis about their necks. The men came in flower-print shirts, except Orville Bulman, a sort of jokester who had earned considerable popularity as a painter of fanciful tropical scenes. He came dressed in a somber black suit. And when Frank questioned him about it, Orville said he was dressed as a Hawaiian—a Hawaiian undertaker.

During the winter months, when the Palm Beach social season was in full swing, Frank and Vera attended the charity balls and other events in the town of Palm Beach proper. Frank would work in his studio until the last minute. Vera, in her pink dressing gown, hair in curlers, makeup on, and nails freshly done, would come down the full length of the house from the master suite to the studio and call to him—Come get dressed now, darling—and he would stop what he was doing and go dress for the occasion.

Vera's son, John Stetson, had a law practice in West Palm Beach and went to see Frank and Vera every other day or so. When

Photo: Frank and Vera Netter at The Beach Club, 1975, by Bert and Richard Morgan Studio.

George and Gertie Netter came to Palm Beach, they stayed at a resort in town and visited Frank and Vera on those trips. Frank's children always loved to come for a visit. Max Som came to visit too. The Palm Beach airport was 10 miles up Interstate 95 from Manalapan. It had evolved into an international gateway, through which guests could conveniently travel to Manalapan, and Frank could travel for his research or to see consultants or they could fly in to see him.

ᘓᘖᘓᘖᘓᘖ

Dr. Hugo Keim was chief of spinal surgery at Columbia Presbyterian Medical Center in New York, and he remembered working with Frank:

> Ciba contacted me and asked me to do a *Clinical Symposia*[2] on scoliosis. About three weeks later I got a phone call from Dr. Netter. He said he would be thrilled to meet me and would come up to Columbia Presbyterian. And I said, "Dr. Netter, I have read and seen your work since I was a college student, and all through medical school. You are like one of my icons. There is no way you are going to come to see me. I will come to see you." I just admired him so much for all the tremendous teachings he had done thru his artwork.
>
> So I went to see him at his apartment on Central Park South—he had a lovely apartment there. And we sat and chatted for a while and planned the *Symposia*. . . . He and I met maybe ten times, and he actually came up to Columbia— came into the operating room and watched what we were doing. I remember one particular incident in the operating room, and he said, "Gee, you are using a special retractor in your surgery. Let me see that one." And I held it in the air, and with about four strokes of a pencil he immediately captured it, almost like a photograph. . . . I was holding this thing just

freely in the air, and he immediately copied the angles and the handle and everything perfectly.

I was doing different techniques and . . . had invented a bunch of things, [including] a power tool to do spinal surgery that was driven by liquid nitrogen, that he thought was pretty neat . . . and he wanted to come and see those things. He visited me several times [but] he would wear clothes that were almost threadbare. They had patches on them. He would have a patch on the seat of his pants, or on one of his knees. . . . Here is this famous illustrator and gifted artist who obviously can afford a suit, and he would show up in suits that were really ancient and had patches on them, but I guess he liked them. He was probably a little eccentric, this famous man who would show up at Columbia Presbyterian Medical Center in a suit with patches on it.

With the *Clinical Symposia* you only have 30 pages and you have got to get in 12 illustrations. Between the author and the artist, you have to make it a cohesive bundle to get the point across both to students and sophisticated practitioners. So it was complicated, but Frank was a master at it.[3]

In 1973, Dr. Walton retired from Ciba, leaving Dr. Shapter in charge of both *The Ciba Collection* and *Clinical Symposia*. Dr. Shapter then worked to expand the *Clinical Symposia* publications, and he edited the booklets himself. When Frank did plates for another issue of *Clinical Symposia* with Dr. Keim, this one on low back pain,[4] Dr. Shapter was the editor.

During the making of that issue, Dr. Keim flew to Palm Beach and Frank picked him up at the airport. "He wasn't the most gifted driver," Dr. Keim recalled, "kind of weaving all around. He was so busy talking to me he wasn't paying much attention to driving."[5] Dr. Keim stayed three or four days as the guest of Frank and Vera at their Point Manalapan home. The two doctors would rise early and work a couple of hours. After a quick breakfast, they played nine holes of golf. They had about the same golf handicap, and it was a nice diversion for them. All the while they were on the golf course, Frank was thinking about the pictures, forming a mental image of what he would paint. After lunch, they worked again for a few hours and maybe took a swim in the pool before supper, and then in the evening they worked a few more hours.[6]

While Dr. Keim was visiting Frank in Florida, Dr. Shapter came down from New Jersey to meet with them for a day or two. "He had very peculiar dietary problems," remembered Dr. Keim. "There were like a thousand things he couldn't eat. Vera was very gracious, but she had a hard time preparing meals for him"[7]—not that Vera did the cooking. She had a housekeeper for that, but Vera planned the meals and ran the household as well as the social calendar, and did some typing for Frank.

The issue on low back pain was a great success, published in several languages and distributed all over the world. With that issue, Dr. Shapter changed the series' look. He changed the paper to heavier, whiter nonglare stock, converted the printing process from letterpress to offset, and altered the design. He added a broad blue border on the top and right edge of the cover, and changed the layout of the contents page. *Clinical Symposia* had reached its twenty-fifth anniversary.

๑๏๏๏๏๏๑

Many of the *Clinical Symposia* issues were spin-offs from *The Ciba Collection*, with text adapted for *Clinical Symposia*.[8] A small number of articles—one on angiocardiography[9] and one on mouth lesions,[10] for example—used only radiographs or photographs supplied by the author and had no Netter illustrations at all. But most articles featured Frank's illustrations.

In the late summer of 1973, Frank went to the mailbox and got the mail, and among the pile was the next issue of *Clinical Symposia*. The issue was "The Cell,"[11] illustrated by Dr. John Craig. Dr. Lawrence Ross at Michigan State University was the author, and Bob Shapter, the editor. A note from Dr. Shapter to the readers introduced the new artist and explained that Dr. Craig would be providing pictures for some of the *Clinical Symposia* issues.

John Craig had been a resident at Baylor in 1970 when he entered a national medical art competition.[12] He won first, second, and third prizes, in one year with three different entries, after which a head hunting firm contacted him, and their client turned out to be Ciba. Dr. Craig recalled:

> Bob Shapter called me from Ciba. Basically what he said to me was that they had become concerned that as Frank got older that at the stage the green books were, they were wondering if he was going to be able to complete it. What their real concern was that if he was working on the green book paintings at the same time as he was trying to do the four to five *Clinical Symposia* a year he might not finish the book collection during his productive lifetime. What they wanted me to do was come aboard and pick up part of the load of *Clinical Symposia*. Frank would be free to produce more illustrations for the books.[13]

After Dr. Craig completed his medical training, he joined the faculty at Baylor College of Medicine at Houston and began working on his first *Clinical Symposia* in 1972.

Dr. Shapter never told Frank about the arrangement with Dr. Craig, never told him it was coming. Frank had devoted 25 years of his life to working on these publications, under exclusive contract, agreeing to forego making pictures for anyone else. From the start, his pictures were what had made that Ciba publication the success it had come to be, and they built Ciba's reputation as a service-oriented company. Without consulting Frank, without offering him any say in the matter or the opportunity to choose his own protégé and mentor a young artist, without any forewarning, Shapter had hired another artist. It caused quite a rift between them.

ᏰᏬᏬᏬᏬᏬᏰ

Photo: Netter family dinner, Hampshire House, Christmas Eve 1973, courtesy of John Carlson.

Season's Greetings, Frank H. Netter, 1974.

The picture Frank made for his 1973 Christmas card was a good likeness of Frank and Vera. He made it after a photograph of them seated on a bench by the swimming pool at their Point Manalapan home. But on Christmas Eve that year they were in New York hosting a family dinner in the dining room of the Hampshire House restaurant. Frank dressed for the festive occasion in a red checked shirt, a large red bow tie with white polka dots, and a red sport coat. Cornelia, Jim and his family, Francine, John Stetson, George and Gertie, Gladys Burrows, and Vera's nephew and his wife—all of them gathered in the Hampshire House apartment before going downstairs to the restaurant for dinner. Cameras flashed all evening, generating snapshots of the entire family group and fodder for the following year's Christmas card, for which Frank made a picture of the whole family gathered around the table, an unmistakable likeness of each of them.

ᴏⳡᴏᴏⳡᴏᴏⳡᴏ

Vera kept herself trim and impeccably groomed. She subscribed to *W* magazine, and she had a dressmaker who could copy the designer gowns for a fraction of the cost of those shown on the pages of that publication. With her blonded hair she favored pink, or its pale cousin, beige, or sometimes shades of blue. She did have a black cocktail dress, with chiffon illusion sleeves, but she rarely wore black. When dieting, she simply ate very little at each meal. Once, at Folly Farm, she and Francine had tried the banana diet, eating a banana and a glass of skim milk three meals a day for a week. It took a great deal of willpower to follow those strict plans.

There was the banana diet and the grapefruit diet, the high-protein diet, the low-fat diet and the low-carbohydrate diet. There was always some new or revolutionary diet plan. To Frank, some of the plans were just crazy. One hostess at a dinner party "consumed the entire elaborate meal," he recounted. "After dinner, however, she disappeared into the kitchen and returned with a banana, which she proceeded to eat, apologizing to her guests, with the explanation, 'You know I am on the banana diet.' This otherwise intelligent woman actually believed that there was some mystical property in the banana itself which would cause her to lose weight."[14] Frank could have been amused by it all, except he was appalled by what he saw as hocus-pocus methods promoted by unscrupulous charlatans out to make money. Diets had become a lucrative business, and testimonials, not science, "proved" the effectiveness of a plan.

He was alarmed at how little dieters seemed to know about appetite, weight loss, and nutrition. What they need, he thought, is education. They need a book that will explain in lay terms how the body works, what nutrients it needs, how that food is digested and metabolized, and what controls appetite. Then they will be able to make informed choices on their own as to how to go about weight reduction.

Frank took it upon himself to write a diet book in which he described a diet based on knowledge. *Fad Diets Can Be Deadly*[15] was a hardcover book, 218 pages long, of which 23 pages were Netter illustrations—simple line drawings rendered in pen and ink. For several of the pictures he took inspiration from sketches he used to create the *Ciba Collection* plates. One picture, captioned "Appetite and Satiety Centers of the Brain,"[16] showed two cats, one a scrawny thing refusing to eat and the other obese, eating voraciously, similar to the illustration of the hypothalamic control of appetite found in the *Nervous System*[17] supplement on the hypothalamus. Another, captioned "Frohlich's Syndrome,"[18] was similar to the illustration of that rare disease in *Endocrine System*.[19] Three pictures, of how the vagus and sympathetic nerves influence stomach activity[20] and regulate appetite, he adapted from the plate on hunger and appetite in *Digestive System*.[21]

He targeted his audience and adapted the information to the educated lay reader. In three illustrations on digestion of carbohydrates, protein, and fats,[22] for instance, which were line drawings after plates[23] in *Digestive System*, Part II, he removed some of the details and modified the terminology. He did not show the epithelial cells, and he changed the nomenclature so that "pancreatic amylase" and "pancreatic lipase" became "pancreatic juices"; "to systemic circulation via thoracic duct" became "thoracic duct to bloodstream"; "hydrolysis (partial or complete)" became "fatty acids progressively broken off." In that way, he did not compromise the content. He knew what to put in the picture and what to omit so as to get the message across to the reader.

In the diet book he also included the requisite table of recommended body weights; an explanation of vitamins and minerals, and of the six food groups; a diet plan; a calorie table; and an exercise plan with illustrations of six recommended exercises. He adapted a figure of good posture and another of an exercise for the back from the pictures he had done with Dr. Keim for the *Clinical Symposia* issue on low back pain.[24] Dr. Robert M. Kark, with whom Frank had consulted on *Kidneys, Ureters, and Urinary Bladder*, wrote the short foreword. Frank self-published the book in 1975 but left no notes as to how many copies sold.

◦❦◦❦◦❦◦

The May–June 1976 issue of *The Saturday Evening Post* featured three articles on contemporary artists: Norman Rockwell, LeRoy Neiman, and Frank Netter. Frederic A. Birmingham, who had interviewed Frank, wrote the article titled "Dr. Frank H. Netter: Michelangelo of Medicine."[25] A large color photo of Frank at his drawing board dominates the first two pages, and several of his better known illustrations are reproduced in color on the following pages.

Just after that article hit the stands, Frank and Vera left for a trip to East Asia. They flew to Haneda, Japan, and Frank continued on to Seoul, South Korea. Ciba arranged an exhibit of some of Frank's pictures, and the Ciba-Geigy staff there hosted a luncheon at the Chosun Hotel. The photo album the Koreans gave him as a memento contains several newspaper clippings and photographs of Frank at the luncheon. He was wearing his plaid suit and polka dot tie—conservative for him—and in several he was smiling and appears to have been enjoying himself. There are also two or three photos of him at the lectern giving a talk, and another photo of him leaning back in his chair, knees crossed, puffing on a big cigar.

From Korea, he backtracked to Japan, where the exhibit was displayed at the Tokyo Hilton. *The Ciba Collection* had been translated into Japanese, and Frank and Vera attended a reception hosted by the staff of Ciba-Geigy Japan, who gave them each a nametag with an enormous red ribbon, somewhat akin to a ribbon given to a winner at a horse show. On Vera's black chiffon dress it looked like an exotic red corsage. Frank dressed uncharacteristically in a conservative navy pinstripe suit. As guest of honor, he sat on a panel and answered questions. And afterward a small group of 8 or 10 of them went to dinner at Yamatoya restaurant, sat on the floor, jackets removed, and dined in the traditional Japanese style.

Their hosts gave Vera some lovely gifts, a porcelain sake set and a brightly colored lacquer tea set. They wanted Frank to have a gift from Japan, and gave him a Sony television set; they had it shipped to Florida from Japan, which cost considerably more than buying one in Florida. Frank left no personal diary of the trip, but in photographs of Frank and of Vera at the receptions, they are smiling broadly and appear happy and gratified by the warm welcome they received. They were gone 12 days altogether.[26]

ᘯ᙭ᘯ᙭ᘯ᙭

In the late autumn of 1976, Frank and Vera went to New York to be there when Vera's son, John, underwent a radical neck dissection to remove a cancerous tumor. Frank's fraternity brother and dear friend, Max Som, performed the operation. Recognized for his great skill as a surgeon, he had led Mount Sinai to the forefront of head and neck surgery.

Max's son, Peter, who has since become an eminent head and neck radiologist, was at that time a young doctor at Mount Sinai and had a small office in the hospital. "Can I sit here?" Frank said, standing at the door of Peter's office. He was waiting for Max to come out of surgery, but to Peter he was like a favorite uncle. Frank saw that Peter was struggling to visualize a particular area in the neck and offered to make a picture of it and send it to him.[27] Peter did not ask. Frank just offered.

On the same day as John's surgery and in the same hospital, it just so happened, Francine gave birth to a daughter, Caroline Nancy Carlson. "When Dad walked into my room at the hospital to see the baby and me," Francine remembered, "he was giggling. He told me that some young doctors had recognized him and as he walked by in the hallway, and he heard them whispering, 'That's Dr. Netter! That's Dr. Netter!' And that really tickled him."[28] A pediatric fellow came to the room just then and told Francine and Frank that baby Caroline had a hip click, so named for the phenomenon that occurred in congenital dislocation of the hip.[29] She should be fine, he reassured them, if for a few months she wore triple-thick diapers or a splint to maintain abduction.

After returning to Florida, Frank made pictures of the neck, paintings in gouache, and as promised, sent them to Peter Som. "There were four drawings that he had done—magnificently rendered. They were just beautiful," Peter said. "They are unsigned but they were typical of his painting of anatomy. He was very generous [to do that]."[30]

Not forgetting his granddaughter's hip click, Frank went through the files in his Florida studio and retrieved a letter he had received some months earlier from Dr. Robert Hensinger at the University of Michigan. Dr. Hensinger was the chief of the Pediatric Orthopaedic Service there, and he had written to Frank proposing a *Clinical Symposia* issue on congenital dislocation of the hip. His interest piqued by Caroline's hip click, Frank wrote back to Dr. Hensinger, and they agreed to collaborate on an issue.[31] "I thought it was a great way to get information out to the public about dislocation of the hip," said Dr. Hensinger. "I was very excited about that. His books were very, very popular with physicians."[32]

On a Friday in the spring of 1977, Dr. Hensinger went down to see Frank at Point Manalapan and stayed the weekend. Frank and Vera had a little cocktail party at their home, and then they took him to the Manalapan Club for dinner. It was largely a group of retired people, and Dr. Hensinger was at that time in his forties; nevertheless he had a great time, as he recalled.

They worked on the *Clinical Symposia* issue about congenital dislocation of the hip, the point of which was early recognition of the condition and how to deal with it. It tends to run in families, girls being more susceptible because of hormonal differences. Restricted intrauterine fetal movement, which can result from a variety of causes, is a contributing factor.

The next time Dr. Hensinger went down to see Frank, Dr. G. Dean MacEwen went with him. Dr. MacEwen was an orthopedist at the Alfred I. duPont Institute, in Wilmington, Delaware, and Dr. Hensinger had previously worked on his staff.[33] They were both attending a meeting of orthopedists at The Breakers Hotel in Palm Beach, and they drove over to Point Manalapan together to see Frank. Dr. Hensinger recounted:

> I gave a slide presentation about the problem and our treatment of those things. And I gave him articles to read, that I had copied, and I gave him some text that I was working on. I presented that all to him. He thought that was interesting. As we drove back to The Breakers, I told Dr. MacEwen, "I don't think he understands. I don't think he got it." I was worried about it, because I did not think he got much of an understanding of what it was all about.
>
> And Dean said, "Yeah, I think you are right. We'll see."[34]

The weeks went by, and then the package came with sketches for the 16 plates. "They were just fantastic. They were just wonderful,"[37] remembered Dr. Hensinger. Frank had taken in all the material Dr. Hensinger had given him, and then he went to the library. Whether that was in Florida or at the Academy of Medicine in New York, or if he had had materials sent to him, he got the information and read about it and thought about how to put it all together. Dr. Hensinger added:

> It was just amazing how perceptive he was. It is not a topic [with which] he had any familiarity. But he was able to put it all together. That was the way he learned. He learned things by drawing them. That was his learning style. As he learned more about dislocation of the hip, he would make the drawings.[36]

The cover picture showed an infant looking very much like Caroline, lying on her back, undergoing a hip exam. One thing that had concerned Dr. Hensinger about pictures of the hip examination in previous publications was that the infant was always shown from the bottom up, showing the genitals. The infants were usually girls, so the view was of the buttocks and vagina. But Frank turned the infant around, so that in his picture the view is from the head of the infant looking down to the hip examination. Very simple, but it was amazingly effective. The head of the infant is closer to the viewer, a unique angle, yet it shows the hip examination more clearly than in the previous views. It was as he had learned so many years before when he was a teenage student at the National Academy School, to draw the figure from the opposite point of view.

"When the *Clinical Symposia* came out," recalled Dr. Hensinger, "one of my friends said to me, 'Now you are immortal.' And I said, 'What do you mean?' He said, 'Dr. Netter's drawings are always going to be popular, and you are associated with him.' His work will be enduring. It will be around for a long, long time."[37]

҉

For some time, Frank had known that the first edition of *Nervous System* needed updating. There was no coverage of the peripheral nervous system, embryology, or physiology. Moreover, advances in several aspects of medicine—radiology, surgery, and disease—made a revision of the volume necessary. Dr. Shapter made the first move. He drew up a plan of what the revised edition should be,

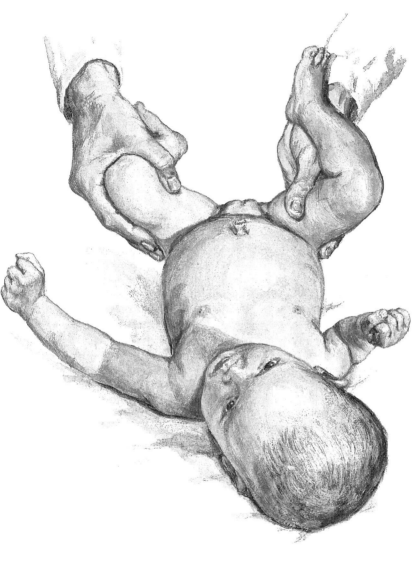

"Congenital Dislocation of the Hip," Frank H. Netter, Clinical Symposia *volume 31,
number 1, 1979, cover, courtesy of Elsevier.*

what the content should be. He independently created an outline and presented it to Frank. Frank did not like that Shapter did that. This was Frank's project. Dr. Shapter should have consulted him, worked with him on the outline.[48]

Phil Flagler joined Ciba-Geigy in 1976 after a career at Smith, Kline & French Laboratories and at a small educational publishing company. Dr. Shapter left the employ of Ciba-Geigy shortly thereafter, and Phil became director of medical education and began work with *Clinical Symposia* and *The Ciba Collection*. Phil was trim and tall—about 6′—with sandy-colored hair sprinkled with gray. He was a polite, affable gentleman who understood medical publishing and could manage the business side of the organization.

Phil was on the phone with Frank once a week or so, keeping up with what was going on, solving whatever problems might come up, talking about what they were going to do next. "I would make two trips to Palm Beach a year and spend a couple of days, talking about whatever the problems of the day were, whatever the project was, and helping solve whatever problems there were. So, I really got to know Frank and Vera quite well. We would always have a pleasant dinner somewhere."[39]

Gina Dingle came to Ciba-Geigy in July 1977. Phil hired her. She was slim, thirty-something, about 5′5″, with neatly bobbed dirty-blond hair. She was an energetic professional and developed a good working relationship with Frank. He dealt with the making of the illustrations, and Gina, as managing editor of the *Ciba Collection* publications, dealt with the administration of it all. Gina recalled:

> I was in charge of developing the book from the actual mechanics of the whole thing. I had a couple of technical manuscript editors who did the first edit. Their job was to cut it down to size. After that, it came to me and I did the second and the final edit. I fit the galleys to the page. I made the cuts where they needed to be made to fit the text. I went through every single illustration and every single leader line. I cross-checked all of the requested corrections and all of that.[40]

After Dr. Shapter left in late 1976 there was no physician on the staff until Phil hired Dr. Alister Brass at the end of 1977. He was an Australian and an accomplished medical editor as well as physician. He was an interesting, dynamic man, Gina recalled, full of life, with a great enthusiasm for everything.

By mid-1978, Alister had assumed the role of directing editor for the publications. When he began, there was no plan laid out for *Clinical Symposia*, no schedule for what issues were coming out. Alister would go and talk to the *Clinical Symposia* authors about upcoming issues. He created a plan for *Clinical Symposia* issues two years into the future, and with that, increased to six the number of issues per year.

Gina recalled:

> The *Clinical Symposia* editors never had that much contact with Dr. Netter. For the book, the meetings were regular and plentiful. My experience with Dr. Netter was always from the practical standpoint. He and Mrs. Netter were very nice to me when I was down there. I used to go to their house, and Dr. Netter would pick me up from the airport. They were really very kind to me when I was traveling on my own. I usually stayed at The Breakers. Twice I stayed at the Brazilian Court. There was a motel down the coast where Alister preferred to stay. When I went down with Alister, he and I would stay in this motel, which was right on the beach, and then I would go for long, long walks on the beach in the evening. When I traveled with consultants, we stayed at The Breakers. Then I would take a taxi to Dr. Netter's house.
>
> When I was with him everything was very focused, very businesslike. We had very little time. I would go down for two or three days. We would start work at eight, break for lunch, go back after lunch, sometimes finish at six or seven, go to dinner, and not [work] during the meal, but have a windup meeting after dinner. Time was of the essence, really. I needed to get as much of his attention as I possibly could.

When Dr. Netter came to see us in New Jersey, I picked him up from the airport, and he would light up his cigar in my car. I would try to hold my breath! He always had a cigar. Even when I would turn up on their doorstep at 8 AM, Dr. Netter was already part way through a cigar. "Oh, hello, dear. Come in," he would say. He was a wonderful man. I loved him. I remember sometimes being in the city with him. He loved New York, and he would say, "My family had property on that corner" or "My family had property on that other corner."

One day at Point Manalapan Vera said, "Come and have a look at this!" And there was this great big closet full of these beautiful clothes from all the best men's tailors. They all looked brand new. But he was Netter. He was colorful! The first time I saw him, he was at the door of the building where my office was. And he was wearing this tie. It was a hand-painted tie. It had a palm tree painted on it and some water in the background. I think he must have had it from the 1950s. Only Netter could get away with it. No doubt it was a very good one. He always wore a cravat. I never saw him with an open-neck shirt that he did not have the cravat. I never saw him in a knitted shirt, like a golf shirt. He always was in a cotton shirt, whether short sleeves or long sleeves, usually short sleeves in Florida, and he had a red cravat with white polka dots that he seemed to love.

For lunch, he always had a dry martini, up. He did not drink wine; he drank hard liquor. At dinner he would have a scotch. He always had a martini at lunchtime. Very rarely he had wine with dinner. When we would go out for dinner at a restaurant, he would have a scotch and water. He once told me that wine was not his favorite ticket. It was a matter of taste. When we were working at Point Manalapan we would go into town for lunch. Once in a while Glenna [the housekeeper] would make lunch, but not often.[41]

CHAPTER 20

TEAM LEADER

PHIL FLAGLER HAD A staff of 18 people in the Medical Education Department at Ciba-Geigy, which included not only the editorial staff but also a distribution group, people who took and fulfilled orders and worked the phones, a full-scale marketing organization. In addition, there were the outside consultants—the graphic artists, the book designer, and publishing people—who worked with the staff almost daily.

Guest editors on the *Ciba Collection* publications were subject experts who helped compile the material but did not alter the language. Editors on the Ciba-Geigy staff were the ones who sat with pencil and pen and edited the words the physicians wrote. Conversely, the staff editors never developed medical content. Phil described the process of finding experts:

> We all used all of our contacts to find people to be guest editors and contributors. Frank would suggest people; we would suggest people; we'd toss them around and eventually settle on somebody we thought would be good. In the earlier years, Frank was the key to that, because he had so many well-known contacts. One thing led to the other in terms of authors. He would start to work with somebody at Baylor, for example, and in the process meet somebody there who was a really good hematologist. And he was impressed by him, and a couple of years later we might be doing something along those lines, and he would remember, and we'd check him out and eventually settle on somebody like that.[1]

Frank painted the pictures and other physicians as well as scientists contributed the text.

Gina Dingle recounted:

> The doctors who did the text got a nominal sum, a very small fee. You couldn't even call it a fee. It was an honorarium, in the true sense of the word. Basically they didn't work for the honorarium; they worked because they wanted to collaborate with Dr. Netter. There was an honorarium for *Clinical Symposia* as well, but it would not buy lunch. It was so little. However, that piece was irrelevant. Anyone who was invited, everyone who was invited, was only too happy to accept.
>
> One person turned us down because he was taking on a big job at the Mayo Clinic and he really had no time. And we wanted him in the capacity of section coordinator. The section coordinator—the guest editor—was of course an expert in his field. And he was supposed to read the text and make sure it was on track and did not go off on a tangent. The role was significant.[2]

As managing editor for *The Ciba Collection*, Gina had hands-on oversight over everything for those books, while a separate staff edited *Clinical Symposia*.[3] In *The Ciba Collection*, the text just covered the topic quickly and Frank's pictures brought to light the different aspects of the conditions.[4] But *Clinical Symposia* presented the latest findings and techniques, so the text necessarily went into more depth.

John Craig made illustrations for some of the *Clinical Symposia* issues,[5] and by 1977 he had assumed roughly half the load for that publication, about three issues per year. John never worked on pictures for the *Ciba Collection* books. John's style was different from Frank's, and the editors never mixed the art in a publication.

Frank did all the *Ciba Collection* atlases, and two or three *Clinical Symposia* issues per year. The topics in *Clinical Symposia* that Frank prepared were sometimes taken from the book, just adapted to a longer length, in which case they reused pictures Frank had prepared originally for *The Ciba Collection*, perhaps with the addition of one or two more to make up the 12 or 16 plates for *Clinical Symposia*. Sometimes it went the other way: He prepared a *Clinical Symposia* issue knowing that the pictures would end up in one of the books.

Finding authors for *Clinical Symposia* was like finding the authors for the *Ciba Collection* books. "We got ideas from all over the place," explained Phil Flagler.

> Physicians would write in and say, "You really ought to do this" or "You really ought to do that." And one of us would come in after having talked to some doctors and say, "They all seem to want to hear about this or that." So it was not a planned thing. We took targets of opportunity. We never had problems with subject matter. It would come along out of the contacts we had, most of them being Frank's.[6]

Doctors and researchers sent proposals for *Clinical Symposia*, and sometimes the topic was too narrow[7] or the publication schedule was too tight to accept a proposal.[8] Sometimes the material was just not suitable. At other times, the topic might instead be considered for inclusion in an upcoming atlas.[9]

Dr. Jay M. Arena, at Duke University Medical Center, prepared a popular *Clinical Symposia* monograph on poisoning, published originally in 1951,[10] and republished[11] several times with author-supplied pictures. Frank did just the cover illustration. Not until it was revised in 1978 did the article include a full complement of Frank's illustrations accompanying Dr. Arena's expanded text.[12]

Sometimes the Ciba-Geigy team and Frank went down a path toward a *Clinical Symposia* issue and it did not pan out. Probably no one was more persistent than Dr. J. William Futrell, who was at the University of Virginia when he began corresponding with Frank in September 1977, suggesting a monograph on the lymphatic system.[13] The correspondence continued for eight years, yet the proposal did not result in a publication. Likewise, Dr. James Urbaniak at Duke University sent a comprehensive proposal[14] for a monograph on

Sketch: "Poisoned Boy," Frank H. Netter, 1978, from the University of North Carolina Wilson Special Collections Library. Note the heavy outlines where the artist used a hard pencil to go over the sketch to transfer the image to illustration board for painting the final picture.

replantation of amputated hands and digits, very descriptive of the anatomy, that Frank and Alister Brass at Ciba-Geigy both liked for an issue of *Clinical Symposia* and also for inclusion in the volume on the musculoskeletal system.[15] Yet Ciba chose not to underwrite the publication, thinking it did not have enough general appeal.[16]

Frank ultimately was the team leader in deciding what topics to illustrate in both *The Ciba Collection* and *Clinical Symposia*. As to a proposal on arthroscopy, he wrote to Alister in 1980, "I do not understand your objection to this subject. This is currently the most pertinent and rapidly expanding field in orthopaedics. . . . It definitely belongs in the musculoskeletal atlas. Dr. Lanny Johnson [is] the outstanding pioneer in this field. I suggest you communicate with him."[17] That contact resulted in a *Clinical Symposia* on arthroscopy published in 1982.[18]

The Ciba publications never promoted a pharmaceutical product. They were strictly educational materials developed to promote the company as being service oriented. There were advertisements in the booklets, but these ads were unrelated to the articles. Ciba, and later Ciba-Geigy, sent *Clinical Symposia* free of charge to doctors and students as goodwill, and they sold the *Ciba Collection* books at close to cost, as a service to the medical profession. Phil Flagler explained:

> The idea was not to make a profit but to come as close as possible to making the operation self-sustaining. Frequently it was not, but we tried. Every company is always looking to keep costs under control, and Medical Education had to defend itself every year at budget time. But to whomever it was that was saying, "This operation doesn't do us any good," I would say, "When was the last time somebody asked you who you worked for and you said, 'Ciba-Geigy,' and they said, 'Oh, *The Ciba Collection*,' or, 'Oh, *Clinical Symposia*,' or, 'Oh, Frank Netter.'" So as often as we had to fight for our place in the company, people knew of Ciba-Geigy not because of our drug products but because of the whole Netter operation.[19]

ଡ଼୦ଡ଼୦ଡ଼୦

At the time Phil Flagler joined Ciba-Geigy in 1976, Frank already was making pictures for volume 7, *Respiratory System*.[20] Dr. Matthew B. Divertie, professor of medicine at the Mayo Medical School, in Rochester, Minnesota, was the consulting editor who pulled together the volume and reviewed all of the text with the illustrations. Dr. Alfred Fishman, chief of the cardiovascular pulmonary division of the University of Pennsylvania, helped lay out the project and select many of the contributors, as well as consulting on 11 plates in the section on diseases and pathology of respiration.[21]

They used Frank and Ed Crelin's work on embryology,[22] incorporating plates from *Clinical Symposia*[23] issue on the development of the lower respiratory system, only slightly modifying the text to fit it into the volume. They also used plates on bronchial asthma[24] from the *Clinical Symposia* monograph that Frank had done on asthma with Dr. Earle B. Weiss, and just updated the text but not the illustrations. Nineteen superb pictures of the gross anatomy of the thorax and lungs[25] came out of Frank's work with distinguished bronchopulmonary anatomist Dr. John Huber.

Dr. Wallace T. Miller, a colleague of Dr. Fishman's from the University of Pennsylvania and recruited by him, worked with Frank on all 17 plates in the radiology section.[26] Dr. Fishman also asked Dr. Murray D. Altose, a young faculty member in the pulmonary function lab at the University of Pennsylvania, to consult with Frank on 21 plates[27] in the section on pulmonary physiology. For the better part of 1976–1978, Frank would visit every three months or so, at first when Dr. Altose was in Philadelphia and later when he moved to Case Western Reserve University. They would meet for one or two days and go over the sketches in considerable detail. Some they created from scratch and some they adapted from those in previously published articles. Frank would ask questions about what precisely something meant in a particular illustration, and Dr. Altose would explain it to him. "He always challenged me to explain every single physiological concept so that he could understand it," recalled Dr. Altose. "But as demanding as he was, it was never aggressive or threatening."[28] All the pictures they did together for the *Respiratory System* volume were also used in an article on pulmonary function testing,[29] published in a *Clinical Symposia* issue a few months after the book came out. Dr. Altose modified the text to fit the *Clinical Symposia* format, and that issue was popular with the medical students, he recollected.

Dr. Henry Heinemann, at Cornell University Medical College in New York, consulted on two plates[30] on the physiology of vaso-active substances. He told Frank that Drs. Una and James Ryan, at the University of Miami School of Medicine, were doing work on lung vascular endothelial cells.[31] At the time, the Ryans' work was new, very cutting edge. Using electron microscopy, they had shown the structure of the lungs both on the airway side and on the blood side. Dr. Una Ryan explained it:

> The endothelium was not just this cellophane lining that stops the blood from falling out into the tissues. It was intricately detailed. It had its own sort of micro-structure, and some of the little "caviolae," little caves, contained enzymes and could process substances in the blood as they went through. And Frank literally drew it. I still go to lectures where people will start a lecture with that picture. It has become part of the understanding of pulmonary metabolism.[32]

Dr. Una Ryan was a striking woman, vibrant and slim with clear skin and shiny black hair, and she had a great deal of enthusiasm for her work. She was a Howard Hughes investigator, and Frank met with her in the conference room of the Howard Hughes Medical Institute, where there was a big table to spread out the electron micrographs. She remembered:

> He was sort of a god to me. I didn't recognize that he was a person at all until I met him. And it was absolutely wonderful. I loved him. He would sketch things out and ask questions: "Would it be better to have the inside of the blood vessel dark, or would it be better to have the tissue dark and the middle white?" He seemed very interested that I was discovering mechanisms through visual means.[33]

During those long, intense sessions, Dr. Ryan had sandwiches brought in for lunch, and at those times he put the pencil down and she put the pictures down, and then they talked about the work he was doing for the book, about art and science, and about electron microscopy and other new technologies. She had done some fashion modeling and had a dress with a silkscreen print of electron micrographs of insects.

> He asked me about those fabrics and how they printed them. It was not the sort of detailed drawings that he did; it was the patterns of insect mitochondria. I told him I thought they would make wonderful wallpaper. He laughed about that.
>
> He could see that I was partially Asian—I am half Chinese and half English—and he asked me about my background, and he seemed interested in the fact that my grandfather was a British doctor who had traveled over the Himalayas taking smallpox vaccine [to China].[34]

And he told her about his trip to China, and that his grandfather too had traveled to China. Out of their collaboration came three pictures for the book,[35] but it took hours of thinking and talking about how to represent the concepts. A great deal of creativity went into it. "I just had this very warm feeling about those conversations," she recalled, "and most of all I loved doing the work with him. He sent me the books autographed, and sent me proofs too. He was very thoughtful, an absolute gentleman and really, really talented."[36]

The section on pulmonary diseases was far and away the largest, 149 plates. Frank's friends at The Mount Sinai Hospital in New York—Max Som, Alvin Teirstein, and Jacob Churg—consulted with him on a dozen plates[37] in that section. Before each of his several trips to New York to meet with one or more of them at Mount Sinai, Frank researched the subject matter and prepared himself to discuss the topic at length. He had known them all for years, and he told lively stories at his meetings with them and was their garrulous leader, Dr. Teirstein remembered, which made the meetings fun.[38] Yet Frank was organized and productive; and they completed the pictures and text within the allotted time.

Dr. Morton N. Swartz was head of the infectious disease unit at Massachusetts General Hospital, and Dr. Fishman recommended him to work on 11 plates[39] in the pneumonia segment in *Respiratory System*. Frank went only once or twice to see Dr. Swartz at Harvard, and they decided how best to show the condition using gross appearance of organs, microscopic appearances of the inflammation and bacteria, x-rays, and data charts; and they talked about the complications, say of pneumococcal pneumonia. The rest they did by correspondence. Frank would send sketches to Dr. Swartz, and Dr. Swartz would send Frank histological sections or pictures of cultures of bacteria or x-rays. Then Frank made the pictures that showed the complications in the heart on one figure, and in the pleural space on another, septic arthritis. "He was what you might call an old-fashioned gentleman," recollected Dr. Swartz. "I could picture him holding the door open for a woman to pass through and holding a car door for her to get in—a very nice, gentle soul, I thought."[40]

Dr. Marvin Sackner was the director of medical services at Mount Sinai Medical Center in Miami Beach and a well known pulmonologist. He consulted with Frank on four illustrations in the section on therapeutic procedures,[41] and he asked Drs. José F. Landa and Edward D. Michaelson to help on five more.[42] One plate they did on arterial blood gas analysis[43] consists of four vignettes; it showcases Frank's consummate skill in depicting hands—the hands of the patient and the hands of a technician withdrawing arterial blood into a syringe.[44]

ᘒᘐᘒᘐᘒᘐ

Frank was nearly done with the plates for *Respiratory System* when he asked Dr. Milton H. Uhley, at Cedars–Sinai Medical Center in Los Angeles, to write a piece on subdiaphragmatic pressure to save choking victims—the Heimlich maneuver—for inclusion in the volume. The Heimlich maneuver was introduced in 1974, and in 1977 Frank was working on the plates. For the book, Frank prepared two composite plates[45] showing the mechanics and techniques of the maneuver.

It was a new procedure, a forward-thinking topic. Alister Brass invited Dr. Uhley to expand the text from the *Respiratory System* volume for a *Clinical Symposia* issue on the technique.[46] The issue had two distinct sections: a "Description of the Heimlich Maneuver"[47] and a "Historical Review of the Literature on Choking."[48] Dr. Uhley asked Dr. Henry Heimlich, who had first described the technique and after whom it was named, to prepare the description, while Dr. Uhley prepared the historical review. This monograph was a bit unusual, in that its target audience was not limited to medical professionals but included the general public. "Anyone who could be a rescuer needs to know how to do the maneuver and anyone who could choke needs to know the Heimlich sign,"[49] explained Dr. Heimlich.

For the monograph Frank made nine additional plates showing choking victims and rescuers administering the thrusts—really great pictures of people. Dr. Heimlich explained:

> The first major picture in the *Clinical Symposia* is very important. It shows a man who is choking, and he is running to the men's room. That is extremely important, because in those days, people were ashamed to be choking. So Frank spread that word right in the beginning with a major picture. If you are choking, you give the Heimlich sign to indicate it and you get people's attention, instead of running out of the room. It is a beautiful thing, the way he did it, as was everything he did. [This] was the first widespread article on the Heimlich maneuver. It was very widely distributed. I am sure that this article saved many lives, by spreading the word on how to do it.[50]

ᕙᖍᕙᖍᕙ

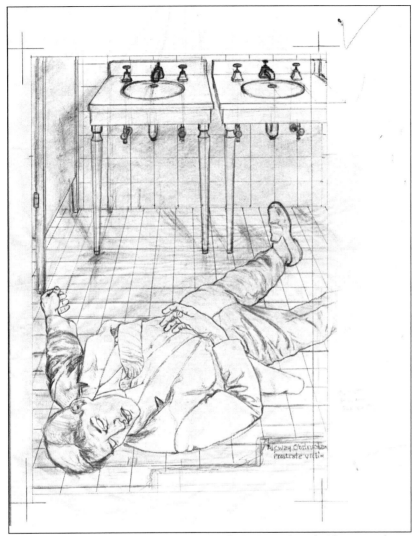

Sketch: "Recognizing the Choking Victim," Frank H. Netter, from the University of North Carolina Wilson Special Collections Library.

There was quite a variety of subject matter in the pictures Frank did for *Respiratory System*—beautiful anatomic illustrations for which he was famous—pictures of patients being treated, pictures of microscopic matter, and diagrams of complex physiologic concepts. Frank made the decisions as to what to pictorialize and how much emphasis to place on each topic. In the four decades since Frank was in school, interest in various lung diseases had shifted. The advent of antibiotics, improved living conditions, and advances in diagnostic techniques had brought about a decreased incidence in tuberculosis and pneumococcal pneumonia. At the same time, demographic changes in the population, smoking habits, pollution, and certain occupational conditions resulted in an increase of lung cancer and emphysema. In the introduction to the volume, he wrote:

> The artist must portray his subject matter as effectively as possible within the allotted pages. What to leave out becomes, at times, as important as what to include. . . . My goal was to picture or diagram the essence of each subject, avoiding the incidental or inconsequential.[51]

The project, begun before 1975, finally came to fruition with the publication of *Respiratory System* in 1979. By the time Alister Brass joined Ciba-Geigy at the end of 1977, they were already making the color separations. "We added three illustrations on computed tomography of the chest," Gina said, "and Alister was involved in developing those."[52] Otherwise, his name is on the *Respiratory System* volume as the directing editor, but Dr. Matthew Divertie was the editor.

For the section about the author in the front of the volume, Frank made a crude portrait of himself at his drawing board. His taboret, art supplies, the skeleton, swing-arm lamp, books, all the accoutrements of his work are there, and in the background through the window are palm trees and the Intracoastal Waterway.

At the completion of each of the books—and it took three or four years, five for *Respiratory System*, to get the book assembled—Ciba-Geigy would host a dinner party. They would invite the authors and editors, as many as could attend, Frank, and the staff members who had been involved in the process. They often planned those

"Self Portrait," Frank H. Netter, *ink on illustration board 1979, from the collection of* Francine Mary Netter.

parties to coordinate with a medical conference, which many of the authors would be attending.

The paintings themselves were housed in a fire-protected and climate-controlled vault, which the Medical Education Department had specially installed in Ciba-Geigy offices in West Caldwell, New Jersey. They were not often removed from the vault, but on the occasions they were exhibited, they attracted a huge crowd. Ward Newschwander did the display booths at the conventions, and he had responsibility for arranging any exhibits. Ward worked for

Phil and was associated with the Medical Education Department at Ciba-Geigy probably longer than anyone except for Frank Netter. For the launch of the *Respiratory System* book at a convention of internists in Washington, D.C., Ward organized an exhibition of a few of the original illustrations from that volume. Ciba had a booth at which the new book was featured, and the exhibit was of great interest not only to the 40 doctors who worked on the book—they had not seen the original finished art prior to that— but also to all of the doctors attending the convention. They came in crowds to see the original pictures.[53]

CHAPTER 21

REVISING NERVOUS SYSTEM

ONE OF FRANK'S FRIENDS and neighbors in Point Manalapan was Dr. Charles H. Frantz. He and Frank were about the same age, and they played golf together. Dr. Frantz was retired from a distinguished career as an orthopaedist and was especially interested in helping child amputees. He had helped establish the Area Child Amputee Program at the Mary Free Bed Rehabilitation Hospital in Grand Rapids, Michigan, and had created a system for classifying congenital limb defects.

On the golf course and in their meetings socially, Dr. Frantz was always encouraging Frank to do some pictures on the musculoskeletal system and on congenital limb deformities in particular. Accordingly, Frank asked him to help organize an atlas on the musculoskeletal system for *The Ciba Collection*. Dr. Frantz then began laying out the volume and contacting potential consultants, including Dr. Harold Kleinert, at the University of Louisville, about replantation of limbs and digits, and Dr. Charles Rockwood, at the University of Texas Health Science Center at San Antonio, about a section on trauma.

Dr. Franz also introduced Frank to Dr. Alfred B. Swanson, an orthopaedist who had been partners with Dr. Frantz in Grand Rapids, and to his wife, Dr. Genevieve de Groot Swanson, who was a plastic surgeon on the faculty of Michigan State University, in nearby East Lansing. Frank then worked with the Swansons on a *Clinical Symposia* issue on the reconstruction of the arthritic hand and foot.[1] The Swansons went into their files and showed Frank the slides and films of joint replacement of the fingers, wrist, and great toe. On one occasion, Al Swanson came to Florida and even played golf with Frank and Charley Frantz. Frank went up to Michigan in 1977 to consult with Al and even went to the operating room with him. Then Frank made the sketches, which they all reviewed together before Frank made the finished pictures.

Frank then began collaborating with Charley Frantz in preparing a *Clinical Symposia* issue on congenital limb deformities. But no sooner had they begun that project than, in 1978, Dr. Frantz died, and Frank's work with him on this project, as well as on the musculoskeletal volume, was interrupted. Al Swanson stepped in for Dr. Frantz for the completion of the project on congenital deformities.[2] Again Frank went to Grand Rapids to meet with Al, who showed Frank a film of a girl who had no arms and was sitting on

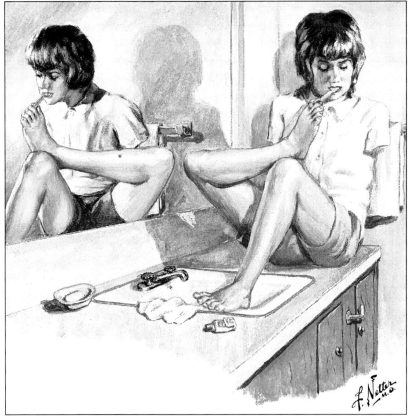

"Congenital Limb Defects Classification and Treatment," Frank H. Netter, Clinical Symposia *volume 33, number 3, 1981, plate 6, courtesy of Elsevier.*

the edge of the sink brushing her teeth with her feet. "Stop the film!"[3] Frank said, and Al had a still print of that frame made up to give to Frank to take back to his studio. He made a picture of that young girl, sitting on the sink brushing her teeth, and, as an artistic flourish, Frank added her reflection in the mirror over the sink, which was not in the original photograph.[4]

Dr. J. Harold Walton, who had been the editor of *Clinical Symposia* from its inception, died in early 1979,[5] and Mary Earl McKinsey became its managing editor. She edited the issue on congenital limb deformities, which Ciba published in 1981. It was dedicated to Dr. Frantz, and in the foreword both Frank and Al told of their respective professional and personal connections to Charley Frantz.

ତ⚬ତ⚬ତ

With the loss of Dr. Frantz as guest editor for the musculoskeletal volume, Frank placed that project on hold and in 1979 began working on the second edition of volume 1, *Nervous System*. Alister Brass was the editor, and he traveled to Florida a number of times to talk with Frank, plan the volume, and decide what new pictures needed to be added and what could be taken from the first edition.[6] Plans called for a complete revision, expanding the volume to two tomes, Part I[7] covering the anatomy and physiology, and Part II,[8] neurologic and neuromuscular disorders. It was Dr. Shapter's outline that they used after all.

There were relatively few contributors to the revised *Nervous System*, Part I,[9] although each was responsible for a large number of the plates. As one would expect, British neuroanatomist Professor G.A.G. Mitchell worked extensively with Frank in preparing this volume and contributed to 94 of the 188 plates.[10] One of the more striking plates is on the anterior aspect of the skull in section I, "Bony Coverings of the Brain and Spinal Cord,"[11] in which Frank used different colors to demarcate the different bones. And 15 plates[12] on the embryology of the nervous system were taken from an issue of *Clinical Symposia*[13] that Ed Crelin had done with Frank in 1974. Those plates were all included in the revision with only the text slightly modified.[14]

Dr. Barry W. Peterson was a junior faculty member at Rockefeller University in New York. Frank somehow found him and went to Dr. Peterson's office on York Avenue to work with him. Frank would light up his cigar and they would talk about neural pathways or the flow of ions through ion channels. "He didn't just want me to tell him what to do," said Dr. Peterson. "He wanted me to give him the guidance of where to look to get started."[15] Then Frank would go off, perhaps to the Academy of Medicine, and read what Dr. Peterson recommended, research it for himself, and return with innovative ways to illustrate some of the things. Dr. Peterson explained:

> Occasionally we would get into a situation where there were very complex neural pathways, like the plate that talks about input pathways to the cerebellum.[16] Frank came up with a cutout section of the brain stem to view it from underneath. If you sit there and puzzle through it, it is a very good way to visualize those pathways. I never would have thought of such a thing. It is a clever concept. He shows the plane of section at the lower right.
>
> I was not making much money then. I got about $150 a plate, and it is not a lot of money, but it was a little extra something and it was fun to do. I would explain the topic to him, we would discuss it, he would go make the pictures, and then we would discuss it some more, maybe do revisions, and then I would write the text to go with them.[17]

It took Frank and Dr. Peterson about three years—from 1979 to 1982—to complete the 52 plates[18] they did together for *Nervous System*. There was a piece on the resting potential of ions, which was more biophysics than anatomy, and Dr. Peterson asked Dr. Alex Mauro, who was a biophysicist and not a physician, to review that portion and check it for correctness.[19]

Dr. Jerome Sheldon came to work with Frank through Dr. Marty Grossman, at the Miami Heart Institute, in Miami Beach. He had done a *Clinical Symposia* issue with Frank in 1980 on colonoscopy,[20] and during one of their meetings, Frank told Dr. Grossman he was planning an issue on the nervous system and wanted to include illustrations of the blood vessels as seen by modern neuroradiology. Dr. Grossman recommended Dr. Sheldon, who was a young neuroradiologist in practice at Mount Sinai Medical Center there in Miami Beach.[21]

Their first meeting was in the radiology department conference room at Mount Sinai. Dr. Sheldon explained the technique and procedure for a neuroangiogram and showed Frank angiograms with normal findings. Then Frank wanted to see the neuroangiology suite and talk with the technologists who performed the studies. He spent the better part of the afternoon talking with them. The last name of one of the technologists was Netter, no relation, but they all had a big laugh about that.

Dr. Sheldon described the various arteries and veins, and Frank sketched them right then and there, making the pictures of the blood vessels and their relationship to the anatomy of the brain. They also reused some of the plates that Frank had done with Dr. Abraham Kaplan for the first issues of *Clinical Symposia* and the first edition of *Nervous System*. Dr. Sheldon supplied the text and new labels on those older pictures, and Frank painted out the airbrushed backgrounds, painting them white to coordinate with the newer pictures, which did not have airbrushed backgrounds. The plates Frank worked on with Dr. Sheldon were for a *Clinical Symposia*[22] issue that came out in 1981. They were later incorporated into *Nervous System*, Part I, with updated text that Dr. Sheldon prepared.[23]

Those pictures that Frank made with Dr. Sheldon were the first pictures to be published that related the cerebral blood vessels— arteries and veins—to the underlying anatomy. Radiographs are a two-dimensional representation of three-dimensional anatomy, but Frank drew the vessels to look like an angiogram and then superimposed the anatomy. Clinicians need to understand anatomy and pathology, and Frank's pictures communicate complex anatomical relationships. Some anatomy professors may want more detail in the pictures, but too much detail obscures the message.[24] Deciding what to leave out of an illustration is as important as what to put in it. Frank was a master at knowing what to leave out of a picture. He included everything that needed to be there and nothing that did not need to be there. Some parts of a picture are detailed and some parts are not, and that brings the message into focus.[25]

ᐒᐭᐒᐭᐒᐭᐒᐭᐒ

When the first edition of *Nervous System* was first printed in 1953, it contained no coverage of the hypothalamus. That was added as a supplement a few years later. It was a paperback in the same format and same size paper as the hardcover book. Dr. Jay B. Angevine, Jr. used it when he was in medical school at Harvard. He shoved it under the front or back cover of the main text and carried them around together. In later printings of the first edition, the hypothalamus supplement was bound in the back of the hardcover book, though still as a supplement. The pictures on which Dr. Angevine consulted for the second edition of *Nervous System* were those in that hypothalamus supplement, as well as two plates on the pituitary that Frank had done for *Endocrine System*.[26] Plate by plate,[27] they reviewed the pictures on the telephone and sent materials through the mail. They did not change any of the illustrations, only the captions and leader bars.

The "Naked Angry Man," as Dr. Angevine called it, was a powerful, well-known picture.[28] It illustrates the rage reaction and spans two facing pages of the book. Frank himself posed as the model for it. For the new edition, they changed just the leader line colors, and Dr. Angevine rewrote the legend. He reviewed the text from the first edition supplement and suggested changes to that. "And there were quite a few," Dr. Angevine recalled. "The changes didn't reflect any ignorance or sloppiness on Frank's part. They were just changes in the growing knowledge and progress in the way we looked at things."[29]

Jay Angevine did not meet Frank face-to-face until after the book was published in 1983, when he went to a meeting of the American Association of Anatomists at the Copley Hotel in Boston. He and other contributors attended a dinner given by Ciba-Geigy in celebration of the book's publication, and Frank got up and spoke. He thanked the people for coming, and then told them that he had a letter he wanted to share with them. The letter, he said, was addressed to the corporate offices of Ciba-Geigy and was from a physician in Elmira, New York, who, for reasons to become clear, he would not name.

Serious in his demeanor, Frank began to read the letter: "Gentleman: I received your data on the *Nervous System*, Part I, *Anatomy and Physiology*, and a contemplated second part for 1985, advertised as a production of Dr. Frank Netter. On a personal basis, I know that Dr. Netter is deceased"—Frank could no longer keep a straight face and started to giggle as he continued to read—"and consider this not a proper way of merchandising. It is all well and good to use his illustrations, but the public should be advised that this is a revision by someone else and not by Dr. Netter."[30] Everyone had a good laugh over that.[31]

๑๏๑๏๑๏๑

Bob Van Mierop, the cardiologist with whom Frank had consulted on *Heart*, moved from Albany to the University of Florida in Gainesville. Whenever Frank was going to Gainesville researching some pictures, he dropped by to see his friend and colleague. Dr. Van Mierop recalled:

> While he was visiting us here, [Frank met] Dr. Gerold Ludwig Schiebler, who was at the time chairman of the Department of Pediatrics, and also was one of those remarkable persons.

> Every year for several months he [Dr. Schiebler] went to Tallahassee, our capital here in the State of Florida, to attend the legislature. He was our representative to the legislature, an official lobbyist. He somehow convinced one of the legislators to introduce a resolution in honor of Frank. [In 1979, Florida State Legislation Resolution of Commendation[32] unanimously passed.] Frank was very pleased with that.[33]

Medical societies and universities honored Frank as well. At a gala ceremony at the California Masonic Memorial Temple in San Francisco in March 1981, the American College of Cardiology gave Frank its Distinguished Service Award at the 30th Annual Scientific Session of the College. In May of that year, Frank received an honorary doctor of science degree from the New Jersey College of Medicine and Dentistry. Frank flew up to Newark for the ceremony, donned the academic robes they gave him and processed with the scholars to receive the honor.[34]

On April 28, 1981, Frank turned 75 years old. Vera was then 80 years old. Her eyesight was failing and she was growing frail. Nevertheless she threw a birthday party for him at the Manalapan Club. She invited their friends and neighbors for a festive evening of dinner and dancing and well-wishing, and in the photos of Frank and Vera dancing together, she in a pink dress and he in a white sport coat and boutonnière, they are clearly having a good time.

That milestone was also marked at Ciba-Geigy. Phil's staff assembled a "birthday book"—a photo album with letters from Ciba-Geigy headquarters in Basel and Ciba-Geigy offices all over the world. The letters poured into Summit. There were letters from Richard Kogan, the president of the Pharmaceuticals Division, and from Felton Davis, Jr., who was senior vice president of public affairs. Letters came from Switzerland, Germany, Denmark, Norway, Sweden, Finland, Italy, Spain, France, Belgium, Japan, Brazil, Argentina, Mexico, Canada, Australia , and South Africa.

Frank was a private person. He liked his golf and sometimes fishing, and while peer recognition pleased him, he shied away from notoriety. He was surprised when Phil presented the book to him. He looked at all the letters from the Ciba-Geigy senior officers around the world, sending birthday congratulations, praise for his work, and thanks for his contribution not only to Ciba-Geigy but to medicine and to humankind, stating that his work will be remembered and studied for generations.

"Everyone at Ciba-Geigy—not everyone, but people thought about it—knew that Frank was getting older," remembered Phil. "The operation would have to find someone to take his place if it were to continue."[35] Would Frank retire? The question was on everyone's mind, and sometimes on their lips.

"I am often asked, 'When are you going to retire?'" wrote Frank in his notes. "But Ciba won't let me retire. In fact, the medical profession won't let me retire. And, anyway, what would I do if I were to retire? I would make pictures. And that is what I am doing."[36]

CHAPTER 22

THE BREAKERS

THE HISTORIC BREAKERS HOTEL is a luxurious palace directly on the oceanfront in the heart of Palm Beach. Its long main driveway runs arrow-straight from South County Road east to the hotel's Italianate structure on the shore of the Atlantic Ocean. At the front entrance to the hotel, the drive encircles an imposing Florentine fountain from which Breakers Row runs north to an apartment complex, part of the hotel property, adjacent but still separate, offering the conveniences of the hotel but the privacy of a residence. Residents there have their own doorman, their own beachfront, their own swimming pool, a parking garage under the buildings, and a boardwalk along the ocean that connects back to the hotel.

By the spring of 1981, Frank and Vera had sold the Point Manalapan house and rented a three-bedroom luxury apartment on Breakers Row. The living room, its walls painted flamingo pink, they furnished with a pair of Ultrasuede chesterfield sofas in the same flamingo pink, facing each other in front of a fireplace—actually a decorative imitation of a fireplace—with a wooden mantel that Frank painted in trompe l'oeil marble. A cabinet Frank had painted in the Italian style, with scenes of Roman ruins, housed the Sony television given to him by Ciba Japan. Frank's landscape of the East River hung over the Steinway piano, and his collection of oil paintings by various artists, including the sketch of uncertain provenance of *Las Hilanderas*, decorated the other walls.

Off the hall close to the foyer, Frank had his studio. Seated at his drawing board beside the north-facing window, he had a view of the ocean on his left, and on the right, his taboret. On the wall in front of the drawing board, rows of shelving held his library, his mementos, photos of his children and a photo of Max Som, four hole-in-one trophies, and among the many awards, a bronze sculpture of a small book with a caduceus and a paintbrush, presented to Frank by New York University School of Medicine.[1] A small round conference table and chairs sat in one corner of the room. Behind his workstation was a bank of cabinets providing storage and counter space, and the closet housing his files and supplies. Not to be missed along the hallway just outside the studio was the *Life of a Doctor* series.

With all those accoutrements, the first thing that hit you, the first thing you noticed when you walked into the studio, was the smell of his cigars, not offensive so much as a signature of the man who occupied that room. Vera asked him to confine his smoking to the studio, and the smell in that room underscored his presence.

It was a good life, an easy life, which allowed him to keep working. Frank and Vera walked on the boardwalk over to the hotel for lunch or to attend one of the myriad charitable functions held in the hotel's ballrooms. Frank swam in the pool at Breakers Row, played golf on the hotel's course overlooking the ocean, and frequented the driving range conveniently located just across South County Road. He would go over there and hit a bucket of balls just to loosen up after sitting all day at the drawing board. He made friends with the regulars and admired a 90-year-old who came every day to hit golf balls. In 1981, the Christmas card Frank and Vera sent, their first year at The Breakers, was a picture Frank made of the two of them—she in a red dress and he in green pants—standing in front of the Florentine fountain, red poinsettias and green palm trees in the background.

⚬❧⚬❧⚬❧⚬

Some years earlier, in 1978, the meeting of the American Medical Association was in San Francisco and had a big session on neurology, remembered Dr. Royden Jones, who was an assistant professor of neurology at Harvard and a neurologist at the Lahey Clinic in Massachusetts. He normally did not attend those big conventions, but as he was interested in the neurology session and in seeing San Francisco, he went to that one. Ciba had a booth featuring some issues of *Clinical Symposia* and the *Ciba Collection* volumes, including *Nervous System*,[2] which, compared with subsequent volumes, was relatively superficial but nevertheless presented the anatomy in clear detail. Roy Jones stopped at the Ciba booth and started chatting with one of the Ciba reps from Medical Education. One of the more difficult areas to teach medical students, Dr. Jones said, was part of the anatomy of the peripheral nervous system. Had Dr. Netter ever considered doing a *Clinical Symposia* issue on that topic, he asked, and gave the rep his business card, going on to the meeting and never giving it another thought.

More than a year later, Dr. Jones received a handwritten letter from Frank Netter saying that he had heard about the inquiries and inviting him to come down to Palm Beach and talk to him about it. Frank had a project underway in orthopaedic surgery that he wanted to expand to diseases of the peripheral nerves, and he wanted Dr. Jones to work with him on it. Dr. Jones read the letter again and without further hesitation called Frank and accepted. Gina Dingle made the arrangements.

On that first trip to Palm Beach Dr. Jones stayed at the Brazilian Court, a small boutique hotel just off Worth Avenue in the heart of Palm Beach, and Frank came by in his Plymouth and picked him up. "He was such an engaging and pleasant and low-level ego," Dr. Jones recalled. "I kind of expected someone who was very artsy, and whose ego you couldn't get through a door perhaps. But he was just the opposite, and we hit it off from [the first] moment."[3]

They worked together in the studio. Frank showed Roy what parts of the orthopaedic project he had, and they began work on a *Clinical Symposia* issue on diseases of the peripheral motor–sensory unit.[4]

Frank and Vera had just recently moved over to The Breakers to those newly opened apartments. One day Frank and Roy drove down to Point Manalapan to meet one of Frank's friends, a businessman who was part owner of the Cleveland Browns, and

Frank pointed out his former home. But Roy found The Breakers apartment delightful, right on the beach within walking distance of town.

ᏸᎥᏸᎥᏸᎥᏸ

In 1980, Mary McKinsey at Ciba contacted Dr. Seymour Diamond, one of the pioneers in the treatment of headaches, and invited him to work with Frank on an issue of *Clinical Symposia*. "Dr. Netter's work was so well recognized that even though I was very busy I thought it was an honor to be able to work with him,"[5] Dr. Diamond recalled. He went once to Florida to see Frank, and then Dr. José Medina, Dr. Diamond's colleague and coauthor, worked with Frank on the pictures. Most of what they put into that *Clinical Symposia* issue[6] was based on the work of Dr. Harold G. Wolff, who was a prominent headache researcher in the 1950s and early 1960s. Dr. Diamond's work was more clinically oriented, but the basic concepts are the same, although there were some additions in where the trigeminal nerve, the fifth cranial nerve, was implicated.

Frank also revised some of the more popular previously published issues of *Clinical Symposia* on the basis of new findings.[7] In 1982, working with Dr. Aram Chobanian, who was by then the head of the Division of Medicine's Hypertension and Atherosclerosis Section at Boston University School of Medicine, he expanded their 1972 issue on hypertension.[8] For the original one, Dr. Chobanian had been a junior author with Drs. Robert Wilkins and William Hollander and had very little contact with Frank. For the 1982 update, Dr. Chobanian was sole author, although his contact with Frank was primarily through phone and mail. One picture they created showed people with high blood pressure stepping up onto increasingly higher levels of platforms, illustrating the step-care approach to managing hypertension and the levels of treatment that could be employed, depending on degrees of severity.[9] They worked on a third revision several years later,[10] when Dr. Chobanian was dean of the Boston University School of Medicine, and he traveled more and went to Florida to work with Frank. There were substantial changes from issue to issue.

Because Frank objected to a manuscript on cardiac arrhythmias that had been proposed for a *Clinical Symposia* issue, Alister Brass asked Dr. Stephen Scheidt, at Cornell, to review it. When Dr. Scheidt independently agreed with Frank's assessment, Frank wrote to Alister, "I am glad to see that you have finally satisfied yourself that I know what I was talking about. . . . If you really want to do this subject, I suggest you get Dr. Scheidt to do it. I will then do my best to illustrate it."[11] But he warned Alister that the topic did not easily lend itself to illustration.

Dr. Scheidt flew down to Florida three or four times in 1982 and taught Frank how to read ECGs. When they were working in the studio, Dr. Scheidt saw the *Life of a Doctor* series, and since he, like Frank, had trained at Bellevue, albeit somewhat later—Frank in the early 1930s, Dr. Scheidt in the 1960s—that prompted them to swap stories about their training. "Once you have been at Bellevue, you don't forget it," explained Dr. Scheidt. "In some ways it was a wonderful place. You had enormous experiences."[12]

Dr. Scheidt did not think it was a good idea for Frank to try to draw the ECGs, "because you can't draw some of the high-frequency things, and there is slight variability in your paintings and the electrocardiogram is a mechanical device that [always] moves at exactly the same speed." [13] But Frank made the pictures of the tracings anyway, and their collaboration came out so well that Ciba-Geigy expanded the topic to two *Clinical Symposia* issues, published in 1983[14] and 1984.[15]

⟨∘❧∘❧∘❧∘⟩

After Dr. Frantz died and left no guest editor for the musculoskeletal volumes, Frank turned again to Dr. Robert Hensinger and asked him to take up the reins as guest editor for Volume 8, *Musculoskeletal System*. Bob Hensinger was a pediatric orthopaedist, and he told Frank that he did not feel comfortable editing the material on adult problems, that what he really wanted to do was a *Clinical Symposia* issue on the limping child. But Frank needed to complete the series of *Ciba Collection* books, and Dr. Hensinger agreed to edit that part of the book dealing with children. He helped Frank outline the volume and locate consultants.

Dr. Carl Brighton was chairman of the Department of Orthopaedic Surgery at the University of Pennsylvania. After Dr. Hensinger attended a talk Dr. Brighton gave on the electrical stimulation of bone in fracture healing, he told Frank about it; and in November of 1981 wrote to Dr. Brighton about contributing to the *Musculoskeletal System* volume, specifically to a section on osteoporosis and electrical stimulation of bone.[16] Frank was keen on including pictures on osteoporosis, especially since Vera suffered from back pain characteristic of the disorder and appeared to be developing the same stooped posture as had her older sister, Beatrice, who before she died had a pronounced dowager's hump.

Frank followed up Dr. Hensinger's letter with a phone call to Dr. Brighton,[17] who said he was delighted to work on the part about electrical stimulation of bone, but for the part about osteoporosis he would ask a young professor on his staff, the chief of the Division of Metabolic Bone Diseases, Dr. Frederick Kaplan, to work on it. After that phone call, Dr. Brighton gave Dr. Kaplan that special assignment. "Young man," Dr. Kaplan recalled Dr. Brighton saying to him, "next week you are going to the library and you are going to do some research on osteoporosis and write a paper to send to Dr. Netter. He needs background information on osteoporosis for an atlas on the musculoskeletal system."[18]

Nobody knew much about osteoporosis in 1982, but the young doctor dutifully went to the library and started reading. In April 1982, Frank wrote to Dr. Brighton inquiring if they had yet gathered the material on osteoporosis, and Dr. Kaplan soon completed the paper—it was triple-spaced, a little over 100 pages—and gave it to Dr. Brighton to forward to Dr. Netter. Dr. Kaplan recalled that he was thrilled to have prepared this document for the man who prepared material for every medical student in the world.

Fred Kaplan was a native of New Jersey, where his parents still lived. He had studied for both his undergraduate and medical degrees at Johns Hopkins University, and then did a residency in orthopaedics at the Hospital of the University of Pennsylvania. That was followed by a fellowship at Children's Hospital of Philadelphia. It was an unusual choice of specialty for someone of his 5'4" stature, as orthopaedics is often considered the domain of the burly surgeon and Dr. Kaplan had the wiry build of a professional jockey. Yet he was as talented a clinician as any and a meticulous researcher, a caring and compassionate physician.

The weeks went by after Dr. Kaplan prepared the research paper on osteoporosis, and not until July did he receive a letter from Dr. Netter, thanking him for the material he and Dr. Brighton had sent.

> It covers the topics [electrical stimulation of bone and osteoporosis] very completely . . . however . . . the problem will be one of condensation to fit them into the space which we will have available in the atlas on the *Musculoskeletal System*. It seems to me that the text you sent me on osteoporosis would be just about ideal for an issue of *Clinical Symposia* with, of course, the addition of my illustrations and I am proposing to our editors that we should do such an issue on this important and extremely prevalent disorder.[19]

It was mid-October 1982 when Dr. Kaplan went down to Palm Beach to work with Frank on the sketches for a *Clinical Symposia* on osteoporosis.[20] He recalled:

> I still remember the morning I flew down. I still remember the excitement in my mind that I was going to spend three or four days down there with Dr. Netter. I had not met him yet, but Dr. Netter had said, "I'll pick you up at the airport. I will be there waiting for you."

So, I'm on the airplane and the door opens in Palm Beach and I walk out of the plane, and there are a lot of people getting off the plane, and families waiting. Those were the days, of course, that you could just come right up to the gate. I had seen many pictures of Dr. Netter, so I knew what he looked like. And there I see this man, in patent leather shoes splattered with paint, sort of khaki pants and a Hawaiian shirt. And I think, "Oh my goodness! This is actually him. This is actually Dr. Netter."

I get off the plane and I am carrying a bag, and I say, "Dr. Netter?" And he says, "Dr. Kaplan, it is so nice to meet you." I say, "Call me Fred." So he says, "Let me help you with your bag." And I said, "Dr. Netter, I am not going to let you carry my bag!" So I carried the bag.[21]

They went to Frank's car, and then drove the six miles, over the bridge to Palm Beach and down County Road to The Breakers, to the apartment. The dining room table was set, and they had a beautiful luncheon in the apartment, Frank and Vera and Fred. They spent about two or three hours just talking. As Dr. Kaplan described it,

I remember even before going into his studio that afternoon, I felt like I was in the presence of a great man. . . . Frank Netter is probably the greatest educator—medical educator—of the twentieth century. I couldn't believe I was sitting there talking to this man who was extraordinarily humble.[22]

Their routine was simple. In the morning Dr Kaplan walked over from The Breakers Hotel to The Breakers Row apartment, and they worked on the pictures. They talked about osteoporosis, and Frank made sketches that were to become pictures. In the afternoon, Frank played golf and Fred took a swim. Then in the evening, they met for dinner either at The Breakers or at a restaurant in Palm Beach.

The *Clinical Symposia* were never intended for the experts but instead for medical students and for the general practitioner. In reality, all sorts of people used them—people in general medicine and internal medicine, physical medicine, pediatrics, radiology, athletic training, emergency medicine, physical therapy, chiropractic—all sorts of people.[23] When Fred was explaining bone formation and bone resorption, they got stuck on how to pictorialize it so as to convey the concept in a simple way for the general practitioner. Frank said, "Let's take a break. I am hungry. Are you hungry, Freddie? Vera went out, but I think she made a pot of coffee for us."[24] So they went in the kitchen, and Frank opened up the freezer and took out some sticky buns in a box. They stuck them in the toaster oven and forgot about them, burning them. The apartment filled up with smoke, and they opened the windows and turned on the ceiling fan in the kitchen to blow the smoke out. Just then, Vera walked in, and of course she smelled the smoke. "What are you boys doing?" she said. And she made them unburned sticky buns, and then Frank and Freddie—Frank always called him Freddie— went out for a walk on the beach.

They were walking along the beach, kicking the sand, and perhaps it was children he saw playing with their buckets in the sand that gave Frank the idea. He would show the osteoblasts—the cells forming bone—as little people bringing buckets of sand to make the bone, and the osteoclasts—the cells resorbing bone—as people taking the sand away. And they went back to Frank's studio, where he made a picture of little workmen with a *B* on their shirt— osteoblasts—carrying buckets of sand and dumping the sand into the reservoir, and other workmen with a *C* on their shirt—osteoclasts—opening a spigot and taking sand from the reservoir. If more "sand," so to speak, is deposited than is removed, it results in a net increase in bone mass, and conversely, if more "sand" is removed than is deposited, then there is a net decrease in bone mass, the result of which can be osteoporosis. And that analogy fit well with Dr. Kaplan's article describing the mechanisms for bone mass regulation.[25]

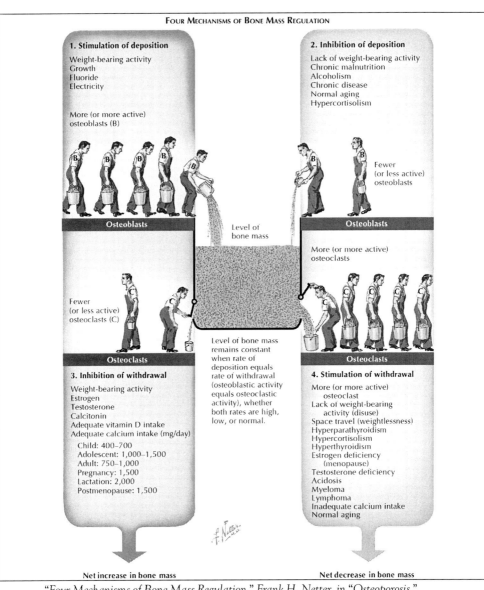

"*Four Mechanisms of Bone Mass Regulation*," Frank H. Netter, in "Osteoporosis,"
Clinical Symposia *volume 35, number 3, 1983, plate 5, courtesy of Elsevier.*

When it was time for Fred to leave, Frank drove Fred back to the
Palm Beach airport. Fred carried his valise and his briefcase, and
as Frank said goodbye, he looked at Fred and said, "Freddie, where
is your jacket? You know, it is cold in Philadelphia."[26] In that few
days' time, Frank had become someone who cared about him.

CHAPTER 23

THE ARTIFICIAL HEART

THE UNIVERSITY OF UTAH Medical Center sits high on a hill above Salt Lake City. When the winter wind blows off the Great Salt Lake, snow may fall in huge amounts on the medical center. On the night of December 1, 1982, a raging snowstorm covered the roads with a slippery fluff and impassable drifts. Cautiously avoiding the storm that could keep them from returning, the operating team at the medical center stayed at the hospital all night, ready for the surgery scheduled for the morning.

The patient was Dr. Barney Clark, a dentist from Seattle. He was 61 years old and had suffered for years from congestive heart failure. When referred by his cardiologist, he was a very sick man. His legs and ankles were puffed with edema, his skin was tinged blue with cyanosis, and his abdomen was swollen with fluids as his failing heart struggled to push life-sustaining blood through his body. Traditional therapies had been ineffective. Heart transplantation was still a new procedure, and surgeons were then not doing transplants on anyone his age. Barney Clark was at the end of his life.

He lay near death in a dark room in the cardiac intensive care unit, his heart failing minute by minute. Monitors reported multiple varying arrhythmias. By late evening the surgeons feared that Dr. Clark would not live until morning. In the middle of the night, they wheeled him into the operating room, where Dr. William DeVries excised both ventricles of Dr. Clark's quivering heart and replaced them with the Jarvik-7 artificial heart. Circulation of the blood was routed through the heart, and the patient was moved to recovery. Dr. Clark was alive, supported by an artificial heart.

It was the first case of its kind, where a total artificial heart was used not as a bridge to transplantation but as a permanent implant.

Up the snowy hill eager news reporters clambered for the story that hurled both Dr. Clark and Dr. DeVries onto the front page of newspapers and televised news broadcasts across the country. The operation caused a sensation.

Across the continent in Palm Beach, Frank Netter watched the television reports and read with great interest the stories in the newspapers about the artificial heart. "Fantastic!" he said. "It was a bold and courageous new approach, a completely new modality."[1] Yet its development had been built in a steady progression of knowledge built upon knowledge.[2] In his career as both doctor and medical illustrator, Frank had seen many of the medical developments that led to the artificial heart. He had witnessed the advent of cardiac surgery, ushered in by the heart–lung machine. Heart transplantation came in 1968, and he had made the definitive illustrations of both heart[3] and kidney[4] transplantation. But rejection of donor organs was still a major drawback to transplantation. Not until late in 1983 would the immunosuppressive drug cyclosporine be approved for managing rejection.

An ongoing shortcoming of organ transplantation is that the need for donor organs far exceeds the supply. That a donated heart depends on the death of the donor presents a conundrum, as the donor heart must still be functioning at the time it is harvested. Great discussions ensued about the ethics of heart transplantation and life support systems, from which emerged a new definition of death based on brain death.[5] The availability of a permanent artificial heart would overcome those drawbacks inherent in transplantation. The supply could conceivably be adjusted to meet demand, and since the artificial heart was constructed of inert material, the recipient's immune system would not reject it. It was indeed exciting news.

⊛⊱⊰⊛⊱⊰⊛

Dr. William DeVries was tall and lanky, with a shock of thick blond hair. His hands were large and strong, not the small delicate hands with tapered fingers one would expect on a surgeon performing such intricate work.

His grandmother—his father's mother—"was a Dutch lady who barely spoke English," Dr. DeVries remembered.

> Her husband had had a hardware store in Holland, and he made enough money to bring everybody over, a family of eight. In steerage, it was not fancy, but they came over in 1924. My father was the oldest son. He had not graduated from high school yet, and his father told him, "Make sure all your brothers and sisters get educated!" So he worked so all of his brothers and sisters got to go through high school. Then he went back to finish high school and went on to medical school. But that is the way they were. You did what your dad said, without question. Families like that where so many of them are successful—those are the only families you hear about. The other ones you don't hear about.[6]

Dr. DeVries's father was the ship's doctor aboard the destroyer USS *Kalk* during World War II. William was just a baby, only a few days old, when the *Kalk* left the Brooklyn Navy Yard, passed through the Panama Canal to the Pacific, and continued on to the South Pacific. She was off the coast of New Guinea on May 27, 1944, when a Japanese bomb hit her, killing the young doctor. William's mother was descended from the first Mormon pioneers who had migrated to Utah, and after she was widowed, she returned to Utah from Brooklyn with her infant son, William, who grew up not knowing his father.

William DeVries graduated from the University of Utah, and perhaps inspired by the story of his father, entered medical school. As a medical student he came under the tutelage of Dr. Willem Kolff, the inventor of the artificial kidney.[7] Dr. Kolff had come to the United States from the Netherlands in 1950. He spent 17 years at the Cleveland Clinic—perfecting the artificial kidney and developing an oxygenator for the heart–lung machine—before he came to the University of Utah in 1967 to start a department of biomedical engineering developing artificial organs.

Dr. Kolff had several projects going, to develop an artificial eye, an artificial ear, artificial limbs, and an artificial heart. The experiments his department did on animals in 1970 demonstrated that they could keep a sheep alive with an artificial heart for little more than two days. But the poor creature was so weak, it just lay on the floor.[8]

Upon graduating from medical school, the young Dr. William DeVries went east for a residency in cardiothoracic surgery with Dr. David Sabiston, Jr. at Duke University. Nine years later, in 1979, Dr. DeVries was back in Utah working with Dr. Kolff. A young resident, Dr. Robert Jarvik, had designed an artificial heart, which the team had implanted in calves and sheep—animals that approximated the size and weight of humans. The animals were walking around and exercising on a treadmill, even being taken outside while connected to a portable heart driver machine.[9] Dr. Kolff wanted his protégé, Dr. DeVries, to implant the artificial heart in a person.

But for use in people, the heart needed further modification. First of all, the heart would have to fit into the human thorax. The research team made a cast of the thorax and challenged Dr. Jarvik to create an artificial heart that would fit in the available space. Then, after seven months of submitting mounds of paperwork and then waiting and waiting and waiting, the team finally obtained approvals from the US Food and Drug Administration to use the artificial heart in a human.

After Dr. DeVries operated on Barney Clark, his name got into the newspapers and he started receiving letters from people who had known his father.

> One of them was from a doctor in Portland, Oregon. Another was from a bank president in Tampa, Florida. They said, "I saw your name in the newspaper and want to know if you are Henry's son." I had probably 30 or 40 letters from people,

all sailors who were on the ship with him. One was from the ship's captain who had buried him at sea. And they wrote back five-page letters saying how they knew him and what they did, and that he was the chaplain on board as well as the doctor.[10]

Bill DeVries thus came to know about his father, about his habits and the music he liked, what tunes he sang in the shower, whatever the sailors remembered.

ᐁᐧᐁᐧᐁᐧᐁ

Soon after the first of the year, Dr. DeVries was asked to speak at a medical conference in Las Vegas.

> I remember going to Las Vegas and taking my grandmother—my mother's mother. She loved the slot machines. She just loved them, and so I would take her down in the morning and put her by the slot machines, and then I'd check her out at lunch. And she would introduce me to everybody she had met. Then I would get her at 3 or 4 o'clock in the afternoon and take her out to dinner, and of course she had met everybody and she introduced me around to all the people at the slot machines. I had never taken a trip with her [before], and I really learned a lot about my grandmother during that time.[11]

Frank Netter was also on the speaking program at the medical conference; he and Bill DeVries were sitting together on a panel of people who had changed the world of medicine.

> I saw him sitting next to me, and I was absolutely just taken away. I could not believe that Frank Netter was sitting next to me. He knew who I was, and I was telling the story of Barney Clark. He knew all about it. Just cold he knew about it—knew

about what we were doing, how we were doing it, everything about it.

It was wonderful, that time in Las Vegas, meeting Frank Netter, talking to him. He was a very personable, wonderful guy, very easy to talk to. He was like my father, about the same age my father would have been then. He was always pleasant to everybody. He didn't talk much about himself, and I had to kind of drag it out of him about how he got where he was and what he did, and his army experiences, and [how] his mother encouraged him to do something useful, and he finally decided to do this [medical art].

When I met him at that conference, he said, "I will call Ciba. They give me a lot of latitude to do whatever I want to do. I really want to see the artificial heart. I think I can do a [*Clinical Symposia* issue]." I thought it was fantastic. He did not have to say any more. He was full of imagination and [looking to the] future. He knew that this would be an important thing for him to do. I thought it was great because he was one of the best-known medical teachers. I didn't think I would ever get to meet him.[12]

◊◊◊◊◊◊

Clinical Symposia was in its thirty-fifth year in 1983. Alister Brass was editor of the January–February issue. In a career move, he left Ciba-Geigy and went to California briefly, but because of illness he soon retired to his native Australia, where he later died. Dr. David Shephard stepped into the role of directing editor of *Clinical Symposia*. When Frank called to inquire about doing a *Clinical Symposia* issue on the artificial heart, the team—Phil Flagler, David Shephard, and Mary McKinsey—agreed that it should take priority on the publication schedule. The artificial heart was a target of opportunity, as Phil said, a hot topic. And Frank proceeded immediately. As he wrote in his notes,

I was thrilled when Bill DeVries asked me to come to Salt Lake City to "portray for posterity," as he so nicely put it, "the first definitive artificial heart implantation in a human." I was delighted to think I would play a part in recording this completely new departure in cardiac therapeutic modality, this completely new approach to the management of intractable heart disease.[13]

Many pioneers contributed to the development of artificial circulation. The "father of open heart surgery," Dr. C. Walton Lillehei, in a daring operation in 1954, had used cross-circulation between a parent and child—venous and arterial cannulae to and from the groin of the father—to support heart–lung function during the first surgical repair of a child's ventricular septum. Using a roller pump designed in 1934 by Michael DeBakey, the heart–lung machine,[14] which Frank illustrated in 1958,[15] soon superseded cross-circulation. Such mechanical support expanded the scope of heart surgery, making possible corrections that previously had been too risky to attempt. In the years following, the cardiac pacemaker[16] came into use to manage heart block and arrhythmias.

In the mid-1960s Dr. DeBakey worked on the development of an artificial heart in his laboratories at Baylor University. In 1969, Dr. Denton Cooley implanted an artificial heart—one designed in Dr. DeBakey's laboratory—as a temporary bridge to transplantation in a man who could not be weaned from the heart–lung machine after heart surgery. In 1981, again as a bridge to transplantation, Dr. Cooley implanted an artificial heart—the design of which was based on Dr. Kolff's work.

The Jarvik-7 heart was not a temporary remedy. It was a permanent implant. And Barney Clark was alive and alert with the Jarvik-7 implant. "Many had thought of the idea but the difficulties had been too great," Frank wrote in his notes. "The Utah team had to a large extent mastered it."[17]

ↀↂↀↂↀↂↀ

Frank studied all the literature on the artificial heart, and in February he went to Utah to meet with Bill DeVries and the Utah team that included Drs. Kolff and Lyle Joyce, the assisting surgeon and co-investigator.[18] They sat down with Frank, put the model heart on the conference table, and told him how the heart worked.

"He had a very clever mind," recalled Dr. DeVries. "I could tell he had studied everything he could find on the artificial heart. He knew what was important and what was not important and asked all the right questions. He had much more insight into what was going on than many of the experts in the field."[19]

"It struck me how humble he was," remembered Dr. Joyce. "He was excited to learn, and he was a master at learning. He had prepared himself so well. I felt he knew the operation."[20]

The Utah team told him about putting an earlier model of the heart in the animals, and how they then had to modify that to fit into the human chest cavity. They explained how the heart driver resided outside the body, and that they had devised special skin buttons securing the drive lines passing through the skin to minimize the chance of infection. They told him all about the years of research, the problems, and successes; and they showed him all they could about the project.

Frank wrote in his notes:

> Only when I arrived in Salt Lake City did I come to understand the tremendous effort and thought and planning that had gone into the project. The heart, after all, is just a pump, and it did seem that it could be replaced by a mechanical pump. But what a pump! It must fit into the human anatomy. It must pump just enough blood for the body's needs—not too much and not too little. The distribution of the blood flow must be balanced between the pulmonary circulation and the systemic circulation to avoid congestion of the lungs. It must not damage the delicate red blood cells, which it pumps. It must not cause clotting of the blood, and it must have a power source to keep it beating regularly and continuously. . . . I was

tremendously impressed by the years of persistent effort with which they had pursued their vision, overcoming so many seemingly insurmountable obstacles—a vision which their scientific intuition told them could be accomplished.[21]

Bill DeVries remembered taking Frank to visit Barney Clark, who was up out of bed. A tracheostomy inhibited his speech, but he could stand up and take a few steps with the aid of a walker, albeit connected by two 8′ long tubes to the heart's pneumatically driven power source, which made a constant noise as compressed air drove the artificial pumps inside his chest. With the heart driver housed in a cumbersome cabinet on wheels, Dr. Clark managed to move through the halls of the hospital to the sunroom and in the elevator to radiology. For physical therapy, he even had a bicycle specially rigged so he could sit in a chair and pedal away.

Before the surgery in December, Barney Clark had been "a desperately ill patient for whom there was no other hope."[22] He was a tall man with a broad chest, allowing for placement of the heart. A dentist by profession, he had been trained in and understood the scientific process, how knowledge is built one step at a time. He had agreed to be part of that and submitted to surgery so future generations might benefit from the medical knowledge gained. This was his gift to humankind.

Una Loy, Dr. Clark's wife, was constantly at her husband's bedside. She fully supported her husband's altruistic decision to undergo this ordeal so that the knowledge gained might help others. She shared a deep faith with her husband, and their devotion to each other was evidenced in how they looked at each other, how she tenderly stroked his forehead, and he, with his heart—the seat of love—excised, with the artificial heart in its place, telling her he loved her still.

Frank made at least one sketch at the bedside of Barney Clark.[23] Another sketch he subtitled, "Mrs. Clark and her sister-in-law sorting through some of the many thousands of good-will letters and get-well cards from all over the world." And Bill DeVries gave him photographs of Dr. Clark, some taken when he was so sick prior to the surgery and some taken when he was recovering after the surgery.

On that first visit to Utah, when Frank was making a pencil sketch of the artificial heart, Dr. DeVries asked him if he wanted a picture—a photo or schematic—to take with him. Frank said no, he did not want a picture. How he could remember it, Bill DeVries did not know. But Frank captured the important part and left out the unimportant part.

> Netter would make a picture of the heart and make it look like a heart. If you were talking about a valve, then he would add to the details of the heart valve. He might blend out some of the anatomy of the coronaries. He embellished the important part and phased out the piece that was not important. That is why he was so good at teaching. He was one of the great medical educators of all time. You cannot treat patients without education.[24]

The Utah team took Frank to see the animals and the animal heart, and to observe the surgery when Drs. DeVries and Joyce were operating on one of the animals. "He wanted to see everything. He was like a little kid," recalled Bill DeVries. "He was so excited about it, to see what was going on." There was a man working at the periphery, and Frank began talking to him, asking questions, Dr. DeVries remembered.

> He was talking to a janitor. We were busy sewing away, and he was over there talking to this guy whose job was to run and get things. [Frank] was over there behind the anesthesiologist screen talking to this guy who had just cleaned up the floor. He was asking him how long he took to do it, and what area had the most blood on the floor. It was just amazing to listen to him talk to this guy. But he was just that way; he was an honest person. He was just a child of the universe. He was

never better than anybody or worse than anybody. If he was not interested in it, he did not tell you he was. He was the sweetest man, a human being. You couldn't ask for a better person.[25]

With the sketches he made in Utah and the photographs Bill DeVries gave him, Frank went home to make the finished pictures. Frank made pictures of Drs. Kolff and Jarvik, of early models of the artificial heart, and, of course, of the Jarvik-7 heart. He made a schematic of how the heart functioned, and a picture of Dr. DeVries with the heart driver. He made pictures of the animals—calves and sheep—exercising on treadmills. And he made a picture of the cast of the human thorax that ensured the Jarvik-7 would fit in the available space. Frank made six plates of the surgical procedure, clearly showing the incision, the excision of the diseased heart, the suturing of the artificial heart connectors, the surgeon's hands, the artificial heart implant, and the skin buttons. For the final plate, of what advancements were envisioned for the future, Frank himself modeled as the patient wearing a portable power source for the artificial heart.

He made pictures of the heart and of the surgery, but his pictures of Barney Clark are most descriptive of what the artificial heart accomplished. Frank captured the cyanotic skin, the swollen limbs, and the barely conscious Dr. Clark as he was before the surgery—an image he took from photographs Dr. DeVries gave him—and how he appeared after surgery, as Dr. Clark grew stronger, sitting up, exercising, smiling with his wife. Frank explained in his notes:

> I became more convinced that the artificial heart would eventually serve both as a temporary life saving expedient in many cases while waiting for a donor heart to become available for transplant, and also, probably more significantly, as a definitive replacement for a hopelessly defective heart. I wanted to portray it in all its aspects—the historical, the mechanical,

the anatomical, the functional, the physiologic, and also its prospects for the future.[26]

Frank returned to Utah the second week of March[27] to review the pictures with the Utah team for accuracy and visited Barney Clark again, who, at 90 days after surgery, was up and around, and the doctors anticipated his hospital discharge. "He made sure everything was exactly right," said Dr. Joyce about Frank. "He came back [to Utah] and sat down with us and checked to make sure it was correct. He was so thorough; it was easy to see how his work was so perfect."[28]

William DeVries and Lyle Joyce prepared the text for this *Clinical Symposia* issue. Any interaction the Ciba-Geigy team had with either Frank or the authors for this issue was minimal; this was Frank's show. Of all the projects he illustrated, Frank wrote in the foreword, the artificial heart implantation was "not only the most interesting, but the most stimulating and inspiring."[29]

Barney Clark's health took a sudden downturn, and he died from an intestinal infection in March 1983, 112 days after surgery, but the artificial heart continued to function until the Utah team switched it off.

ᐤᕀᐤᐤᕀᐤᐤᕀᐤ

In the spring of 1983, 30 years after publication of the first edition, Ciba published the revised *Nervous System*, Part I, *Anatomy and Physiology*. Alister Brass was credited as the editor and Gina Dingle, the managing editor. Pierre Lair prepared the graphics, but with that volume, Phil Grushkin designed a new cover for *The Ciba Collection*. Gone was the black square over which the gold lettering had always been printed, replaced by gold letters against the green buckram. The larger font is elegant, but without the contrast of the black background, the words can be more difficult to read.

Ciba-Geigy launched the book at the American Neurological Association annual meeting, held in New Orleans that year. They staged an exhibit of some of the art and had a nice dinner party, where Frank was honored. The contributors and the staff in Medical Education who had worked on the book were all invited. Frank also invited Dr. DeVries to come to the exhibit, attend the party, and enjoy that beautiful city. "I really tried to get out to see it, but I could not make it," said Dr. DeVries. "I was too busy in the hospital. That's one of the things I'll always regret—not taking the time to do that."[30]

The party was not formal or stuffy, and people enjoyed themselves. Frank stood up and spoke—just briefly, saying that he was frequently asked to talk.

> I can put the whole philosophy of speech making in the terminology of the lingerie business. It is very simple. There are four kinds of speeches, likened to a lingerie shop. The Kimono Speech loosely covers the entire subject and reveals very little detail. The Girdle Speech covers a good deal, but aspects are stretched. The Panty Speech covers the subject but is short enough to be interesting. And the Bra Speech has many varieties; all contain vital material, but are limited to cover just the essential points.[31]

He then thanked them for their help on the book, for the knowledge of the collaborators, for the assistance of the Ciba team and for their friendship, and concluded:

> My pictures keep buzzing through my head, resolving themselves when I lie in bed, when I am on the golf course, when I am dining with friends. . . . Once I have visualized the picture clearly in my mind it is a simple matter to transfer it to paper. Now . . . the next volume of *The Ciba Collection* is already buzzing through my head.[32]

A few weeks later, Mary McKinsey and her team at Ciba-Geigy were readying the pictures for publication of both the osteoporosis publication and the artificial heart publication. Fred Kaplan took his father, who lived near the Ciba-Geigy facility in West Caldwell, New Jersey, to see the completed osteoporosis pictures. While there, they saw the pictures Frank had made for the artificial heart issue. Dr. Kaplan wrote to Frank to tell him how much he enjoyed seeing the pictures and asked if he might have some of the preliminary sketches from his osteoporosis article. Frank replied that he was delighted that they had seen the illustrations on the artificial heart operation. "That was one of the most fascinating projects I have ever been engaged in and I am very proud of the pictures I did for it."[33] And while he had discarded most of the sketches he had done for the osteoporosis article, he enclosed the two he had left.

Publication of the *Clinical Symposia* issue on osteoporosis[34] was in the summer of 1983; and in the fall, 11 months after the historic operation on Barney Clark, the *Clinical Symposia* issue on the artificial heart[35] came out.

Dr. William DeVries left Utah in 1984 to go to Louisville, Kentucky, he recalled.

> I remember my nurse coming over saying, "You've got one more appointment."
>
> It was my mother. She said, "I need to talk to you about your dad. You are leaving, and I think that you need to know what he was like." I never told her about those letters, and I learned more about him from them than I did from my mother. I often think about all the publicity and the two things I really cherish about that. One is I got to know my dad. And the other, I got to know Frank Netter. It was just serendipitous that that happened.[36]

CHAPTER 24

A Body of Work

I

N 1983, DR. GEORGE H. Thompson had been in practice about seven years and was interested in Legg–Calvé–Perthes disease, a hip disorder of childhood affecting the capital femoral epiphysis. At the recommendation of Bob Hensinger, Frank wrote to Dr. Thompson, asking if he would be interested in coauthoring with Dr. Robert Salter, from the University of Toronto, an issue of *Clinical Symposia* on the disease.[1] Of course he said yes, and he sent Frank a short monograph and about 50 photographs and diagrams with legends. Frank sketched out his interpretation and sent back sketches with comments in the side margins—what do you think about this, and is that correct? After a couple of iterations, Frank made the finished pictures.

As they neared the end of the effort, Dr. Thompson attended a meeting of the American Orthopaedic Association, which just so happened to be at The Breakers. Frank invited Dr. Thompson to come over to the apartment. He walked from the hotel along the boardwalk overlooking the ocean over to the apartment, and they spent about an hour reviewing all the pictures. That was the same day Dr. Henry Mankin, a distinguished orthopaedic surgeon from Harvard and an expert in musculoskeletal tumors, was coming over to talk about a lump Frank had found in his groin.[2]

Dr. Mankin visited Frank in the apartment that afternoon. They discussed some of the pictures for the *Musculoskeletal* volume, and when Frank told him about the lump, Dr. Mankin referred him to Dr. William F. Enneking, an orthopaedic oncologist at the University of Florida. What followed is best described in Dr. Enneking's own words:

> I had no direct contact with him, only admiration and respect from afar after each succeeding symposium, which I pressed

upon my medical students whether orthopaedic or not, until the summer of 1984 when I was contacted by his orthopaedist in Palm Beach concerning a mass Frank had developed in his right groin. He asked me to see him in consultation, which I did soon thereafter.

Frank had developed a mass, or lump, just below the front of his upper thigh where it joined his abdomen. He had two things that at first glance seemed relevant: a mild case of neurofibromatosis with multiple small superficial lesions (about 10% of people with von Recklinghausen's disease develop a malignancy and his mass was very close to the large femoral nerve—a likely location) and a history of an injury to the lower margin of his pelvis some 20 [years] previously after which he developed myositis ossificans in the muscle immediately adjacent to the recent development. MO, as it is called, rarely develops malignant transformation but was a possibility. I immediately consulted Dick Hawkins, a radiologist with enormous experience in angiography. Dick was one the most capable radiologists in pinpointing the precise location of such potential malignancies, and this was most important— both for diagnosis and treatment.

He reported to me that the mass was immediately adjacent to the femoral nerve but not attached or arising from the nerve. That made transformation from a benign neurofibroma very unlikely. It was not attached to the long-standing MO but draped over it like a skullcap, and with such intense vascularity that it was very likely malignant. This was very important information. Next a chest x-ray was obtained to exclude the possibility of a potential malignancy that had spread to the lung via the blood stream, a not uncommon sequence. The radiologist called to report that indeed it had, that there were multiple small densities in both lung fields with all the characteristics of metastatic malignancy. When with faint hope I asked if it was possible that the nodules could represent neurofibromas in the overlying skin, he excitedly said,

"I didn't know he had that"—he had not seen Frank, only his x-ray, and I had neglected to write that on the request form for the films. He soon called back saying, "I put some paper-clips over some of the lesions and sure enough that's what they were." What a relief! By putting a metal object that will show up on the x-ray directly on a neurofibroma on the skin and repeating the x-ray, if the clip corresponds exactly to the questionable lesion, it correctly identifies the lesion as on the skin rather than within the lung tissue itself.

Next came the conversation with Frank. If the biopsy was benign it could safely be removed with no nerve or artery damage and little likelihood of recurrence, but if it were malignant, to obtain a margin that was adequate to have lit-tle risk of recurrence, it would likely mean that portions of the femoral nerve, artery and vein would have to be removed with the mass. Given the vagaries of angiography—this was before CT and MRI were available—it might become evident during the procedure that amputation was the only certain way of obtaining a safe margin. If in fact that was the case, how did he want me to proceed: perform a safe amputation or a risky local removal preserving the nerve and blood vessels. He responded, "How about just a biopsy, close the wound, verify the diagnosis and then decide?" This was cer-tainly a reasonable alternative but carried risks of its own; the obvious vascularity of the lesion meant significant bleeding from within the potential malignancy, leading to high risk of spreading the process over a much wider area and making even amputation unreliable. Furthermore, doing the biopsy with a tourniquet in place to prevent bleeding, making the diagnosis immediately on frozen section technique, and pro-ceeding immediately with the removal by local resection or amputation was the safest way to go. Frank thought for a moment and then said, "My golf game is not all that good as it is but an amputation sure would not help, so let's go with the local resection."

The procedure was done the next day. When I went to see Frank in the preoperative area he said he had one other request. "When the tumor is out, please preserve it for me, as I want to make a sketch of it and include it in my medical record." The biopsy clearly showed the mass was a malignant tumor, although the pathologist was uncertain as to its exact type. Accordingly, the resection was carefully done without harm to the adjacent nerve and vessels, and after the tourniquet was released, the margin of the wound was seen to be perilously close to the capsule about the tumor in several places.

I had relayed to the pathologist Frank's request to preserve the tumor until he could complete his sketch. By the next day his condition had stabilized, he was returned to his room on the orthopaedic floor, and after he had recovered from the effects of the anesthesia he asked for the specimen and his drawing pad. He took only a very few moments to compose his sketch, handed it to me and asked me to put it in his chart.

My daughter (coincidently named Francesca and throughout childhood known as Frankie), a third year medical student, was assigned to my service, and although she was not directly involved with the surgical procedure she was involved with his postoperative care. While checking through his chart the next morning she came upon the sketch of his tumor. She promptly took the chart to his bedside and asked him to sign it. Then she went to the Xerox copying machine in the nurses' station and made a copy of the autographed sketch. After she proudly displayed his well-known signature to some of the other students the Xerox machine got quite a workout.

Needless to say I was quite concerned about the proximity of the edge of the tumor to the margin of his wound—a matter of a few millimeters—when I received a call from the pathologist. She told me that they had done a variety of special stains on the tumor tissue in order to clarify the precise type of tumor and had concluded that it was a type of lymphoma that was known to be quite sensitive to radiation therapy. This was very good news for it meant that once his wound was healed, radiation therapy could be given to the area surrounding the resection site that would significantly reduce the risk of a local recurrence of the tumor.

Subsequent consultation with the radiation therapist resulted in a plan for four weeks of daily radiation treatments, and because of the long distance between Palm Beach and the university in Gainesville he would stay in the hospital for the treatments. A few days after the treatments were commenced Frank became quite restless. He had become quite friendly with Dr. Chappie Conrad,[3] our tumor fellow who had assisted with his operation, and asked him if he could come down to our study and research center to have a look around. Chappie took him there, and Frank, after seeing the myriad of material on bone and soft tissue tumors, immediately began questioning him about the possibility of doing a Ciba symposium on those subjects. Chappie was quite thrilled with the prospect of working with the famous Dr. Netter, and so arrangements were made for him to have time off from his duties to work with Frank during the month-long period he would be receiving his radiation treatments.

Now most patients who are given the amount of radiation therapy that Frank was receiving find it quite debilitating and are glad to have long periods of rest between treatments. Not Frank! I would find them both in the Study Center at all hours surrounded by open books, scattered sketches, looking through microscopes and scribbling away for hours on end. The result of these labors was two wonderful symposia.[4] . . . Plaques received from Ciba commemorating these works now occupy a prominent place in the Orthopaedic Center for Study and Research at the University of Florida.[5]

Frank took small commuter planes back and forth from Palm Beach to Gainesville for the treatments. On one of his trips, he walked into the office of his friend and colleague, cardiologist Bob Van Meirop, with whom he had worked on the *Heart* volume. Dr. Van Mierop remembered being surprised to see Frank.

> He was a patient at the hospital. He said they had found a node in his groin, I think his right groin, and they were trying to find out what it was. And it turned out to be not good. I do not remember the exact diagnosis, but he became sicker and sicker. He came by several times, when he came back to Gainesville for the treatments. I always enjoyed his visits.[6]

For over six months, into the spring of 1985, Frank and Chappie Conrad worked together, going over case histories and picking out examples for the soft tissue *Clinical Symposia* issue[7] and for the bone issue.[8] They reviewed every case, every pathology report, every x-ray, and every clinical scenario. Frank picked up all the nuances and subtleties, Dr. Conrad recalled.

> It was incredible how at the age of 79 he could sit down and work for eight to ten hours. We would sit in those offices and go through the pathology. He would say, "That is a pretty good example of a giant cell, don't you think, Chappie?"
>
> And I would say, "Yes." We had all the different tumor types. We had little slide collections, arranged in notebooks, and he and I must have gone through at least 100 or 150 cases looking for good examples. I still have some of the old sketches he did. I saved them, because they are really cool, just the old pencil sketches of the bone.
>
> He never gave any hint that he was suffering very much [but] he didn't like those little planes very much. One time before taking him to the airport, I brought him home and introduced him to my wife. He lit up a stogie in the living room and smoked up the living room. After he left she said, "Next time you bring that gentleman by, do not let him smoke up the whole house."

When I said, "That guy is the most famous medical illustrator in the world!" she looked at me like I was exaggerating, and I knew she would not understand.[9]

After Frank had finished with his treatments and they had collected enough examples for the publication, Chappie went down to Palm Beach two or three times, stayed at The Breakers, and worked with Frank there. "In The Breakers," Dr. Conrad recalled, "you had to have a tie to go into the dining room, and he lent me one of his polka dot cravats [an ascot] and I put it on and went down and ate dinner in the beautiful huge dining room with just a golf shirt and one of Frank's ties."

> I had a really nice working relationship with him. He was very generous to me. I have a great picture of him at his drawing board. I remember [in Frank's apartment] the pictures of a doctor's life, and he told me about his life in New York and about his being an art student, and being a medical student with an artistic interest. He told me he signed a ten-year contract with Ciba to illustrate the human body, and he renewed the contract six or eight times. It is a wonderful thing how he overlapped all the different parts of medicine from one field to the next, between medicine, and surgery, and orthopaedics. Medical instruction has changed a great deal over the years. They do barely six weeks of gross anatomy [now], and as a result, the students struggle with musculoskeletal problems. It makes teaching anatomy a bigger challenge for the surgeons. It is a faster race track all the time, [with new discoveries being added to the four-year curriculum].[10]

CHAPTER 25

MAKING PICTURES TO TEACH

THE REVISION OF THE *Nervous System* book was in two parts: Part I, *Anatomy and Physiology*, had been released in 1983, and Frank was working on Part II, *Neurologic and Neuromuscular Disorders*, which was more clinically oriented. Frank had asked Dr. William Fields, in Houston,[1] to be the guest editor. He was an expert in cerebrovascular disease and had previously worked with Frank on a *Clinical Symposia* issue on stroke.[2] But by 1983 Dr. Fields seemed to have lost interest in the *Nervous System* revision and they were not getting anywhere with it.

Frank was working with Roy Jones on the *Clinical Symposia* issue on peripheral nerves when partway through the project, Frank pulled out some notes and told Roy that this was what he and Bill Fields had done on planning Part II of the revision of the *Nervous System*, and what did he think. It was superficial and not anywhere near the depth that the nervous system demanded, Roy politely said. There had been so many new discoveries in the 30 years since the first edition. It was uncommon in current clinical practice to see the large tumors pictured in the first edition of the *Nervous System*, partly because radiological advances and improved diagnostic techniques had enabled early detection and treatment. Frank then asked Roy to step in as guest editor.

Shortly after Dr. Jones returned to the Lahey Clinic, Gina Dingle called him and asked him to come to the Medical Education offices in West Caldwell, New Jersey. Frank flew up, and they sat down and outlined what should be in the volume. The Medical Education people limited the number of new illustrations they could include, perhaps for budget reasons, but also, more significantly, to free Frank to work on the *Musculoskeletal* volume, which would complete *The Ciba Collection*. Only then would it seem reasonable to revise the books and print new editions. *Nervous System*, Part II, had about 210 plates and used many from the first edition and select *Clinical Symposia* issues.

Gina Dingle remembered working on it.

> When he did the cerebral palsy series,[3] he wanted to make too many illustrations. So I said, "Dr. Netter, we can only make seven." He felt a great sorrow that these young children were getting such a handicapped start in life. Many of his children illustrations—most of them—I find very poignant. There is an added dimension to them that goes beyond a rendering of the clinical condition. If you look at his clinical pieces, there is a third dimension to them all. This is not just a picture of a condition. This is a picture of a patient suffering from that condition. That is what sets his art apart.[4]

Between 1983 and 1985, Roy Jones went down to Florida six or seven times to work with Frank on the volume. He would leave Boston on Thursday night and fly down to Palm Beach and stay at The Breakers. They would work Friday, Saturday, and half of Sunday, then Roy would get on a plane back to Boston. Vera would say hello to Roy in the morning and leave them to their work during the day. They would be at work in the studio at 6:30 or 7:00 o'clock in the morning and not break for lunch until about 2:00 PM. They reviewed each plate, Roy with the pipe he used to smoke and Frank with his cigar. Sometimes Frank would have trouble conceptualizing something, and after lunch would go out and hit a few golf balls while Roy would go back to the hotel and maybe take a swim. Then they would meet again at 4:00 and work until 8:00 or 9:00 before joining Vera for dinner at The Breakers.

On each visit, they would outline 15 or 20 plates, taking about an hour to work through each one. Frank would take notes and the next week send Roy a sketch, some with no more than boxes and notes as to where he was going to place things on the plate. "Carpal tunnel syndrome commonly wakes people up from their sleep,"

Roy explained. "And he sort of rough-sketched out a woman sitting up in bed, shaking her hand, and the clock would show 3:00 AM. [There was also a figure of] someone sitting behind the wheel of a car, and his hand had fallen asleep."[5] The patient's experience was all there in those pictures.[6]

⟨⟩∾⟨⟩∾⟨⟩

For *Nervous System*, Part II, Roy Jones recruited a young man, a contemporary of his, Dr. Louis Caplan at Harvard, to work with Frank on stroke and cerebrovascular disease and on dementia.[7] Lou remembered going down to Florida, bringing copies from anatomical books, atlases, or sometimes a rough sketch he had done himself, and working with Frank.

> It was interesting how he would work. The person he worked with would do the writing and then he would do the drawings. Even though he was a physician and a surgeon, he had not really done any clinical work, so he did not have that much familiarity with neurology. I asked him once how he did it, and he said that he would draw it in his own mind. He would figure it out, and once he pictured it [in his mind] he was able to put it on paper. The sketches initially may or may not have really caught it, but when [I would talk] with him afterwards he would change it in a very simple way that was very impressive. I do not think anybody has ever come close to capturing it the way he did, first with anatomy and also with these little caricatures of people doing different things. He was really able to get the essence across. Also he would ask questions about what you had written to try to get you to separate the wheat from the chaff, just very concisely to convey the basic information. He could tell very well if you hadn't done that or if you put in extra things or it didn't really click with the illustrations. He was really the mastermind behind the different parts.

He was very devoted to Vera but he still liked to work. At that point he still was having some pain [from the cancer treatments], and he would work in the morning and devote the rest of the day to being with her.[8]

With Lou Caplan, Frank did some beautiful pictures of the anatomy of the arteries and of the types and causes of stroke, as well as of clinical manifestations. While they worked, Frank would tell Lou about the other things he was doing. He told him about the artificial heart and how he went to see that. He told him he was planning to illustrate the work Dr. Harold Kleinert was doing at the University of Louisville School of Medicine to reattach a little boy's severed finger, Dr. Caplan remembered.

He always liked to hear about new things. He kept his ear to the ground about new events and new ideas and figuring out how to illustrate them. He considered himself a teacher. He really wanted to use the drawings to teach people about the person and about the illness. It was not just making pictures; it was making the pictures instructive. . . . If you can visualize it and you can see it, it is much more instructive than just reading something. The way he did those, they were very effective. . . . One of the things about his work was that if you looked at it, you immediately knew who did it. It had a kind of personal signature. You did not have to see the signature. It had its own unique character.[9]

Dr. Jones also recruited the chairman of neurosurgery at the Lahey Clinic, Dr. Stephen Freidberg, to work on the brain tumors and spinal tumors sections of the volume. On a week-long visit to his sister in Boca Raton, Dr. Freidberg took the opportunity to spend a few days commuting up to Palm Beach to work with Frank.[10] Out of that effort came 14 outstanding pictures on the diagnosis and surgical treatment for the tumors, which Ciba used in the *Nervous System* volume and in a *Clinical Symposia* issue.[11]

❧❧❧❧❧❧

Roy Jones asked Dr. John R. Hayes at Indiana University School of Medicine to prepare the text to accompany Frank's masterful psychiatric portraits originally published in the 1957 *Clinical Symposia* issue[12] authored by Frank J. Ayd, Jr. They were now included the new edition in the section on common problems in psychiatry.[13]

Frank's medical school classmate Dr. Albert Sabin was at the University of South Carolina, and he sent Frank photos of patients and provided text for the plates on polio.[14] His discussion of the pathology and epidemiology of polio included a brief section on prevention, which clearly explains the difference in efficacy between inactivated poliovirus vaccine—the Salk type—and the oral poliovirus vaccine—the Sabin vaccine.

Dr. Thomas L. Kemper, at Harvard Medical School, contributed text and suggestions for Frank's illustrations for the autistic and dyslexic brain,[15] all his contact with Frank being via mail.[16] The picture Frank made of the boy sitting apart, detached from his playmates, must have been reminiscent to Frank of the oil painting he had made years earlier of his own son, Frankie, sitting apart from Cornelia and Jim playing together.

The chairman of the neurosurgery department at the University of Florida was Dr. Albert Rhoton. He had authored a 1977 *Clinical Symposia* issue on aneurysms[17] and was working with Frank on adapting seven plates from that monograph for this new atlas.[18] He recommended Dr. William A. Friedman, an assistant professor there, to consult on the plates on head trauma.

After meeting once with Frank in Gainesville, Dr. Friedman drove down to Palm Beach several times. There, in the studio filled with art supplies, mementos, and golfing trophies, he showed Frank the photos and slides he had brought. "He put me completely at ease," recalled Dr. Friedman. "I felt he was interested in me as a person and in the topic, head trauma, and what I was doing as a young neurosurgeon trying to apply the latest techniques."[19] The result was a *Clinical Symposia* issue on head trauma,[20] published in

1983, although several of the plates in that publication had previously appeared in two *Clinical Symposia* issues[21] Frank had done in 1966–1967 with Dr. Frederick E. Jackson, at the Naval Hospital in Charleston, South Carolina.[22] Dr. Friedman's *Clinical Symposia* article was then used in its entirety in the *Nervous System, Part II*.[23]

Dr. Marc A. Flitter was a neurosurgeon at Mount Sinai Medical Center, in Miami Beach, whom Gina Dingle contacted to work on the *Nervous System* revision. Frank went to Dr. Flitter's office for their first meeting. "I was awed by his coming to see me," Dr. Flitter recalled. "He was a world-famous medical illustrator, and yet he approached me with no sense of hubris. But rather it was as if he were part of our own medical communications department. He seemed to be unmoved by his fame and remained focused on his art."[24] Frank had a concise plan for the *Nervous System* volume, yet to be sure that the topic was adequately covered he asked Dr. Flitter if more illustrations were needed. Dr. Flitter updated portions on congenital disorders in children—hydrocephalus and spinal dysraphism—and a composite plate on manifestations of brain tumors[25]—to make them more current. There were more changes to the text than to the pictures, so much of the work after that initial meeting was coordinated through Gina, back and forth.[26]

In all, there were 30 contributors to the volume, but Roy Jones did the majority of it. He worked with Frank to lay out the volume, recruited many of the contributors, reviewed their sections, and consulted on 56 plates throughout the book, including plates on childhood disorders, trauma, stroke and infection, multiple sclerosis, spinal cord disorders, and the peripheral nerves.[27]

ভ৹৹ৡ৹ভ৹

Milt Donin had the most eloquent diction, honed from years of presenting both scientific and business materials. He stood about the same height as Frank, maybe a bit shorter, and was trim, with gray hair and a goatee he kept neatly groomed. He had a kind of openness about him and a way of always asking about your family, a likeable sort of gentleman.

Milt had been at Ciba-Geigy since 1975, after 25 years at Squibb, and although he held a doctorate in chemistry, his career had always been geared more toward the business side. After a reorganization at Ciba-Geigy in 1984 Milt found himself without an assignment. He was planning to retire in a couple of years anyway, but until then he needed a job. Milt had worked in research for Roy Ellis, and in the reorganization Dr. Ellis had become vice president for public relations. The Medical Education department was attached to his area.[28] He told Milt that Phil Flagler was looking for someone, so Milt called Phil up, and that led to Phil Flagler's hiring Milt not so much to fill a vacancy formed when David Shephard left the company[29] but to act as Phil's editorial assistant.

When Milt stepped in as editorial director, Gina Dingle handled the editing for *The Ciba Collection*. The *Nervous System*, Part II, was in the production phase, and Milt really could not contribute much to that. So he concerned himself primarily with providing leadership for the *Clinical Symposia* team.[30] It was a small group, just two editors—Mary McKinsey, who was herself preparing to retire soon, and a new editor, Maria Erdélyi-Brown—who handled the articles for *Clinical Symposia*.

Essentially, Milt tried to keep things moving along smoothly. At that point, Frank was angry with Phil over the plan for succession. Frank was soon to be 80 years old, and Phil had John Craig lined up as a possible successor. Milt recalled that the team at Ciba-Geigy took Frank's position to be that he wanted to do it all, that he saw no reason why there needed to be a successor, and that he was going to function forever.

There can be no doubt that Frank's ego was hurt. What he wanted was a protégé of his own selection, someone he could mentor and train over time to take up the reins.[31] He envisioned something of an art studio in the style of the grand masters, with the student learning his craft from the master, an art studio funded by Ciba-Geigy. Ironically, it was for a lack of foresight that Frank blamed Phil and lack of foresight of which Phil accused Frank. Frank was so annoyed that he would not talk to Phil.[32] So Milt became the go-between and started working with Frank directly.

There was one time that at Phil's suggestion Milt took a photographer with him to Florida to take some candid photographs of Frank. The photographer took pictures of Frank, of Frank and Milt together, and of Frank and Vera together. One of the poses the photographer set up for a photograph of Frank and Vera turned out exceptionally well. Milt arranged to have that enlarged and framed, and he brought it down to Palm Beach on another trip. Both Frank and Vera were crazy about that photo. "There was just something very magnetic," said Milt about Frank, "something that attracted him to you. He could be a tough customer really, but he could also be very nice. And you just felt that there was something there that you weren't going to find in everyone."[33]

ঙ৹ঙ৹ঙ৹

For a *Clinical Symposia* issue on renal complications of liver disease,[34] Ciba-Geigy editor Mary McKinsey invited Dr. Murray Epstein, at the University of Miami, the world leader in the field, to work with Frank. At Frank's invitation, Dr. Epstein went up to Palm Beach to

collaborate on the publication. Over the three months that they worked together, he drove up to Palm Beach four or five times, and each time the work became more and more focused. They would look at the sketches and come up with different ideas on how to tell the story.

When they started, Frank did not know much about liver disease, and Dr. Epstein told him about the overbearing thirst that occurs in patients with the disease. The treatment

Photo: Frank and Vera Netter in the living room at Breakers Row, c. 1984, courtesy of Novartis.

involves fluid restriction, but the thirst drive is so strong that patients will not comply. He related a story about a patient who was cheating, so Dr. Epstein had the plumber come up to the hospital room and turn the water off in the sink. The patient had no access to fluid either on his tray or from the faucet. Then a day or so later on rounds, Dr. Epstein found the patient drinking from the toilet bowl. Frank thought that vividly captured the essence of the problem, and he made a picture of it.[35] Mary McKinsey apparently was disturbed by it and did not want that picture in the publication. But Frank insisted it be included, and they put it in.

Before coming to the University of Miami, Dr. Epstein had been a flight surgeon in the air force and worked on the NASA space program. One of the things that the team there had developed was a water immersion tank to simulate the physiological effects of astronauts being in space over extended periods. They had a water immersion tank at the University of Miami and used it clinically to look at what regulates volume of salt and water in patients, particularly patients with liver disease. Frank was absolutely mesmerized. He said he had to go and see it in the laboratory so he could make a picture of it, and they then made an appointment for Frank to come to Miami to see it. Dr. Epstein and his team were concerned about Frank driving down I-95 to Miami because it is a busy interstate highway with cars and big trucks zipping along, and he was nearly 80 years old. But on the day of his visit, he drove down alone and arrived at the medical center, where he spent the whole day sketching the tank. They filled it up with water, and one of the technicians got into a bathing suit and climbed in and climbed out, the way a patient would, and Frank took in all of the details. He spent hours walking up and down and around it, to visualize it and to sketch it.[36]

Harry M. had been a patient of Dr. Epstein's for 14 years. He was warm and affable, Dr. Epstein remembered, but he drank, and his condition was a complication of that. Frank looked at the actual data books and made a graph of the data collected from years of study of Harry's case.[37] Harry came to the laboratory, and Frank made a picture of him that wound up on the cover of the issue. Frank was intrigued also with the analogy between the sick patients and healthy astronauts in space flight. He made a plate showing sodium excretion by the kidney and water excretion, comparing what happens during weightlessness in space with what happens here on earth.[38] And another plate he made on the effects of water immersion[39] shows the relationships between the heart and brain, and brain and kidney, a simple but powerful and accurate description of the physiology.[40]

꜀꜀ꙮꙮꙮ꜀꜀

In early January 1985, the Rev. Timothy S. Healy, president of Georgetown University,[41] wrote to Frank inviting him to receive an honorary degree at the medical school's graduation ceremonies. Senator Howard Baker, who was also to receive an honorary degree, was to give the commencement address. Frank accepted the honor with pleasure.

The commencement was in the concert hall of the John F. Kennedy Center for the Performing Arts in Washington on the afternoon of Saturday, May 25, 1985. Frank wore the academic regalia they had ready for him—a robe with three bars of velvet on the full sleeves, on his head the black velvet tam with a tassel attached on top. Frank marched in the procession with Dr. John Stapleton, dean of the medical school; Dr. Matthew McNulty, chancellor of the medical center; the Rev. Healy; and other dignitaries to the stage of the concert hall. It was quite a spectacle. Vera sat with Frank's children in the audience. Milt Donin and his wife were there, representing Ciba-Geigy, at the request of Roy Ellis.

Two hundred one graduates in academic dress sat in the front rows of the audience. After the national anthem, an invocation, and a reading of the university charter, Dr. Stapleton presented the candidates for honorary degrees one by one. No sooner had he presented Dr. Frank H. Netter than the students jumped to their feet and erupted in cheers. "There were other people who were getting honorary degrees, distinguished people, including a senator," recalled Milt. "The graduating class politely clapped for each of them. But when they announced Frank, the class stood up, applauded, and opened their gowns and pulled out their cameras. That was an enlightening experience."[42] Although these students had never met him, never heard him lecture, Dr. Frank Netter was their mentor, their greatest teacher. Faculty members fastened the doctoral hood about Frank's shoulders, its blue and gray lining in the Georgetown colors, As the students' cheering continued, Frank walked to the front of the stage and raised his arms as if to embrace them all. The long sleeves of his academic robe hung down like wings of a mother hen calling her brood to the fold.

Photo: Dr. Frank Netter and the Rev. Timothy Healy, Georgetown University School of Medicine commencement, 1985.

৹৻৹৻৹৻৹

At the Medical College of Georgia, William Stenstrom was the director of the Medical Illustration Graduate Program and David Mascaro was an associate professor in the department. They recruited Frank to be on their advisory council, a position he held for about five years, beginning in 1985.[43] During that time Bill and David went to Palm Beach to interview Frank and made a videotape of him talking about his life, about his art training, and about medical illustration in particular.

They sat in the living room of The Breakers Row apartment and spent an afternoon with Frank, letting the tape run. Frank asked and they told him about their graduate program in medical illustration—how students are selected for admission, the curriculum and graduation requirements, and student placement in positions after graduation. They brought samples of student work, as well as of their own work. They explained how the students are encouraged to explore various media, and also asked Frank about his use of media. Frank told them that he never used pure transparent watercolor because it is difficult to make corrections. He liked oil, but it is messy, he said. But in opaque watercolor, as in oil, he could work from dark to light, and that is what he used primarily.

Frank told them how he came to be a medical illustrator, how he started first in commercial art and then went to medical school, where he began making pictures to help himself learn the anatomy. "I still make pictures for my own education," he said to them. "If they do not mean anything to me they are not going to mean anything to anybody else."[44] The most difficult part of his work, he said, was keeping up with medical progress. At the same time the most stimulating part was meeting doctors in the forefront of medical progress. Bill Stenstrom, unlike Frank, had specialized in his career as a medical illustrator, making pictures almost exclusively of the retina. Specialization, they agreed, may be the trend in medical illustration, because the artist then really knows the subject, which is a prerequisite to making the pictures.

David asked Frank about the reproduction process, if he reviewed the proofs, to which Frank replied that he no longer did that. When they did letterpress, he used to check the proofs, but after Ciba switched to offset lithography, he just had to trust the pressman to watch the print run.

What he did work hard at, Frank told them, was the pictorialization—presenting a subject from just the right angle, including just enough material to identify it but not so much that the essential point of the picture is lost.

> Hands are important for any artist to know how to draw, but especially for a medical illustrator. To show the surgeon's hands, the artist must capture the expression and the tension in the hands and the function that is being performed—pushing or pulling, holding or squeezing.

As he spoke, he put his hand out and with the other gestured to it.

> In order to draw hands, a person must know the construction of the hand, not just the pure anatomy of the hand, because that is superimposed on the basic structure of the hand, the elements of the hand—the palm, the shape of the palm, the arch of the palm, the relative length of the fingers at the various knuckles and the manner in which they open and close— and then portray those things in perspective at different angles. It is simple if you visualize this as a unit and then you can draw it just as you would a still life.[45]

ʘʘʘʘʘʘ

Frank was revising the *Nervous System* volume at the same time that he was developing the *Musculoskeletal System* volume. There was a great deal of intersection between the two disciplines, orthopaedics and neurologic disorders. In the introduction to *Nervous System*, Part II, he wrote:

> Cerebral palsy and poliomyelitis are, of course, basically neurologic diseases, and they are both so presented in this volume. But the after-care, corrective surgery, and rehabilitation of such patients are usually in the hands of orthopaedists. Accordingly, those aspects of these diseases will be covered in the forthcoming atlases on the musculoskeletal system. . . . Intervertebral disc herniation and spinal stenosis likewise fall into both fields of practice . . . [and] many other examples overlap between the two disciplines.[46]

The *Nervous System*, Part II, was published in 1986. Pierre Lair was the book's designer. He was French and had been the design and production manager of *The Ciba Collection* for nearly 12 years when he died in 1985 at the age of 57.[47] Ciba-Geigy dedicated the volume to him.

Gina Dingle went to all of the annual meetings of the associated academies or the societies while Medical Education was working on a particular book, because the authors would be there and she could meet with them. The American Academy of Neurology had its annual meeting in Boston that year, so most of the people invited to the dinner were at the convention, and they set aside an evening for the celebration of the book release.

Ciba hosted a big dinner at the Café Budapest Hungarian restaurant in Boston and invited all of the people whose work appeared *Nervous System*, Part II. It was a real celebration. Gina and the other members of the Ciba-Geigy support staff who were at the convention also came to the dinner. It was not anything extraordinary, the party at the Café Budapest, but it was great fun and the food was terrific.[48] The Café Budapest was considered one of the best restaurants in the city. It was small, almost like a private home, and they had almost the entire restaurant to themselves. There were interconnecting rooms, instead of one huge hall, yet everyone had a clear view of the head table, where Frank was sitting, with Vera at his side. Frank got up and thanked the contributors, naming specifically Roy Jones and Gina Dingle, Phil Flagler and Milt Donin.

The following day, at Roy Jones's invitation, Frank gave grand rounds at the Lahey Clinic. The auditorium there holds 250 people, but for Frank's lecture, there was standing room only. People were even standing out in the hall trying to hear him.[49]

Vera, Frank H. Netter, oil on canvas, 1968, from the collection of Francine Mary Netter.

"*Major Depression,*" Ciba Collection of Medical Illustrations, Nervous System
Part I, *2nd ed., 1983, Section VI, plate 1, courtesy of Elsevier.*

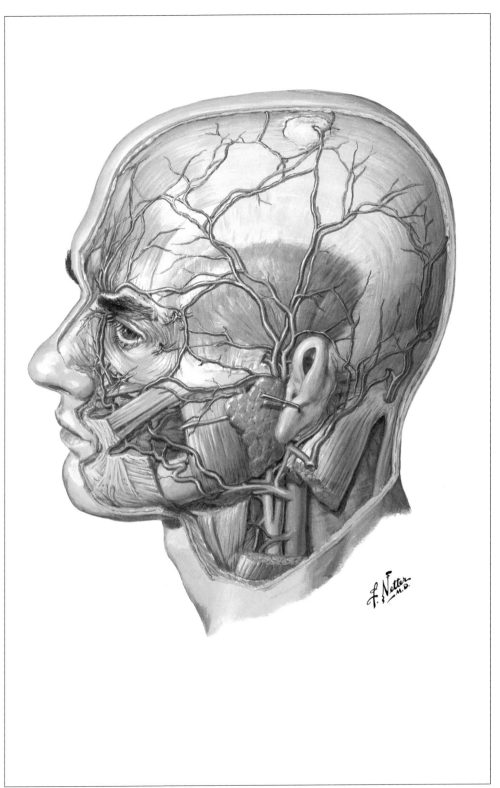

"*Blood Vessels of the Scalp*," Ciba Collection of Medical Illustrations, Nervous System
Part I, 2nd. edition, 1983, Section III, plate 1, courtesy of Elsevier.

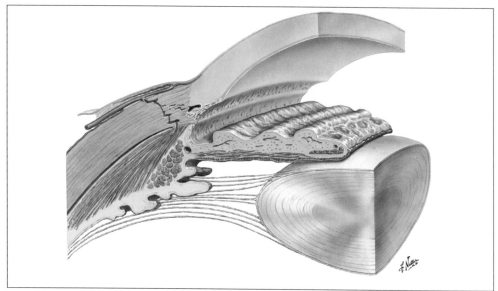

"Anterior and Posterior Chambers of the Eye," Frank H. Netter, Atlas of Human Anatomy, 1989, plate 83, courtesy of Elsevier.

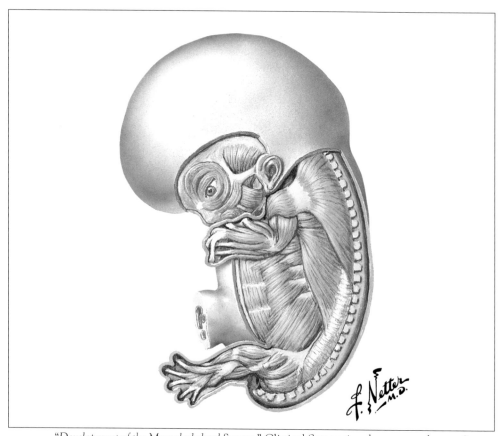

"Development of the Musculoskeletal System." Clinical Symposia volume 33, number 1, 1981, cover, courtesy of Elsevier.

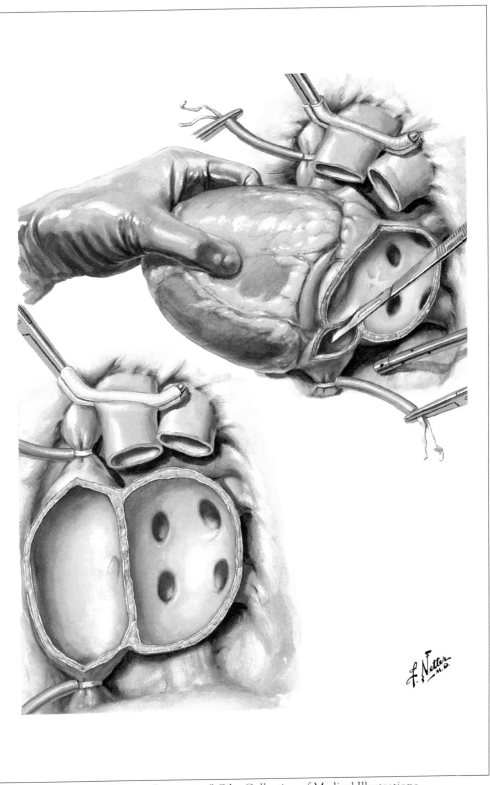

"*Heart Transplantation: Recipient Preparation,*" Ciba Collection of Medical Illustrations, Heart, 1969, Section V, plate 95, courtesy of Elsevier.

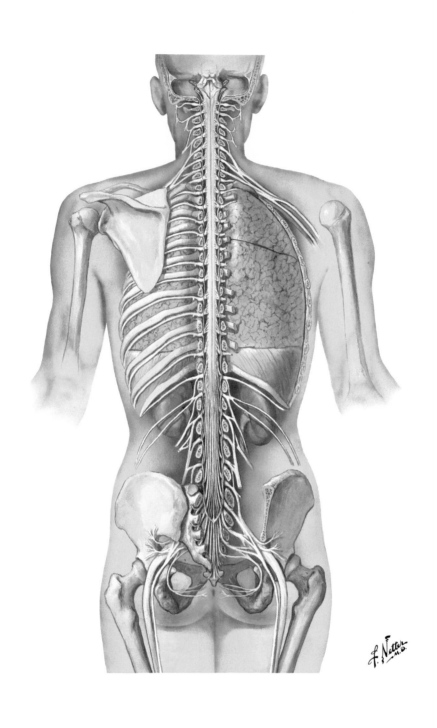

"*Spinal Cord in Situ,*" Atlas of Human Anatomy, *1989, Section II, plate 148,*
courtesy of Elsevier.

CHAPTER 26

MUSCULOSKELETAL SYSTEM

AFTER PUBLICATION OF THE osteoporosis issue of *Clinical Symposia* in 1983, Fred Kaplan used to visit Frank whenever he was in Florida visiting family. He would call Frank and go to The Breakers, and have cocktails with the Netters and go out to dinner with them. Frank asked Fred to help him on the *Musculoskeletal System* volume, and without hesitation Fred agreed to do it.

By the time Fred started to work on it, the outline for the volume had already been through two iterations, one with Dr. Frantz and another with Dr. Hensinger, who wanted to do just the part on children. Fred and Frank went over the material and made a completely new outline of volume 8. It was to consist of over 700 plates in three tomes: anatomy, physiology, and metabolic disorders in Part I;[1] developmental disorders, tumors, diseases, and joint replacement in Part II;[2] and trauma in Part III.[3] They first came up with a broad list of topics, and as the work progressed they filled in the details.

Beginning in 1985 and for the next three years Fred worked with Frank on compiling the art and text for Part I and lining up contributors. Since he was at the University of Pennsylvania, he drew heavily on the faculty there. Most of the contributors worked on two or three plates.[4] Dr. Carl T. Brighton contributed to 7 plates[5] in the physiology section, including those on bone growth and remodeling. Dr. Maurice F. Attie worked on 10 plates[6] on parathyroid hormone. Dr. Michael E. Selzer contributed to 15 plates[7] on skeletal muscle.

Dr. Russell Woodburne, emeritus professor of anatomy at the University of Michigan, was wholly responsible for the anatomy section of *Musculoskeletal System*, Part I. He worked with Frank long distance, sending sketches back and forth in the mail. One of the more profound pictures they did together was of deep dissection of the shoulder and axilla. It is a difficult anatomy, often with individual variation, puzzling even the most experienced surgeons.[8] On the original sketch, Frank made notes in the margin and sent it to Dr. Woodburne asking for clarification, and Dr. Woodburne wrote his reply, also in the margin, and sent it back to Frank. On this sketch one can see a few randomly spaced brown spots—small burns and burn holes—wherever Frank inadvertently had dropped cigar ashes on the thin tracing paper.

In the section on anatomy, Frank incorporated 18 plates[9] he had prepared working with neuroanatomist Professor G.A.G. Mitchell, of Manchester, England. Since 1955, they had worked together on over 100 plates. Eight plates accompanied by text attributed to Professor Mitchell in the *Musculoskeletal System*, Part I,[10] volume were pictures Frank had made earlier for *Nervous System*, Part I.[11]

Frank's longtime colleague Dr. Edmund Crelin, at Yale, was credited with the section on embryology. Twenty of those plates[12] and much of the text for them were from a *Clinical Symposia* issue[13] that they had done together, which was published in 1981, and they added one new plate on sensory nerve distribution during embryonic limb development.[14] And Dr. Henry Mankin contributed to 11 plates[15] in the physiology section. He also wrote the laudatory foreword to the volume.[16]

Fred Kaplan was the major contributor to *Musculoskeletal System*, Part I, collaborating with Frank on over 60 plates.[17] Interspersed throughout the volume were most of the 17 plates Frank had done with Fred for the osteoporosis issue of *Clinical Symposia*,[18] including the picture of the little men filling the buckets of sand[19]—osteoblasts making bone—and other men taking the buckets of sand away—osteoclasts breaking down bone. They did a plate on the musculoskeletal effects of weightlessness in space flight, for which Frank made a picture of an astronaut on a space walk.[20]

When they had done the *Clinical Symposia* issue on osteoporosis, Fred wrote the text first, and then Frank made the sketches

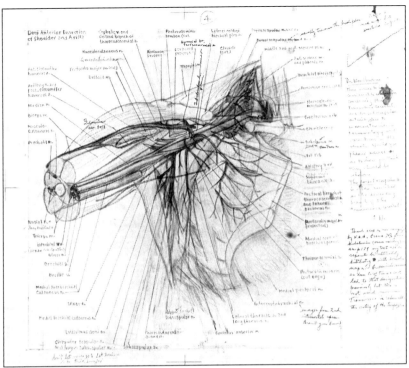

Sketch: Deep Dissection of the Shoulder and Axilla, *Frank H. Netter, with comments in the margin by Drs. Frank Netter and Russell Woodburne, c. 1986, from the University of North Carolina Wilson Special Collections Library.*

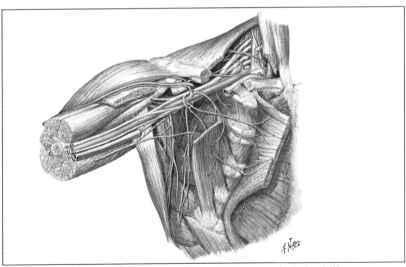

"Shoulder and Axilla: Deep Dissection," Ciba Collection of Medical Illustrations, Musculoskeletal System *Part I, 1987, Section I, Plate 24, courtesy of Elsevier.*

from the text. But now Frank made the sketches first and sent them to Fred, who wrote the text from the sketches. When the pictures were done, Frank gave Fred some of the sketches they had worked on together for the *Musculoskeletal System* volume. "You can have them," he told Fred. "I just throw them away."[21] But Fred framed them and hung some in his office and some in his home.

ↄ|ↄ◌|◌◌|◌

For the Part I tome, Fred thought they needed a little more on the growth plate. Frank had thought they would just show the growing ends of the bone, but Fred said that so much more is known about it. So Frank asked Fred to teach him about the growth plate. "Do you have a lecture on it? Bring it with you the next time you come down. I have a slide projector, and we'll project it in my studio. We'll look at it together," Fred remembered Frank saying.

On his next trip to Palm Beach, Fred brought his lecture on the growth plate, the one he customarily gave to medical students. He recalled taking the slides to The Breakers to show Frank:

> I had slides on the biochemistry of the growth plate and some on the new molecular biology and some on genetics. We came back from lunch and he said, "Let's see your lecture. Pretend you are doing a lecture in medical school and I am the whole class." He had to understand it before he could make a picture. And I realized that I was about to teach the greatest teacher in the world so he could present it pictorially to medical students everywhere.
>
> "Dr. Netter," I said, "I feel a little embarrassed about giving this lecture like this."
>
> "Aw, come on, Freddie, this is great stuff," he told me. "Let's see what we know about the growth plate."
>
> And I gave the lecture in about an hour—the only time I ever had a student smoke a cigar.[22]

They then put together a diagram that talked about the regions of the growth plate, the names, the functions, the blood supply, the oxygen, the cellular respiration, the mitochondria, the calcification, the matrix vesicles, the proteins, the diseases, the genes, the mechanisms of action of these genes on the different parts of the growth plate. Then Frank filled in his comments in pencil. Fred took the diagram back to his hotel room that evening and worked on it, and brought it back the next day. And Frank said that it was wonderful. That was the original sketch for the plate in the section "Structure, Physiology, and Pathophysiology of Growth Plate"[23] in *Musculoskeletal System*, Part I.

Fred became a frequent visitor on Breakers Row as work on the atlases progressed, and he got to know some of the people who worked there.

> There was a doorman—Jim, I think his name was. He was the doorman who let me into the complex. He got used to seeing me, and he said to me one morning, "Is Dr. Netter a very famous doctor?"
>
> And I said, "Oh, he is an extremely famous doctor."
>
> So he said, "Is there a condition where your face is all kind of scrunched up?" And the doorman kind of mimicked this funny facial expression.
>
> And I said, "Yes. Why do you ask?"
>
> And he said, "Well, Dr. Netter asked me to sit there one day with my face like that so he could draw my picture."
>
> So I told Dr. Netter what the doorman said, and he laughed, remembering the picture he had made of facial nerve palsy[24] for the *Nervous System* volume, and he said that sometimes it was hard to find a patient with the condition he needed to depict. He always liked to do pictures of real patients.[25]

One of Fred's patients had an extremely rare genetic disorder called fibrodysplasia ossificans progressiva—FOP for short. In people with osteoporosis, bone is resorbed faster than it can be made.

But in people with FOP, muscles, ligaments, and tendons turn to bone, crippling those patients and freezing their bodies so that they become as rigid and motionless as marble statues. It is conceivable that Lot's wife, who was said in the Bible to have turned into a pillar of salt, suffered from FOP. Fred brought a photograph of his patient to show Frank and suggested that they include a plate on FOP. It is a rare disease but helps illuminate the normal.[26] Frank asked about the young woman he saw in the photograph—What is her name? Where does she live? When did it start? How does it progress? Her name was Carol, and from the photograph Frank painted her picture.[27] Fred wrote the text and provided the radiographs showing ossification of the soft tissue—tissue normally not visible in that way on x-rays.

⟋⟍⟋⟍⟋⟍

When they worked together at Breakers Row, they would break for lunch and drive into Palm Beach to have lunch in town or go over to the golf course and have lunch at the restaurant over there. Once when they were together in the studio after lunch, there came in the mail a large envelope that had come from Bratislava in what was Czechoslovakia, which at that time was in the Communist bloc. Frank opened it, and inside was a letter from a medical student who was studying the anatomy of the brain. He had found Frank's pictures to be an inspiration, but his medical school library had only one copy of Frank's book, which was falling apart at the binding from overuse. To study the anatomy of the brain, the letter continued, he had made a model of the brain stem, which he was enclosing. Then from the large handmade envelope Frank pulled out something made out of construction paper. It had 10 different layers to it, held together by staples, and if you flipped the layers you could see the different levels of the brain stem. Each one was a cross-sectional cut, and the student had put the layers together so that he could study the anatomy layer by layer. Fred recalled what happened then.

Frank hands it to me and says, "What do you think?" He read me the letter, which was in English.

I looked at this very crude model of the brain stem that the student had made out of construction paper with each of the parts labeled, and said, "Dr. Netter, it is really crude."

And he says, "Yes, Freddie, it is primitive, but you know what? This boy, look what he has to study! They have one copy of my book in the whole medical school, and it is falling apart. And this boy took the time to look at my book and study the anatomy of the brain stem, and inspired by my pictures, he made this to study. This is amazing. This is not like studying in New York or Chicago or Philadelphia, where you have all the books you could want. They have one copy, and this boy went out of his way to do this, and then to write me a letter. I am going to write him a letter right now and thank him for sending this to me. And you know what? I am going to call Gina and tell Ciba to send him a set of atlases."[28]

The Ciba–Netter partnership which has so illuminated the Western world had penetrated the curtain that was still iron. I was watching the highest form of diplomacy on the most professional level: a bullet fired not at the heart, but from it.[29]

ᦞᦞᦞᦞᦞ

One evening during the course of the three years they worked on the volume, they were working late in the studio. Vera came in and said it was getting to be about eight o'clock, time for dinner. It was summertime, in early August, when the late daylight still streamed in through the north-facing studio window. They had been working hard all day and agreed they should take a break. They went to the bar area beside the living room, and Fred took a glass of wine while Frank made himself a martini. Fred saw a small bronze statue on the bar, he remembered.

I had never seen anything like it. It was a martini glass, a bronze martini glass, and at the base of it was a little sculpture, a head stuck on the martini glass, no shoulder, just a head. So I said, "This is very unusual. What is this?"

And he said, "My friend Rube Goldberg gave me that."

"Rube Goldberg? The fictional character?" I said.

And he stopped making the martini and turned and looked at me, a stunned expression on his face. And he said, "What do you mean, fictional character? Rube Goldberg was a real person. He gave me this."[30]

That launched an interesting discussion about Frank's growing up in New York and the rich cultural experiences he had had. He talked about being a young man in New York and how he did not start out in medicine but started out as an artist. He told Fred stories about how he did window displays, made pictures for magazines, and painted stage sets. He talked about the Netter family coming from the Alsatian region of France and about Jacob Mordecai Netter traveling around the world. All of his cousins and siblings had distinguished careers, and so should he, his mother told him. He could make pictures for fun, but he should be a doctor. She said artists live a dissolute life, drinking and cavorting with nude models. And with a twinkle in his eye, Frank looked at Fred and said, "I don't know. It sounded pretty good to me, Freddie."[31]

Then, of course, he went to medical school. "In your first year of medical school, it must have been incredible," Fred recalled saying. "Did you make pictures then? I bet your teachers were very supportive of you. They must have seen your talent."

"No, they were not, Freddie, it wasn't like that back then. I wasn't Frank Netter then. I mean, I was Frank Netter, but I wasn't famous then." And he told Fred about his experience in the anatomy lab with the professor who told Frank to stop making pictures of the cadaver, and to go home and read the book.

Then Frank said something that surprised Fred. "It wasn't easy being Jewish, going to medical school back in the '20s." Fred, who is himself Jewish, said, "Dr. Netter, I didn't know you were Jewish." Frank told him how he did not believe in religion, that more people were killed in the name of religion than anything else. So he did not practice religion.[32]

Frank told Fred about interning at Bellevue and becoming a surgeon when the Great Depression came. He told him about the man living at the fancy address with the little boy who had appendicitis and the utility company had turned off the electricity because he could not pay the electric bill. He told Fred about the die-cut heart he did for Ciba, and how that was so successful that he did other organs. It was such good advertising, he said, that Ciba offered him an exclusive contract, and that was how he started working on the series of atlases.

> He became to me like an uncle, someone I loved whom I could talk to and of whom I could ask advice. And we would talk about a lot of things, about Jimmy Durante and Rube Goldberg, and about going to nightclubs. He loved to talk about the nightclubs. He made a picture even when he told a story. And he painted the story of a rich cultural environment in New York, this true melting pot of so many different cultures.[33]

ৡৡৡৡৡ

Ciba-Geigy took an unprecedented step when it named its new Scientific Information Center in Frank's honor—the Frank Netter Library, in Summit, New Jersey, dedicated on April 30, 1986. "The significant thing about it," Gina Dingle said, "was that Ciba-Geigy had a practice of putting letters or numbers on buildings, so there would be Building A, Building B, etc. The Netter Library was the exception and was the only building named after a person. Otherwise we were in Building U."[34]

Frank and Vera came up to Summit for the formal dedication. Gina came, and Phil Flagler and Milt Donin came. Fred Kaplan came up from Philadelphia. Roy Ellis was there, and Douglas Watson, the new president of the Pharmaceutical Division, was there, as were the recently promoted former president, Charles O'Brien, and other officers of the company. Three newly completed buildings composed the research complex—a state-of-the-art laboratory, an office building, and the library—all designed by architect Henry Klemp.

On the wall by the door to the library was a larger-than-life relief sculpture, a head-and-shoulders portrait of Frank. Fred Kaplan remembered:

> They gave everybody a small version of the big medallion that was on the wall of the Netter library on the Ciba campus. It was a picture of Dr. Netter holding something in his hand. And he looked at me and said, "Freddie, what do you think that is that I am holding in my hand?"
>
> I said, "Well, Dr. Netter, I think it is paintbrushes, isn't it?"
>
> And he said, "I don't know. It could be paintbrushes. It could be pencils, or it could be cigars. I guess it must be paintbrushes. I wish it were cigars, but I think it is paintbrushes."[35]

In the front of the library building a lectern was set up, and a few folding chairs were by the door for the guests. Doug Watson addressed the assemblage of Ciba-Geigy employees standing in front of the building, as did Charles O'Brien. It was a nice event, coming on the heels of an article about him, "Frank Netter, MD: 'command performance' in medical art," that appeared in the April 25, 1986, issue of *JAMA*.[36] He had just had his eightieth birthday, so naming the library in his honor and publishing the article about him were in a way birthday presents.

Then it was time for Frank to speak. He was dressed in a light-colored suit, a yellow shirt, and a white-striped tie—conservative by his standards. He stood at the lectern and told the story he had

Photo: Frank and Vera Netter with Dr. Frederick Kaplan and Gina Dingle at the dedication of the Frank H. Netter Library, April 1986, courtesy of Dr. Frederick Kaplan.

told so many times before—about his long relationship with Ciba and subsequently Ciba-Geigy, from the time it had it offices in a loft building on Greenwich Street in New York before moving to Summit. Now here was this beautiful new facility. But Frank faltered in his speech somewhat, hesitating, searching for words from a script memorized a long time ago. Age and ill health were taking a toll on this once debonair man.

ᏭᎣᏭᎣᏭᎣᏭ

Musculoskeletal System, Part I, was published in 1987. Ciba-Geigy had a book release at the convention of the American Academy of Orthopaedic Surgeons, which was held in Atlanta that year. Most of the contributors were there at the convention, and as was its practice, Ciba-Geigy hosted a celebration one of the evenings. There was a large contingency from the University of Pennsylvania, including Dr. Brighton and many of Fred Kaplan's colleagues.

Dr. Mankin came from Harvard. At the commemorative dinner at a restaurant in town, Dr. Mankin said a few words, after which Frank got up and thanked all the consultants, as well as Phil Flagler, Milt Donin, and Gina Dingle.

Musculoskeletal System, Part I, was praised by reviewers and well received by the doctors. The

Photo: Frank Netter with Drs. Al and Genevieve Swanson, Peachtree Plaza Hotel, Atlanta, 1987, courtesy of Drs. Al and Genevieve Swanson.

most succinct book review was by Richard E. Senghas in the October 1988 issue of *The Journal of Bone and Joint Surgery*,[37] who wrote that the *Musculoskeletal System*, Part I, was another one of the artist's outstanding books.

The Swansons, Al and Genevieve, were also attending the orthopaedic convention as well as conjunctive meetings of the American Society for Surgery of the Hand. They were already working on pictures for the *Musculoskeletal System*, Part II, and met with Frank in their room at the Peachtree Plaza Hotel. Gina was there too, keeping track of the work that needed to be done. Al and Frank spread out the *Clinical Symposia* issue that they had done in 1979, "Reconstructive Surgery of the Hand and Foot,"[38] and the preliminary sketches Frank had made for the forthcoming volume. Al showed Frank the silicone implants for the great toe, and they discussed the pictures and worked out the details for the next tome.[39]

CHAPTER 27

ATLAS OF HUMAN ANATOMY

OVER THE YEARS, RICHARD Netter collected issues of the *Mercury*—CCNY's comic publication—with Frank's pictures in them, articles about Frank in *Flair* and *The Saturday Evening Post* magazines, and Frank's Christmas cards. He had a full set of Frank's books in his office. Some of his earliest memories were of Frank copying cartoons from the newspaper. When as a child he had lived with his cousin Frank and his great-aunt Esther, he had loved to watch Frank draw comics.[1]

That inspired Richard to try his hand at drawing himself. He would turn the paper sideways, and in elegant script write out his name—or your name if you were sitting beside him. Then he would turn the paper back to its correct orientation and make a cartoon profile out of the name. Somehow, it always worked out that there was a taller letter for the nose and one that formed the mouth and chin. He would add hair, and it never looked at all like the person, but you knew who it was because of the name. At Christmastime, Richard made the funniest cartoons, some with profiles of the names of family members doing the zaniest things, and had them printed up as Christmas cards to send out. One year's card read "Holiday wishes from our house to yours" and showed the floor plan of an apartment. But it was the craziest layout. He had a 20' long living room that was 2' wide, and the master bedroom had no doorway to go into it, and there were nine toilets lined up in a row in the middle of the family room. It was just nutty, and the more you studied it, the more you laughed.

Richard's fraternity at Cornell was Phi Sigma Delta, and for years he organized fraternity reunions held at the Harmony Club in New York City. Dr. Martin S. Wolfe was also an alumnus of Cornell and had been in that fraternity. He knew Frank from working with him in 1983 on a *Clinical Symposia* issue on diseases of travelers,[2] when he made two trips to Palm Beach to work with Frank in his studio at The Breakers, and both he and Frank puffed on the Macanudo cigars that Dr. Wolfe had brought as a gift for Frank. Dr. Wolfe recalled getting together with Richard at those fraternity reunions, and how Richard seemed so proud that his cousin had produced something of great value to so many people.[3]

Having followed his father into the law, Richard achieved considerable success as a partner in a Fifth Avenue law firm. In his spacious law office at Singer Netter Dowd and Berman on the seventeenth floor of the Squibb Building,[4] an enormous partners desk occupied the middle of the room and a large Diocletian window overlooked Fifth Avenue. As Frank's attorney after George retired, he advised Frank about estate planning, about his contracts with Ciba-Geigy, and about other legal matters.

Phil Flagler said of the contract negotiations between Ciba-Geigy and Frank:

> I enjoyed Frank's friendship very much. But every time there was a contractual renewal, and the debate about the terms of the new contract came about, we had to be adversaries, which really didn't please either one of us, but that was our job. Those were always very difficult, because he was a tough negotiator. He was a good businessman. And he always set up some person or event or something that he could get his heart into, be mad about and really argue about. We would have to work through that. Some were more difficult than others, but that is where Richard Netter came in.
>
> I had the utmost respect for Richard. He kept it all together. I would go in to New York, and we would chat back and forth and he would then get on the phone with Frank, and I would come in again and we would chat some more, and I would go back to the Ciba-Geigy people and say, "You know, Frank wants this, that, and the other thing." Then the board would

meet, and I would get a response. It would just go back and forth, and back and forth. Some of it got unpleasant, but we always managed to get it together, but again I thank Richard for that. He was always a realist, always searching for the appropriate compromise. He was really good at that. I found him to be a delightful man. I think that over the years, Richard and I became really good friends.[5]

Milt Donin recalled the negotiation in 1986, in which he participated:

Richard was a tough guy to deal with. No matter what we came up with, it wasn't sufficient, and finally Phil was about ready to say to hell with it. We had a meeting with Roy Ellis, and Phil was saying, "I think he is pushing us too far."

The question was raised, should we continue? Roy said, "You should give it one more try."

And we did. We went back one last time to negotiate with Richard, and to our delight he said, "I'm going to call Frank and tell him this is the best we can do." So it was arranged that we had the final contract typed up and ready for Frank to sign. Frank came up from Florida for a meeting in Richard's office.

Frank immediately started raising objections to various phrases in the contract. There was one that seemed to be a real stickler, and since I was really the junior member of this body, I was sitting there making some notes and at some point I said, "Excuse me, may I suggest something?" And I suggested a rephrasing, and Frank said, "Okay. That's it, I'll sign the contract. Let's go to lunch."[6]

Down the elevator and out onto Fifth Avenue they came. "Where did you go to law school?"[7] said Richard in his basso voice, joking with Milt about his negotiating skills. All four of them, relieved and jovial, walked up Fifth Avenue to the Harmony Club for lunch.

ᘒᖇᖱᖱᖱᘒ

Roy Ellis was senior vice president for medical and public affairs and had oversight of the Netter publications, so Phil and Milt reported to him. He had met Frank on occasion at the launch of a new volume of *The Ciba Collection* and found Frank to be genial and unpretentious. Generally, Dr. Ellis did not get involved in the contract negotiations except to ensure that the terms were financially sound. A physician himself, he saw the need for a first-rate atlas of anatomy using Frank's pictures. *Gray's Anatomy*,[8] so well known, is far more text than illustration, but even those illustrations lack the clarity and brilliance of Frank Netter's pictures. While there were many, many paintings in the Netter archive at Ciba-Geigy that could be used to create an anatomy atlas, more were sure to be needed. Frank was also enthusiastic about the idea, Dr. Ellis recalled.[9]

The president of the company, Charles O'Brien, did not at first endorse the anatomy atlas project. It stalled until finally Dr. Ellis decided he would somehow convince the executives within the company to allocate the money for it, and he told Phil to go ahead with the project. That decision, Dr. Ellis recalled, was a major inducement to Frank's signing the contract.[10]

Atlas of Human Anatomy[11] was a colossal project. It would be a single volume of Frank's pictures, facilitating the study of anatomy. Reproduction of the color plates would use the finest printing techniques of the day. Frank had made thousands of pictures for Ciba, and in planning for the atlas, the team first had to evaluate what art they had and what they still needed.

ᘒᖇᖱᖱᖱᘒ

Phil conducted a search for an anatomist to act as a guest editor to pull the *Anatomy* atlas together. He contacted a few anatomists, including Dr. Sharon Colacino, who was assistant professor of anatomy at Columbia University College of Physicians and

Surgeons, in New York. She had written a letter of inquiry to Ciba some years earlier, and Phil Flagler replied to her asking if she might be interested in doing this project. He asked her to do a wish book, choosing what she would put in it.

She took about six months to design *Atlas of Human Anatomy*. First, she designed what she wanted in an anatomy atlas. Only then did she go to *The Ciba Collection* and to *Clinical Symposia* to select the artwork. She went through all of Frank's published illustrations to find what already existed that would fit her design. She prepared an outline of the book and sent it off to Phil.

Frank liked Dr. Colacino's proposal. He telephoned her and invited her down to Palm Beach. They spent about three days together on Sharon's first visit, reviewing her outline and planning for the atlas, she recalled.

> When I first went to Florida to meet with him, I was in absolute awe. In the medical field his name just meant so much, and I was not sure he would work with me, because I was very young—I was in my forties. But he was just a nice human being, and we really hit it off from the beginning. He was delightful.
>
> On that very first visit we went out for lunch one day, and banana cream pie was on the menu. I said, "Frank, they have banana cream pie. I love banana cream pie." And he said he did too. So I asked him, "Well, isn't it bad for you?" And he said, "No. It just greases your arteries." He made me feel as though I could tell him what I thought, and I did.[12]

Frank had done over 4000 illustrations during his 50 years with the Ciba Pharmaceutical Company, and from those they selected the illustrations they wanted to use. They compiled *Atlas of Human Anatomy* primarily from the gross anatomy sections of the *Ciba Collection* books. Frank had also done a series of pictures for the upper respiratory system, but for some reason those had not made it into the *Respiratory System* volume, although they included them in the first edition of the *Anatomy* atlas.[13] There were a few shortfalls, and Sharon worked with Frank to determine what pictures he needed to make to fill the gaps.

Most of the collaboration they did long distance over the telephone, she in New York and he in Palm Beach. Once a week they had a long telephone session to go over the work. They reviewed all of his pictures for correctness in light of new medical knowledge and current terminology. "At one point I said, 'We are never going to get done,'" Sharon remembered. "He knew my name, but he always called me 'kiddo.' He said, 'Come on, kiddo. Look at it one book at a time.'"[14] Volume by volume, they waded through the anatomy illustrations in *The Ciba Collection*. Initially, they identified 19 illustrations that had to be done to round out the atlas. But as the project progressed, the number of new illustrations Frank made grew to nearly 50, which was relatively few, considering that there were 514 plates in the book. He also redesigned the overlays for all of the illustrations, while Sharon checked every leader line and label and updated the nomenclature to conform to the fifth *Nomina Anatomica*, then the current standard for medical terms.

Over the next three years, 1987–1989, they worked on the atlas. For the last two years, she stopped teaching and devoted her full energies to working on the atlas. She made three more trips to Palm Beach to work with Frank face-to-face. They would start work early in the morning and work hard for three days each time. They also talked about golf and about the three trophies on his bookcase for the holes-in-one that he had hit, all on the same hole on the same golf course, the oceanfront course down on Florida Route A1A, near Point Manalapan. She recalled:

> In his studio in Palm Beach, I was looking out the window and there was a building there. He said, "Kiddo, when I first moved here I had a beautiful view looking north along the oceanfront, and then they built this building." He used to tell me, "I can paint a squirrel better than anybody," recalling his [childhood] art lessons. And he told me a great story about

how he discovered he could earn a living making pictures, how the advertising manager made a mistake and paid him five times the price he asked.

I love to read mysteries, and he liked mysteries as well. We got to laughing and talking about his military days and his job separating all the bones in the museum. He said, "I got so bored that I started reading murder mysteries." Anyway, he gave me the name of an author—Mary Roberts Rinehart, he read everything she wrote[15]—and I bought some of her books and I read them.[16]

He told Sharon about his trip to China and about seeing a C-section done under acupuncture anesthesia. "That really blew his mind," Sharon recalled. "I think it would have blown my mind, too!"

In working with him, I came to recognize that he was one of the most phenomenal students that I have ever known. "I must understand it. I must internalize it," he said. He would study so much before he sat down to make a picture. The other thing he said was if you are having trouble understanding something, try to draw it. To draw it you have to know it. If you don't know it, there will be a blank place in the drawing.[17]

ᢒᡟᢒᡟᢒᡟᢒ

Halfway through the work on the atlas project, in 1988, Milt Donin retired. He was not part of the team that saw the atlas to completion. He had been at Ciba-Geigy for more than 12 years but had spent only the last few years of his career in the Medical Education department, and the company had a small retirement party for him. Frank made a portrait of Milt that Phil Flagler presented to him, and Milt just cherished that.[18]

When *Good Morning America* did a piece on Frank, Michael Guillen was the science editor on the show. He spent over a day with Frank interviewing him and four hours interviewing Sharon Colacino. They then edited the footage down to a five-minute segment that aired on August 1, 1988.

Phil Flagler then convinced Ciba-Geigy to make its own film about Frank and his work, a biographical piece running about 40 minutes. In the winter of 1988 he took a film crew to Palm Beach, and they took footage of Frank at the apartment and on the grounds of The Breakers. They showed him in his studio painting some of the pictures for the next volume of *The Ciba Collection, Musculoskeletal System*, Part II. They showed him sitting outside on the terrace, and in another scene sitting with Vera in her office, reading the mail. They showed him hitting balls on the golf course, walking on the boardwalk along the beach, and sitting in the living room with Vera at the piano in the background. When she protested that she could barely play the piano, they told her not to worry, they would overdub something played by Vladimir Horowitz. She got a laugh out of that.

When making the movie, Frank had in his own mind an outline of what he was going to say, and it was difficult for him to be spontaneous. In the film, telling the stories he had told many times before, he appeared somewhat stiff and rehearsed, as he told how he had learned to draw squirrels and wanted to learn to draw people. So he watched people, he said, and before you can learn to draw, you must learn to see. He explained how he tried to make the people in his pictures appear as living, breathing human beings. "They are not machines," he said. "We are not repairing a television set."[19]

Phil spent a great deal of time working with the film crew, and he was a bit edgy about how Frank would react to the finished piece. He took a videotape of it down to Palm Beach to show Frank and Vera, and the three of them sat in the living room at Breakers Row and watched the tape. As Frank and Vera watched the movie, Phil watched them intently for their reaction. When it was over, they seemed rather cool about it, and Phil came away wondering. Two days later Frank called Phil and praised the movie. The problem with the showing in Palm Beach had been that neither Frank nor

Vera could hear the soundtrack. When they viewed it again privately, they could actually hear and see the movie and were enthusiastic about the film.

᎒᎐᎒᎐᎒᎐᎒

For the final work session before *Atlas of Human Anatomy* went to press, Frank came up to New York to work at the Ciba-Geigy facility in West Caldwell, New Jersey. All of the paperwork was there. They had black-and-white dummies of each page laid out one after the other on tables placed end to end around a large conference room. And at that meeting, in June 1989, they checked the graphics and finalized the order in which the illustrations were to appear in the book. Sharon remembered:

> It came down to the last three or four days before everything went to the printer. We were walking down the hall at Ciba-Geigy. There was a man in work clothes in the hall, and Frank stopped and talked to him: "Hello. What's your name? What do you do here?" I was immeasurably impressed that Frank was so concerned about the man who worked in the mailroom.[20]

The book designer with whom Ciba-Geigy contracted, Phil Grushkin, supervised production of that first edition of the atlas. He was the person who was the lead, the point person, in putting the book together.[21] His expertise was with art books, and he put that atlas together as an art book. Phil insisted on a number of quality-control procedures, including a numbering scheme for each plate to identify it four ways: by Ciba-Geigy's archival registration number, by plate number, by page number, and by the art's position on the printing press. Caroline "Jeffie" Lemons was the person at Ciba-Geigy who kept track of the artwork and typographic details. She documented the numbering scheme of the artwork on a pagination grid.

Photo: *Sharon Colacino, Phil Grushkin, and Frank Netter checking the graphics and finalizing the sequencing of illustrations for* Atlas of Human Anatomy, 1989, *courtesy of Sharon Colacino Oberg.*

The finished artwork was photographed and was reproduced as large-format color transparencies. Ciba-Geigy contracted Gamma One Conversions photographic studios in New York to make the color transparencies of the illustrations and provide color retouching by hand. Phil supervised the retouching to ensure that the colors of the transparencies exactly matched the original art.

The next step in preparation for printing was the color separations. It was a monumental task to print the 514 plates and make them look as if they had all been painted at the same time, when in actuality they had been painted over a period of 40 or more years. The color correction was delicate and required both digital correction and handwork. Phil Grushkin and Phil Flagler—Phil and Phil—considered several printing companies and finally selected Daiichi Seihan, in Tokyo, to do the color separations and printing. Daiichi Seihan produced the four-color separations used in the printing process, and then, using a computer with a mouse, they corrected the color, pixel by pixel.

Phil and Phil proofed the colors, comparing each plate not only with the original transparency but also in relation to its placement in the paging scheme, so that the color of bone on one page, for example, was consistent with the color of bone on the following page. The colors from one to the other needed to be uniform. Phil Flagler remembered:

The color separations had to be nigh well perfect or they changed the information the pictures portrayed. If the face was too yellow, it gave the person jaundice, which may not have been the intent. The color had to be just right, and that was not an easy proposition, particularly in those days.

There was a major transition starting in the '60s and going through the '70s and '80s, when all the technology moved from handwork to the beginnings of computers and digital manipulation, all the way up to the *Anatomy* book, which was done [with] a combination of computer technology and highly technical handwork. And the only place we could get the handwork really done well was in Japan, because when things went to the technical route here in the United States, they went completely, and the finesse we needed was not available with that technology. We had a group of people who were always working on the technology and trying to find better ways to do things. If you can, imagine doing basically by hand the paste-ups for all of those pictures with all of the legends and the lines going to the various structures. Just pick out one of the pictures in the *Anatomy* book and imagine not only laying it out and proofreading it but then translating it to print. It was an amazing operation.[22]

Sally Chichester was the freelance proofreader, and after she and Sharon checked the labels and leader lines on photoprints of Frank's tissue overlays, Jeffie input the labels. Phil Grushkin prepared the mechanicals himself, using photocopies of Frank's original art and corresponding tissue overlay. Frank had done the hand-lettering on the overlay so meticulously that it closely matched the finished type, making Phil's job considerably easier.

The printing itself was yet to come. When Phil and Phil left for Japan to supervise the printing, they had yet to finish proofing the color separations for the second half of the book. Phil Grushkin hand-carried the mechanicals for the index onto the plane, and at the last minute Sharon sent updates by Federal Express to them in Japan.

Phil and Phil spent three weeks in Japan, shuttling between two Daiichi Seihan printing plants, each plant with two presses running full speed ahead. As they were checking the proofs, Phil Grushkin's numbering system was invaluable in quickly identifying where each piece of art was on the sheet of 16 plates. The subsequent bookbinding process would place the pages in order and cut the sheets.

After three weeks of around-the-clock effort, the tag team of Phil and Phil headed for home in mid-July 1989. The bound books came by ship less than a month later.[23] Ciba-Geigy simultaneously released both hardcover and paperback editions, the hardcover being the physician's library reference and the paperback, the student edition. Medical schools across the country and around the globe immediately put the paperback to use in the gross anatomy labs.

ᘖᘙᘖᘙᘖᘙ

Unlike *The Ciba Collection*, Netter's *Atlas of Human Anatomy* has no text. It relies on Frank's vivid illustrations to tell the story. Frank knew exactly how to highlight the pictures, how to put the spotlight in just the right place, so as to bring out the message of the story. As Sharon put it,

> He knew what had to be in a picture and what to leave out. Not every little detail had to be in the picture, just the essential pieces of information. He did that so well. If you pick up a Gray's [*Anatomy*] or a Grant's [*Atlas of Anatomy*],[24] the illustrations are loaded with information and show everything without discriminating the important features, whereas Frank included in his pictures only what was needed to illustrate the point and nothing more.[25]

"The *Anatomy* atlas is the crowning piece of all the work," said Phil Flagler. "From the time we began to work on it until it was complete was at least four years. It is a great book. It is the piece of which I am most proud. Phil Grushkin is a name that should be remembered in all of this. He was a graphics designer of real note."[26]

Netter's *Atlas of Human Anatomy* is indeed a beautiful book. The reviewers unanimously agreed on that point. Lawrence Altman, for *The New York Times*, recommended the atlas to anyone interested in the human body;[27] John Skandalakis, for JAMA, likened Netter's influence on anatomy to that of Leonardo da Vinci;[28] Richard Senghas, for the *Journal of Bone and Joint Surgery*, and Stephen Carmichael, at the Mayo Clinic, both called it a classic;[29] Bonnie Kendall, editorial director for the *Journal of the American Dental Association*, called it a remarkable new book;[30] the *Journal of Neurological and Orthopaedic Medicine and Surgery* called it a monumental work;[31] John Anderson, for *Science Books & Films*, called the book excellent and said that no other atlas of anatomy compares;[32] and Mikel H. Snow, for the *New England Journal of Medicine*, welcomed the volume for its impressive accuracy and unequaled drawings.[33] Phil Grushkin submitted the atlas to the Bookbinders' Guild of New York, and it won the award for the Number 1 Book of the Year in the category of Scholarly Reference, Illustrated, at the New York Book Show.

The frontispiece of *Atlas of Human Anatomy* is a candid photo of Frank at his drawing board. He was wearing a blue shirt, open at the neck, and holding a cigar in his left hand and a paintbrush in his right. He was painting the plate on the arteries and veins of the orbit and eyelids, plate 80. A color copy of plate 115, "Oculomotor, Trochlear, and Abducens Nerves: Schema," is alongside in a loose-leaf notebook, with its tissue overlay showing his handwritten labels. Before they put it in the book, somebody at Ciba-Geigy suggested that they touch up the photo and take the cigar out of the picture. But that cigar was Frank; that was how he worked. They did not touch it.

ଶ୨୦ୠ୦ଶ

Because there were no authors or outside editors on the atlas, Ciba-Geigy did not have a big party for the launch of the volume. Phil Flagler had a party at his beach house for the whole staff and the primary people who worked on the book, people from the Daiichi Seihan New York office, and Phil Grushkin. It was at the party that Sharon saw the volume for the first time.

After the party, Phil and Phil, Sharon, Jeffie, and Sally got on a plane and went down to Palm Beach. They brought copies of the atlas, and Frank autographed copies for each of them. And Phil

Photo: *Frank Netter at his drawing board,* Atlas of Human Anatomy, 1989, *frontispiece, courtesy of Elsevier.*

Flagler brought a special gift for Frank. The team in Japan had prepared a proof of the photo of Frank at his drawing board that appeared in the front of the atlas. Around the margin of the photo, all of the people at Daiichi Seihan who worked on the publication had signed their names in Japanese, and sent that to Ciba-Geigy so Phil and Phil, Gina, Sharon, Jeffie, and Sally could sign it too.

Photo: Team for Atlas of Human Anatomy *with Frank and Vera Netter, Breakers Row, celebrating publication of the atlas, 1989, courtesy of Sharon Colacino Oberg. From left rear: Frank Netter, Sharon Colacino, Phil Flagler, Phil Grushkin. Seated from left: Caroline "Jeffie" Lemons, Sally Chichester, Vera Netter.*

Phil had had it framed and presented it to Frank during their visit. Frank was especially pleased with it.

They had a nice visit with Frank and Vera at Breakers Row that evening. Frank was wearing the same blue shirt as in the atlas photograph and, Sharon remembered, someone teased him by saying, "Don't you have any more shirts?"[34] Frank added an ascot and put a jacket on over his blue shirt, and they all went out to dinner afterward, except for Vera. She was nearly 90 years old and exhibited several of the risk factors for osteoporosis—she was thin, of Northern European heritage, somewhat sedentary, post-menopausal with a lifetime history of dieting, and for decades had eaten a calcium-poor diet. In 1988 she had fallen and broken her hip,[35] and when it stubbornly failed to heal, Frank subsequently took her to the Hospital for Special Surgery, in New York, where she had hip-replacement surgery[36] with a successful outcome. But she had stopped going out to dinner when Frank went with business associates.

CHAPTER 28

UNFINISHED BUSINESS

WORK ON PARTS II AND III of the *Musculoskeletal System* volume began well before Part I went to press. While Part I covered normal anatomy, embryology, and physiology, Part II dealt with developmental disorders, tumors, rheumatic diseases, and joint replacement, and Part III, trauma and fracture care.

Dr. Robert Hensinger worked with Frank as consulting editor of *Musculoskeletal System*, Part II.[1] He had oversight of the part of the book on children, which was its largest single piece. Dr. Richard H. Freyberg, at the Hospital for Special Surgery, in New York, edited the section on rheumatic diseases, and Fred Kaplan suggested some people to work on the orthopaedic diseases, dwarfism, the different types of avascular necrosis, and other problems. Much of the outline they took from a book on orthopaedics by Dr. Robert Salter,[2] with whom Frank had worked on a *Clinical Symposia* issue[3] in 1984. For the section on congenital amputees and those problems, Frank incorporated the outline his friend in Point Manalapan, Dr. Charley Frantz, had made more than a decade earlier.

Sometime before that, Bob Hensinger had written a proposal for a *Clinical Symposia* issue on the limping child, and many of the pictures of the lower extremities that appeared in *Musculoskeletal System*, Part II, were an outgrowth from his proposal. The pictures on congenital anomalies of the cervical spine were from photos of Bob Hensinger's patients. He recalled:

> We tried to keep the text short. It just covered the topic quickly and then the pictures emphasized the different aspects of the thing. The picture of a child with a lumbosacral agenesis[4] is somewhat the way she was in life. She has a little round face

and a pleasant smile. It catches all the information, but he had an ability to make these drawings comfortable to the eye. The kids may have a very severe handicap or deformity, but he did not make them look ugly or distorted. They were just very nice children with a problem.

I flew to New Jersey one time to meet with Gina Dingle and go over the text. She worked very closely with Dr. Netter getting the material ready for publication. They were just very careful not to upset him. They treated him with kid gloves. They were very deferential. They didn't want to do anything that would offend him. I got the sense that if they tried to do something that [he did not like], he was quick to tell them not to do that.

When I first worked with him on the *Clinical Symposia* on congenital dislocation of the hip,[5] he did the whole plate. He did the lettering. He decided about the size of the pictures, the size of the x-rays, the printing, and then its placement on the plate. Every aspect of it was his work. Then as he got older and had less time, he let the Ciba-Geigy team do things to the plate. Using computers, they repositioned the component parts of the plate, and they did the lettering and positioned the legends.[6]

Much of the material needed for this book had been done pre-viously for issues of *Clinical Symposia*, including the plates and text on congenital dislocation of the hip Frank and Bob Hensinger did,[7] as well as the work Frank had done with Drs. Salter and Thompson on Legg-Calvé-Perthes disease.[8] All 34 plates on tumors came entirely from the two *Clinical Symposia* issues that Frank had done with Drs. Chappie Conrad[9] and Bill Enneking on tumors of bone and of soft tissue.[10] The material in the issue on congenital limb malformation, which Frank had completed in 1981 with Drs. Alfred and Genevieve Swanson, just needed some updating.[11] Frank and the Swansons worked together to revise some of the implant draw-ings on reconstructive surgery for deformities of the rheumatoid hand for inclusion in *Musculoskeletal System*, Part II.[12] In the plates on arthroplasty for the metacarpophalangeal joints, they added titanium grommets, which protect the implant from sharp bone ends, and they converted the carpal bones' silicone implants to titanium designs.

Al Swanson was at that time chairman of the Hogden Memorial Lecture[13] at Blodgett Memorial Medical Center in Grand Rapids, and he invited Frank to be the 1989 honored lecturer, to which Frank replied that he would. "The predicted attendance was so large that we had to change venue," Genevieve remembered.

> Hours before the lecture, I accidentally discovered that he was heading for University of Michigan in Ann Arbor. I rebooked his [connecting flight] and successfully paged him as he arrived at the Detroit airport. Northwest [Airlines] delayed the departure [of the plane] for Grand Rapids waiting for him. He still looked out of breath when I picked him up at the airport.[14]

Frank brought along a copy of the movie Phil Flagler had produced, and he showed that at the lecture. The film told his story and afterward he spoke only briefly about his work and about the *Atlas of Human Anatomy*.

For his visit, Frank stayed with the Swansons in their home. In the evening while Al and Genevieve prepared dinner, he took a ballpoint pen and made a sketch of them in their houseguest book—Al with a golf club in one hand and what looked like either a cooking spoon or surgical instrument in the other, and Genny with a handful of notes.[15] They laughed and had a great time, Genevieve remembered.

Over the years Dr. Hugo Keim and Frank did six *Clinical Symposia* issues on spinal deformities. Whenever he visited Frank in Palm Beach they would play golf together, and over the two decades they worked together, their friendship grew. "He was a remarkable man," recalled Dr. Keim. "It was wonderful for me to be able to collaborate with him on his work. It was not just a professional thing; it was kind of a social, pleasurable thing."[16] In 1989 Drs. Keim and Hensinger coauthored a *Clinical Symposia* issue on spinal deformities,[17] and they incorporated that material into *Musculoskeletal System*, Part II.[18]

The section in Part II on total joint replacement covered hip replacement, knee replacement, shoulder replacement, and elbow replacement.[19] Dr. John Insall and his team at the Hospital for Special Surgery, in New York had developed the first successful total knee implant that allowed patients to move naturally. It was a hot new topic, and Ciba asked Dr. Insall and Dr. Russell Windsor to work with Frank on the segment on knee replacement.[20] "To me it was an honor to be an author," Dr. Windsor recalled, "because he only picked the absolute best, the leading figures in whatever field there was. It was something to be an invited author in *The Ciba Collection*."[21]

ↂↂↂↂↂↂↂ

The University of Texas Health Science Center at San Antonio ran a level I trauma center that was recognized as a leading center for fracture care. Their emergency medical service (EMS) program provided education and training in prehospital care through the American Academy of Orthopaedic Surgeons for emergency medical technicians and was instrumental in developing the US Department of Transportation education programs for technicians and paramedics.

Dr. Charles Rockwood was chair of the Department of Orthopaedics at the Health Science Center, and he was known for his work on fractures and had been responsible for establishing the trauma center. Dr. Charley Frantz had told Dr. Rockwood in the 1970s that Frank was planning a volume on the musculoskeletal system, including a section on trauma, but it was not until 1986 that Gina Dingle called from Ciba-Geigy and said Dr. Netter would like to start work on the trauma section. By that time, Dr. Rockwood had retired, so Dr. James Heckman, who had helped Dr. Rockwood run the EMS program, became the editor of *Musculoskeletal System, Part III*. "He had a wonderful secretary called Nita," recalled Gina. "She set up all of the meetings. She scheduled everything. It was actually very trouble-free for us, because all we needed to do was give them a time when we were coming."[22]

Gina went with Frank on the initial trip to see the group in San Antonio for the work on trauma and management in Part III of the *Musculoskeletal System* volume. Frank had done a broad-scope outline of the book, and when he met with Dr. Heckman, they fleshed out the details and subdivided it into sections and the sections into topics. They decided how many illustrations would be devoted to each topic. Dr. Heckman recruited the doctors, experts in their field, to act as section editors for each segment and identify the people to prepare the text. Gina's job was to get in touch with the authors to spell out for them the particulars—that they had a specific number of illustrations that would cover their subject, and what the length of the text was to be. She told them about their honoraria; she told them about the method of communication; and if they needed to have a meeting with Frank, she arranged it. Gina recalled:

> The illustrations—the authors were more in charge of that, although sometimes the guest editor or section editor would put in his 2 cents' worth as well and say we really need to add this. Authors often wanted many more illustrations than were assigned. Many were concerned that some aspect would be omitted, and my job was to tell them that it was being covered, that somebody else was doing that series of illustrations.[23]

Dr. Heckman had substantial input as to what went into *Musculoskeletal System*, Part III, as far as the subject matter. They had some rudimentary material for Frank to reference—Dr. Rockwood's textbook on fractures[24] and case histories of what they wanted to illustrate. Dr. Heckman remembered:

Once we told him what we wanted to do, he would come up with the idea of how to make it look real. He was so good at depicting it in a real-life situation. We would give him the ideas, and a fairly well annotated outline, and he would go back home and make sketches and bring them back and talk to us about them to see if he was on target with the injury. He did not have any problem with the anatomy. He knew the anatomy. He just wanted to make sure that what he was depicting was the way we would manage it prehospital or the way we would treat the fracture surgically.[25]

They included an EMS component in that volume, seven composite plates[26] on how to treat injuries in the field before patients get to the hospital. It was a unique element of the book—principles of prehospital care of musculoskeletal injury specifically for physicians or the medical community in general—for which Dr. Heckman took the outline from the prehospital-care curriculum for their EMS training program. For the section on trauma care, they made a list of common injuries by anatomical site and Dr. Heckman divvied those topics up among members of the faculty at San Antonio who had the expertise and wanted to get involved in working with Frank.

Jim Heckman thought they should include about ten plates on vascular diseases. "Wouldn't it be nice to get Mike DeBakey!" he recalled saying to Frank, just pie in the sky. "And he said, 'Well, let's call him up.'"

I couldn't ask Mike DeBakey to do anything, but Frank called him and got DeBakey involved. And on his trips to San Antonio when he came down to talk to us about fracture work, he would then go over to Houston to work with Dr. DeBakey on the vascular section.[27]

⊶⊶⊶⊶⊶⊶

In Michael DeBakey's office at the Texas Medical Center in Houston, there were beautiful Oriental rugs, crystal, placards, and awards from all over the world. It had more of a museum-like quality than a hospital aura. Many of the items in his office were gifts from his patients, some of whom were fabulously wealthy—including the king of Saudi Arabia and the shah of Iran. Dr. DeBakey had told them to pay whatever they thought the operation was worth, and they gave him his fee many times over. During his tenure as chancellor at Baylor University, he became most effective at raising money. He had a tremendous ability to affect America's medical policies. Politicians would ask his advice on whether the government should fund this or that.[28]

In August 1987, Frank went to see his friend in Houston to review the cases and come up with a plan for the plates on peripheral vascular disease. Frank's outline for the volume included obstructive arterial disease as well as arterial trauma and other arterial diseases, and he made a list of materials he needed, plate by plate, to make the pictures—arteriograms, x-rays, reprints, slides, pictures of the techniques for catheterization and angiography—and he asked Mike to send that to him in Florida. Dr. DeBakey recalled:

> When he came down to do this work, we had dinner together every night. I told him one time, "Frank, your illustrations—you don't even have to put your name on them. I can recognize the fact that you did this, and most people who know your work can immediately recognize the illustration, you did it." Well, that's talent, that's what it is. He was so easy to work with. Frank was kind of a celebrity, and certainly in the medical field everybody knew Frank Netter. The name was familiar even with the medical students. But he was pretty much down to earth.[29]

Photo: Drs. Frank Netter and Michael DeBakey,
Dr. DeBakey's conference room, Houston, c. 1988.

John Craig continued to make illustrations for *Clinical Symposia* issues. He lived in Houston, and during one of Frank's trips to Texas, he invited Frank to have a drink with him at the hotel. Frank lit up a cigar, and they talked about medical art, each with his own approach to it, how Frank took his commercial art training and applied that to medical art, and how John added much more detail in the preliminary sketches than Frank did. They never worked together, and that was the only time they ever met.[30]

ᘓᕲᕢᕲᕢᕲᕲᘏ

Between 1987 and 1989, Frank made at least half a dozen trips to San Antonio to see Dr. Heckman and his team. He would arrive with his cigars and with the sketches for them to look at together. Jim Heckman remembered those review sessions:

> For someone who was not an orthopaedic surgeon, he was very knowledgeable about the injuries. Obviously, he had done some reading of the subject matter in addition to just what he recalled from his past experiences. He was a delight to work with. We would say, "No, that doesn't look quite right," or "Fix that," and the next time when he brought the drawings back, they were right on target. We never got into any arguments about how things should be depicted. It was a fun experience.
>
> His artistic skill and insight were amazing. He could depict things that you would describe to him more accurately and more effectively than almost anybody else. Of course, he had a lot of anatomic knowledge. He did not have a lot of orthopaedic knowledge, but he was still able to capture what we were talking about in a realistic way. We all grew up looking at his illustrations and were awestruck in working with him. He had an innate ability to capture the essence of what we wanted to depict and do it extremely well. In a clinical way, it was not sterile but had a very personal and human character

to it. He was also a fun person to be around. He worked very hard, was conscientious, and was receptive to other people's ideas. There was a certain amount of awe [for us] coming into the project, and once you got over that, you could really respect him for what he was as a person.

We had him over to dinner [at my home] one night. Our son was in his early teenage years and an aspiring artist. He was interested in lots of things, but he spent a fair amount of time painting and drawing. [Frank told] him the story about how his mother told him he needed to get a real job and he could not live off of being an artist all his life. When our son heard that story, he decided to pursue some other profession and have art as an avocation. But Frank would have been a successful artist no matter what he depicted.

He was fairly frail in the last year we worked together. I took him over to the hospital cafeteria for lunch one day and he fell down, going through the doorway, missed the step, and I thought, "Oh my goodness! I am going to be treating Frank Netter's broken hip here in this hospital!" Fortunately he just hopped back up and we went off to lunch and he didn't have any serious problems. [31]

Dr. Fred Corley was in orthopaedics with Dr. Heckman. He made a substantial contribution—27 plates[32] on injuries to the elbow, wrist, forearm, and hand. Dr. Corley enjoyed working on the project. And Frank was interested in their work. He asked questions about the reading on the blood pressure cuff that they used during Bier block anesthesia for reduction of a fracture to the forearm.[33] "He wanted to know how we roll plaster," said Dr. Corley, "and why a short-arm cast came to the end of the metacarpal heads on the dorsum of the hand and the thenar flexion crease on the palmar surface, and how that enhanced function. He had a genuine goodness in him."[34] Frank had done two *Clinical Symposia* issues in 1969 and 1970 on similar topics—"Injuries to the Elbow"[35] and "Injuries to the Wrist."[36] The Ciba team used computers to extract sections from the composite plates[37] in those older publications to use in *Musculoskeletal System*, Part III, although the text was completely new and original to Dr. Corley.

In San Antonio there is a good Mexican restaurant called La Fogata, where Fred Corley and Jim Heckman took Frank to lunch one day. The waitstaff served margaritas and brought out individual bowls of a thick, soupy, piquant salsa and tortilla chips for dipping. Not knowing what it was, and before they could stop him, Frank took a spoonful—a huge gulp—of the salsa. "He turned red from the top of his head to the tips of his toes," Dr. Corley remembered. "He began perspiring profusely. I could just see the headlines in the paper the next day—'Famed illustrator hospitalized after meal with *former* associate professor of orthopaedics at the University of Texas Health Sciences Center.' Fortunately, we got him a glass of milk and lots of water and he simmered down, and we were able to enjoy our meal after that incident. He told me that that was hotter than most of the cigars he had smoked."[38]

Another consultant at the University of Texas San Antonio Health Science Center was Dr. Basil Pruitt. He was a large man with a deep imposing voice, yet a compassionate clinician and leading researcher. He had served for decades at the United States Army Institute of Surgical Research before coming to the

Photo: *Frank Netter modeling for picture of man being hit by a car, with Vera Netter modeling as the car's driver, c. 1989, from the University of North Carolina Wilson Special Collections Library.*

University of Texas San Antonio. His were patients who were victims of severe, life-threatening burns, and Dr. Pruitt was called the "father of modern burn care." He remembered meeting with Frank on two occasions to prepare the segment on burn injury.[39] They did plates on the classifications of burns; on the three degrees of burns; on measuring the area of body surface burned; on resuscitation, wound care, and skin grafting; and on nutrition for burn victims. The segment was only six plates but clearly told the story of treating patients with serious burn injuries.[40]

To understand the various pelvic fractures, Frank consulted Dr. Peter L.J. McGanity, also at the University of Texas Health Science Center. In making the pictures, Frank modeled for two illustrations

Sketch: "Lateral Compression Injury," showing man being hit by a car, Frank H. Netter, c. 1989; from the University of North Carolina Wilson Special Collections Library.

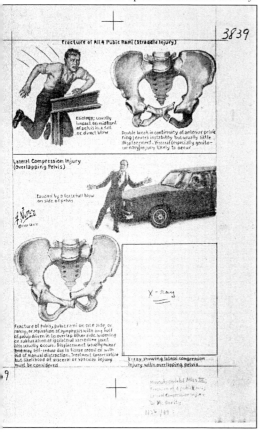

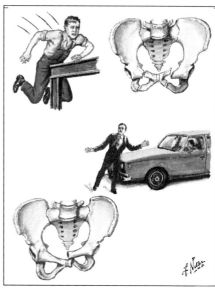

"Lateral Compression Injury," Frank H. Netter, Ciba Collection of Medical Illustrations, Musculoskeletal System, Part III, 1993, Section I, plate 80, courtesy of Elsevier.

of a man being hit by a car. At The Breakers Row apartment, he parked his car in front of the building, and Vera's son, John Stetson, took pictures of him leaning against the car as if being hit. In the finished painting he toned down the outlandish outfit he was wearing in the photograph—red pants and white patent leather shoes splattered with paint. Together, these images are interesting in that they show the progression of his work from photo of the model, to sketch, to finished picture, although the painting is not one of Netter's best. He was aging, with failing eyesight and health, and it shows in the picture. Nevertheless the message of the picture is clear.

ᏩᎤᎤᏋᎤᎤ

A little more than a third of the Part III tome's consultants were in San Antonio. But Dr. Scott Mubarak was a professor of orthopaedics at the University of California, San Diego. He had sent a proposal to Ciba-Geigy to do a *Clinical Symposia* issue on compartment syndrome—fluid accumulation in the muscle compartment in an arm or leg that causes vascular problems, impaired perfusion, and if not treated, even death. At first, Maria Erdélyi-Brown at Ciba-Geigy could not find a place for it in the *Clinical Symposia* schedule, but then Frank wrote to Dr. Mubarak, saying he wanted to include a piece on compartment syndrome in the *Musculoskeletal System* volume. They exchanged letters and talked on the telephone, and Dr. Mubarak put together an outline and sent it to Frank, along with a highlighted copy of the textbook[41] he had written. Frank made sketches for six plates[42] that covered the pathophysiology, diagnosis, and methods of surgical treatment, and sent copies to Dr. Mubarak with some questions about why they were doing this or that. Dr. Mubarak said:

> Other artists for papers that I had written, they don't ask questions like that. He was more than just an artist. He even knew

about the different . . . techniques for measuring the pressure of the compartment syndromes. I did not tell him about them, but he knew about them. He so beautifully conceptualized the patient's disease or problems and told it with pictures.[43]

༺ঔৣৣঔৣ༻

Probably the longest-running collaboration on a topic in that volume was with Dr. Harold Kleinert, who was a professor of surgery at the University of Louisville School of Medicine. It had begun years before when Dr. Charley Frantz—before he died in 1978—had written to him about the preparation of illustrations on replantation of limbs and digits for the *Musculoskeletal System* volume. At that time, Dr. Kleinert had graciously accepted. Yet it was not until 1982 that Frank wrote saying that he was ready to begin work on the subject and requested slides, photographs, diagrams, x-rays, and a preliminary version of the text.[44]

Somehow the work still did not progress. Dr. Kleinert wrote to Frank in a letter dated June 19, 1987, inquiring about it. Frank replied that he continued to be interested in the topic, although because of his work schedule, it would another year before he could begin work on it.[45] In May 1988, more than a decade after they agreed to work together, Dr. Kleinert sent Frank a list of proposed illustrations,[46] and Frank made the trip out to Louisville, where they finally began work on a *Clinical Symposia* issue. Dr. Kleinert and his team[47] demonstrated the replantations of fingers and hands they had done and gave Frank photographs of the amputated part and the replanted part, and in February 1989 Frank sent Dr. Kleinert copies of the preliminary sketches[48] of the microsurgical instruments used in replantation; of the surgical techniques for replantation of a digit, of a tendon, of a thumb, and of a hand; of grafts and reconstruction.[49] The finished replantation pictures were incorporated in *Musculoskeletal System*, Part III,[50] and published at last in a *Clinical Symposia* article[51] in 1991.

CHAPTER 29

GIVING LIFE

I N LATE WINTER AND early spring of 1989, Frank was suffering in discomfort and had his gallbladder removed, not by laparoscopy, which was new at the time, but by open surgery. That is when doctors found an aneurysm of the abdominal aorta.

Aram Chobanian was by then dean of the medical school at Boston University. He had worked with Frank on three *Clinical Symposia* issues on hypertension,[1] but as dean he would go down to Florida on fund-raising missions. Palm Beach was a favorite place where he often attended functions for donors at The Breakers and on occasion would visit Frank and Vera.[2] During one of those visits, Frank confided in Aram that he had an aortic aneurysm, and the two of them discussed it and debated whether the aneurysm was large enough to require surgery.[3]

In 1953, Dr. Michael DeBakey had pioneered surgically excising such aneurysms and grafting Dacron tubes in their place. Frank had illustrated that surgery of the aorta for a *Clinical Symposia* issue[4] published in 1956. Now it was he who weighed the risk, trying to decide if he should undergo surgery to repair the aneurysm or face the possibility of a life-threatening rupture.

❖❖❖❖❖❖

Ciba-Geigy asked Frank to make a painting for a poster in celebration of National Nurses Week, April 30 through May 6, 1989. On Thursday, May 4, 1989, at the National Museum of Women in the Arts in Washington, D.C., the Tri-Council for Nursing and Ciba-Geigy jointly sponsored Salute to Nurses Day. Doug Watson, President of Ciba-Geigy Pharmaceuticals, welcomed the attendees, and Frank presented his painting to the council.

An outlandish image of an aging artist, wearing a black-and-white-checked jacket, a red shirt with small polka dots, and a foulard ascot, Frank stepped to the podium. Without making any jokes for his opening remarks, and in a somewhat distracted manner and privately suffering with the aneurysm, he briefly explained his vision of the helping hand that nurses offer. Reminiscent of Michelangelo's *Creation of Adam* in the Sistine Chapel, of God giving life to man, Frank's picture—the hand of the nurse reaching to the hand of the patient superimposed over the background of an anatomical heart—symbolized the caring that nurses provide. "I like to paint hands," he said, "because hands are so expressive."[5] He unveiled his picture to enthusiastic applause from the audience. That picture was also on the cover of the May 5, 1989, issue of *JAMA*.

Later, as the nurses were talking among themselves, Frank was standing off to the side by himself when a woman approached him. She was middle-aged and slim, her bobbed brown hair neatly coifed. "Uncle Frank," she called to him in a soft Southern accent. It was Mary Mills, Katie's daughter. He had not seen her in nearly 35 years, but no sooner had she said that than he took her by the hand and held on, and he introduced her to everyone as his niece.[6]

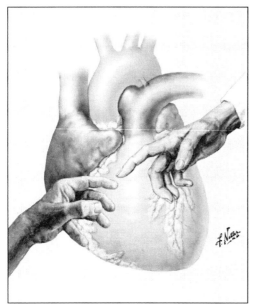

Giving Life, Frank H. Netter, *gouache on illustration board, 1989, courtesy of Novartis.*

ᷡᷡᷡᷡ

Not a week went by before he was traveling again. Drs. Carl Brighton and Frederick Kaplan invited Frank to be the featured speaker and honored guest at the University of Pennsylvania's celebration of the centennial of the orthopaedics department, May 11–12, 1989. It is the oldest orthopaedic department in the nation. For the event, Ciba-Geigy put on an exhibit of 60 of Frank's original paintings, including many from the *Musculoskeletal System*, volume 8. Ward Newschwander arranged the exhibit in the orthopaedic surgery suites. He organized the pictures on hanging panels and on folding screens, some higher, some lower. They also had a setup to show the movie about Frank that Phil Flagler had orchestrated. The celebration was to begin on Thursday when Frank would be recognized as an honorary alumnus. He would speak, and afterward they planned a reception at the art exhibit. The next night, Friday, there was to be a banquet.

Frank flew up to Philadelphia—Vera had stopped traveling with him—and one of the orthopaedic residents drove Fred Kaplan to the airport to meet him. As they were driving out of the airport, Frank in the front, Fred in the back and the resident driving, Frank blithely lit up a cigar. They opened the windows, but still it stunk up the resident's car.

The Dunlop Auditorium at the University of Pennsylvania has a seating capacity of 500 people. On Thursday, May 11, it was filled to capacity, standing room only, with crowds who had come to see Frank Netter. The dean of the medical school, Dr. Arthur Asbury, named Frank an honorary alumnus, and then Frank began to speak. The doors were wide open, and people were standing in the hallway outside listening to him. "I have never seen anything like it," recalled Fred Kaplan.[7] Frank talked about his early days in medical art. He talked about his time in the army and making pictures for the army manuals to show the soldiers how to care for themselves. Then he talked about working for Ciba and becoming the medical artist and educator that people know. He talked about what an honor it was to be at the University of Pennsylvania School of Medicine and receive the honorary alumnus award from Dr. Asbury. Then he said he would sign some autographs and books, and people lined up to talk to him. The line went out the door and spilled out onto the Hamilton Walk, the main walkway through the campus. There were more than 100 people who wanted to talk to him, but he could not talk to them all because he had to go on to the reception.[8]

The wine and cheese reception and viewing of the art exhibit was held in the orthopaedics department. The guest book had over 150 entries from attendees that evening, among them medical students, nurses, doctors. Several hundred more came over the weekend, including Dr. Robert Salter, who came from Toronto, and the librarian from Johns Hopkins, who drove up from Baltimore with her family. Gina Dingle was there for the reception. Phil Flagler was there. Frank's son Jim, who lived in Philadelphia, came, with his wife, Carol, and Frank introduced Fred to them.[9]

Carol Orzel, Fred Kaplan's patient with the disabling genetic condition FOP and whose picture Frank had painted, was at the opening of the exhibit for the centennial, and Fred introduced her to Frank. She could not look up at him because of her ossified tissue, so he pulled up a chair and sat down to talk to her. Of course, with the aneurysm, sitting was easier for him too. As Fred watched, his patient and his greatest teacher talked about her condition, about life, and about art. Fred had given her a copy of *Musculoskeletal System*, Part I, the book with her picture, and Frank signed it for her. Then he turned to Fred. "You have got to work on this one, Freddie," he said. "You can always do something kind. You have to do something intelligent."[10]

Dr. Kaplan remembered:

> In the art exhibit we had about 100 paintings from Ciba. One of them was a painting Frank had made in 1953 of a woman who had fallen down a flight of steps and broken her hip and she was being attended by a young doctor.[11] We were walking around and Phil [Flagler] said to Frank, "Frank, who is that handsome young doctor taking care of this old woman who broke her hip?" And Frank looked at the picture and said, "Why, Phil, that's me!" He had painted himself as the doctor

Photo: Frank Netter with Dr. Frederick Kaplan and his patient, Carol Orzel,
University of Pennsylvania Department of Orthopaedics centennial, 1989,
courtesy of Dr. Frederick Kaplan.

taking care of the old woman. Of course, Phil recognized him;
you could tell it was Frank.[12]

Saturday evening they had cocktails at the Bellevue Hotel and
then went on to a banquet at the Philadelphia Museum of Art. The
orthopaedics department had hired the space, and tables were set
up around the statues. Fred's parents came, and Frank met them.
Gina Dingle and Phil Flagler came, and the orthopaedists all came.
Frank spoke again at that dinner. "Dr. Netter was actually a pretty
shy person," Gina recalled. "He never stood up and thumped his
chest. Mostly he listened to all sorts of accolades. People would rise
and praise him."[13]

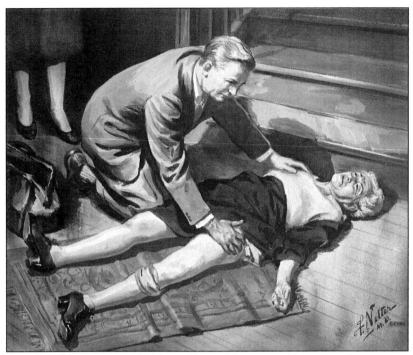

"Disorders of the Hip," Frank H. Netter, Clinical Symposia volume 5, number 2, 1953, cover, courtesy of Elsevier.

The following week Fred Kaplan was off to Houston to work with a group of about 15 other distinguished physicians on establishing health criteria for the astronauts. Frank sent Fred a note on May 15, thanking him and Carl Brighton for their hospitality at the centennial celebration. Fred retuned from the Johnson Space Center on Friday, and then on May 21, Sunday, wrote a long handwritten letter to Frank describing how he had gone into the space shuttle, sat in the commander's seat, gone through the air locks and the payload bay, and walked through a mock-up of the space station, which was still in the planning stages.[14] It was a letter from one friend to another.

ꙮꙮ

The longest tenure at Ciba-Geigy of any vice president of public relations was that of Dr. Arthur Emmett. He had been at Ciba-Geigy in Switzerland, and he came to Summit in 1989 after Roy Ellis retired.[15] The Netter publications were a part of his responsibility in which he took great pride. He had done his medical training in Australia and had known Frank Netter's pictures since his student days. Everybody in medicine in Australia, as in America, knew Frank's work. Dr. Emmett explained:

> He was probably the best-connected man in medicine because he had to meet with so many specialists in so many areas, when he was doing his paintings for different maladies or different illnesses. He met some of the best cardiologists, some of the best gastroenterologists in America. They all respected him and loved him so much.
>
> He was quite old by the time I met him. His paintings were starting to get a little bit shaky. He was clearly a man of great talent, not only with his painting but [also] a great golfer. He was *the* person in medical art. Just nobody could touch him. Other people tried, but nobody could touch him. We had other people backing up Frank, but nothing compared to Frank. Even in his latter years when his brush was not as steady, it was still fantastic.[16]

Phil Flagler, as director of medical education, reported to Dr. Emmett. Over the years Phil negotiated at least four contracts with Frank. The first one ran for a term of five years, but for the later ones, the term got down to two years. Frank was always fighting with management to write him a fair contract, which often meant trying to get enough money.

The contract now on the table was to run for the rest of Frank's working life, and the contract negotiation had been particularly hard. Frank was older and not as productive as he once had been, remembered Dr. Emmett. Some members of the board at Ciba-Geigy were pushing not to renew, certainly not at that price. Phil negotiated the contract for Ciba, and he wanted to make sure they finished the *Ciba Collection* work. Moreover, because it was a considerable amount of money, Arthur had to run it by Doug Watson and get his approval.

Doug Watson was not a physician, but he was president of the Pharmaceuticals Division of Ciba-Geigy. He had previously been at Ciba-Geigy headquarters in Basel before coming to Summit. Mr. Watson, while considerably younger than Frank, certainly recognized Frank's unique talent, the extraordinary partnership Frank had with Ciba-Geigy, and the value the Netter art collection brought to the company;[17] and he wanted to retain that relationship. Frank Netter had the longest association with Ciba of anyone.

Frank went out to the Ciba-Geigy campus in Summit, and the officers of the company entertained him in the executive dining room. So dapper as a young man, Frank came now with a heavily stained necktie, Arthur Emmett remembered.[18] Then Frank and Phil sat down with Doug Watson in Watson's office.

Phil recalled:

> Doug was not buying what Frank wanted. Doug Watson was a nifty Scotsman, very contemporary guy, and at one point when Frank said he wanted something, Doug said, "No way, José." Frank did not like that at all. He felt that this young whippersnapper was being fresh with him. Frank did not do anything except get a scowl on his face, but his body language said it all, and I heard about it afterward.[19]

Frank received a letter in late March from Mike DeBakey congratulating him on *Atlas of Human Anatomy*, thanking him for an inscribed copy, and asking Frank to send an autographed photo of himself.[20] Dr. DeBakey further mentioned their project on peripheral vascular disease that that they had begun over two years prior[21] but that had been delayed for over a year,[22] and, unbeknownst to him, was in peril of cancellation because of the failed contract negotiations. When Frank replied to his friend in a letter on April 10,

1990, sending the photo and asking for one of his friend in return, he explained that the peripheral vascular disease project was in jeopardy because of "a silly disagreement with the Ciba Company, who apparently do not appreciate what I have contributed to their recognition in the medical profession in my 52 years of association with them."[23] In addition, he asked Mike to write to Ciba telling them how important it was to continue the work.

Frank was so upset about what had happened at the meeting with Doug Watson that he called Freddie and told him about it. Fred Kaplan remembered:

> He was very, very upset. He had gone up and he had spo-ken to the president at Ciba, but he was terribly insulted. He walked in and told them how much he wanted, and whoever it was at Ciba said, "No way, José." Dr. Netter mentioned that expression about ten times, maybe more. I do not know if he was more upset that they would not agree to his numbers or whether he was more upset with the way they were treating him, that they would use that expression. He said, "You know I am not just some person off the street, Freddie. Yet that's the way they are treating me." He was so upset, in fact, that I was upset hearing him be so upset.
>
> I do not remember the details, but I remember talking to Phil or to Gina or to both about this, that I wanted to talk to the president [of Ciba]. I called Phil after talking to Dr. Netter, after seeing how upset he was, and Phil suggested I call [Doug Watson] or write him a letter.[24]

Fred wrote an eloquent three-page letter to Doug Watson on April 18, 1990. He outlined his relationship with Frank, and said:

> By establishing, fostering, and cultivating an association with Dr. Netter, the Ciba Corporation has made a noble and inspir-ing contribution that is consonant with the very best tradi-tions of medical education in this century. The distinguished

sponsorship of such an extraordinary genius and talent as Dr. Netter had served your company and the public it serves exceptionally well. The dissemination of his works with his name and your logo are clearly the highest forms of advertising in the pharmaceutical industry. . . .

Even in his vespertinal years, there is only one Frank Netter. Your association with him garners far more attention and is far more valuable than simply the sum of the pictures you have been wise enough to commission.

Ciba-Geigy's fortuitous and nearly life-long association with this unique and brilliant man, this physician–artist of legendary proportions, is, I understand, under enormous strain. . . .

I appeal to you as a leader and a man of vision to continue that association with Dr. Netter . . . it would be tragic and unthinkable to prohibit him from completing the atlases. . . .[25]

Fred sent a copy of the letter to Phil Flagler and one to Frank. He also sent Frank a birthday card for his eighty-fourth birthday.

Dr. DeBakey wrote to Doug Watson as well. In a letter dated April 23, he reiterated how he had been working with Frank since 1942 when they were in the army, how they had done the *Clinical Symposia* issue "Surgery of the Aorta,"[26] and they had started a project on peripheral vascular disease for the forthcoming Part III of *Musculoskeletal System*. He said it was important to complete the project and how eager he was to work on it with Frank. He closed by commending Ciba's contribution to anatomy in supporting publication of *Atlas of Human Anatomy*.[27] Surely that letter got the attention of the executives, because Dr. Emmett remembered that Dr. DeBakey was a strong supporter of Frank's during those contract negotiations.[28]

Frank wrote to Fred on April 25, thanking him for helping Nancy Netter, Jim's daughter, in her application to medical school, as Fred was then chairman of the medical school admissions committee at the University of Pennsylvania. He also thanked Fred for the birthday card and for writing to Doug Watson. He was planning to meet with Phil Flagler the following week, he said, to try to work things out.[29]

In a cordial two-page letter dated April 30, 1990, Doug Watson wrote to Fred Kaplan, thanking him for his concern, and assuring him that he too wanted to come to an agreement. He characterized the disagreement as a family squabble, with two sides to the story. He said that it was Frank who had come to them in midcontract asking for an increase in royalties, but he confirmed that Phil was going to Palm Beach to try to work out an agreement.[30]

"Eventually we got things worked around," said Phil, "so the contract got signed, but it was tense. It went back and forth a number of times before that contract was signed, and Richard was the go-between who could talk sense into both sides."[31] On June 28, Phil wrote a letter to Fred Kaplan thanking him for intervening and telling him that Dr. Netter and Ciba-Geigy were going to get back together and proceed with the *Musculoskeletal System*, Part III.

ଚ୧୦ଚ◊୦ଚ

There was no doubt that Frank was getting on in years. He might have had some concern that because of his health he might not be able to finish *The Ciba Collection*. The aneurysm caused him a lot of discomfort, both physically and psychologically. But more than that, he must have seen that his brushwork was not as it once had been. And for first time in four and a half decades, not since his work during World War II for the Surgeon General, Frank tried to increase his output by using other artists to do some of the painting. He had done a detailed outline and contacted the specialists who collaborated on the topics, and there were but a few more pictures to complete in *Musculoskeletal System*, Part III, the final book in the series.

To help him finish the volume, he asked David Mascaro, the professor in the medical illustration department at the Medical College of Georgia whose work Frank knew from when David and

Bill Stenstrom had come and interviewed by him. David painted 27 pictures[32] from Frank's sketches, completing, among others, the pictures of fracture healing and the complications of fracture, which Drs. Fred Kaplan and Carl Brighton, respectively, worked on with Frank, as well as those on soft-tissue injury and on amputation that Frank had sketched in consultation with Jim Heckman. The signature on the art Frank and David did in that way was "F. Netter, MD with D. Mascaro." It consisted of the "F. Netter, MD" logo with David's name in smaller block letters underneath. David also recommended a former student, Craig Luce, to do some of the painting.[33]

Craig lived in Charlottesville, Virginia, and when Frank called him, he went right down to Palm Beach to see the sketches Frank wanted painted. In the studio he saw some of Frank's finished pictures lined up along the wall, and on the taboret he saw the stack of paint palettes and the Winsor & Newton sable hair brushes— much larger and much more expensive than any Craig used, but of such fine quality that they could point down from the ferrule to the tip to do the delicate work yet handle the sweeping wash work as well. "It was a beautiful studio," Craig remembered. "After our initial meeting I had hoped that we could set up something like a Netter's Studio so that he could direct the work and focus on what he wanted to do, but Ciba-Geigy was not going to do it for him."[34]

Craig worked on ten pictures for Frank, including some Frank laid out with Dr. Fred Corley on the wrist and forearm, including the one on Bier block anesthesia for which Frank had been so inquisitive about the reading on the blood pressure cuff.[35] Craig did the painting in Charlottesville and every few weeks took the pictures to Palm Beach for Frank to review and pick up a new set of sketches to paint.[36] "When Dr. Netter sat down to look at my paintings," Craig recalled, "he was always very concentrated and very critical to make sure that it did what he wanted it to do. I always had something to touch up, so whenever I went down to Palm Beach I made sure that I had another night in the hotel to be able to paint more on it and bring it back the next morning."[37]

Similarly, the signature on the art they did was, "F. Netter, MD with C.A. Luce."

☙❦❧

In the early summer of 1990, Frank was honored at an international conference of medical communicators in the Netherlands. Vera again declined to go with him because of her poor health. The opening reception was at the Rijksmuseum amid works of art by the great Flemish and Dutch painters. Patrick McDonnell, a young Canadian medical illustrator who used computer graphics to make his pictures, recounted that he saw Frank standing under the Rembrandt painting *The Anatomy Lesson of Dr. Jan Deijman* and introduced himself. During the course of the ensuing conversation, Patrick invited Frank to come see the newest in high-definition computer graphics. Frank was interested to see that, and off they went in the car, Frank sitting next to Patrick, telling him he was doing just fine navigating the narrow streets alongside the canals, to the place where Patrick had his computer graphics station.

Patrick showed off his computer and his portfolio of pictures, which Frank found new and interesting. "You copied my picture!"[38] Patrick remembered Frank saying, sort of teasing, when he saw one of the pictures on the computer. But Patrick had not yet seen Frank's picture, although his picture is uncannily similar to Frank's picture of the anterior and posterior chambers of the eye that he had made for the *Anatomy* atlas.[39]

When Frank returned home from the Netherlands, he was a basket case, Vera said.[40] That trip really wore him out. A souvenir he acquired on the trip was a reproduction of Rembrandt's *Hundred Guilder Print*, which he hung in his studio. Patrick subsequently visited Frank in Palm Beach. Frank took him to lunch at The Breakers, and afterward arranged for Patrick to go to Ciba headquarters in Summit and meet with Phil Flagler. "He was very approachable," Patrick remembered about Frank, "even after having received so much recognition. He was doing what he loved."[41]

ๆ๏๏๏๏๏

In July of that same year Frank went to Saskatchewan, Canada, for a meeting of the American Association of Clinical Anatomists. Art Dalley had nominated him for their highest honor: he was to be made an honorary member.[42] Gina went with him on that trip, meeting Frank in Toronto to fly from there to the meeting in Saskatoon. They got on the plane and the plane had to turn around and go back to Toronto, but they checked into the hotel and continued on to Saskatchewan the next day.[43] It was another grueling trip, but Frank wanted to go because it was a big event in his honor. It was as if he was trying to cram every bit of life and every bit of work into his last years. A photograph of Frank taken with Dr. Stephen Carmichael, who had so glowingly reviewed *Atlas of Human Anatomy*, showed that Frank's plaid suit was rumpled and his necktie crooked. He was smiling and appeared to be happy but extremely tired.

Photo: Frank Netter with Stephen Carmichael in Saskatoon at American Association of Clinical Anatomists meeting, July 1990, courtesy of David L. Dawson.

CHAPTER 30

DRAWING CONCLUSIONS

THE TEXAS MEDICAL CENTER is a vast complex of hospitals, schools for the health professions, and related institutions. One of the largest hospitals is the Methodist Hospital, where Michael DeBakey pioneered the cardiovascular surgery service. In September 1990 Francine walked through the cavernous hospital lobby, past a larger-than-life bronze statue of Dr. DeBakey, past a collection of exquisite porcelains, and took the elevator up to her father's room.

Frank had told her about the aneurysm and that Mike DeBakey was going to operate, and since Vera was not up to it Francine had flown out from New York that morning to be by his side for the surgery the next day. She found her father up and walking around in a room furnished more like one in an elegant hotel than in a hospital. They sat together and talked only briefly about the flight and how beautiful the world looks from above the clouds, and about Methodist Hospital and how donations from Texas oil billionaires made it possible. As she left to go to her hotel, she promised to be back in the morning before they took him to the operating room.

At 6:30 the following morning, Francine found him lying on a gurney in the hall outside his hospital room. As she walked toward him, he turned his head toward the sound of her footfalls and smiled when he saw his daughter. "You know what hospitals are like," he said to her. "You have been in hospitals." Down the hall came Dr. DeBakey, tall and thin, wearing green scrubs and cap. Frank introduced his friend to his daughter, and then Dr. DeBakey left to go scrub and an attendant wheeled Frank away.

The waiting room outside a cardiovascular intensive care unit (ICU) can be uncomfortable during the interminable wait for news of a loved one in surgery. Two, three, more hours Francine waited before Dr. DeBakey came out to talk to her after the surgery. There was more disease than they had anticipated, he said. He had a kindly demeanor and led her into the ICU to see her father. She wanted to stay there and hold his hand, but the staff members gave her only five minutes with him. Come back in two hours, they said. She left, called home with an update, wandered around the unfamiliar city and returned to the ICU in precisely two hours.

But before she saw her father again, Dr. DeBakey spoke to her. Frank had taken a bad turn, he said. He put his two index fingers together, pointing one fingertip into the other. Then he slid one finger to the side of the other. The graft had separated, he said. They had had to take him back in to repair it, and he was now recovering. Francine then went in to see him. Frank was on the respirator, not conscious of her presence. She held his hand for the few minutes she was permitted to be with him.

Francine stayed in Houston for four more days, wandering around the city in between 15-minute visits with Frank every two hours. In the ICU, she saw the progress of patients who had come in after Frank, while Frank lingered on the respirator, barely aware of his surroundings. Every day he seemed weaker than the day before. When she could no longer stay away from her obligations at home, Francine got on a plane to New York. At the same time in Philadelphia, Jim got on a plane to Houston and came to take a turn at the bedside. They took turns like that, traveling back and forth to Texas to be with their father, watching him as his mind withdrew into its own world—"ICU psychosis"—turning off the constancy of the surroundings. It was six weeks or more before he was finally weaned from the respirator, finally moved out of the intensive care unit to a private room and finally lucid, but he was terribly weak. Confined to bed, with legs that he could barely move of his own accord, he seemed to grow smaller and smaller.

Vera made at least one trip with her son, John, to Texas to see Frank, and that seemed to cheer him. She walked slowly and cautiously with her artificial hip, not trusting her eyesight, relying on her son to help her, although he himself was alarmingly thin and undernourished. The series of cancer operations he had undergone had removed much of the soft tissue in his neck and mouth, and radiation had damaged the underlying bone, causing him to have had great difficulty eating.

Phil Flagler too made the trip to see Frank in Houston. "It was a very sad time," he recalled. "Mike DeBakey was very good to him and to me. He sent a car to the airport to pick me up, and greeted me at the hospital. Cornelia was at the hospital when I was there. [Frank] was sitting up and chatting, but obviously not doing terribly well."[1] Frank had mustered all his strength to put up a good front for the visit. He kept his illness private.[2]

⊙ʡ⊙ʡ⊙ʡ⊙

Remarkably, Part II of volume 8 of *Musculoskeletal System*[3] was published in 1990, just a year after *Atlas of Human Anatomy* came out. There was very little double duty on the part of the editorial staff at Ciba. Gina managed the editorial functions for the *Musculoskeletal System*, Part II, volume and did not work on the atlas, although Sally Chichester and Jeffie Lemons did work on both books.

Chappie Conrad took time in November to write Frank a letter congratulating him on the volume. Chappie, apparently unaware of Frank's hospitalization, sent best wishes that both Frank and Vera remained in good health.[4] In January, Ed Crelin wrote a letter to Frank saying that he had just received a copy of Part II of *Musculoskeletal System* from Ciba and how beautiful it was. Although Dr. Crelin had contributed to Part I and not Part II, he wrote that in an indirect way his work was included, because one of his former students at Yale, John Ogden, was a contributor. Dr. Ogden had worked on the plate on Osgood-Schlatter lesions.[5]

Ciba-Geigy hosted a party for the contributors to *Musculoskeletal System*, Part II, as it had done for all the previous volumes. The party was in Philadelphia because there was a convention there at that time and most of the authors were already there, and they set aside the evening. Frank was in the hospital in Texas and unable to attend. "We talked to Dr. Netter from his hospital room in Houston," Gina remembered. "He gave his best wishes to everybody."[6]

⊙⁊☉☉⁊☉⊙

Frank's hospitalization was difficult for his children. Jim lived in Philadelphia, Cornelia and Francine, in New York, and Jonathan, in Germany. They wanted to be there for their father, yet he was far away in Texas. The incision wound in his abdomen did not want to heal and his digestion was poor, byproducts of the sacrifice of arterial branches during surgery. He crept toward recovery, inch by inch, sometimes by millimeters, two baby steps forward and one backward.

In May 1991, Frank seemed to be gaining some strength and wanted to go home. Cornelia arranged for an air ambulance for the transfer to New York. The specially equipped Learjet accepted the patient on a stretcher through a rear hatch and, in addition to the flight crew, a pilot and copilot, carried Cornelia and a doctor from the Texas Medical Center, crouching in their seats beside the stretcher. As the distance from Houston to New York was beyond range of the small jet, equipped as it was, the jet landed in Memphis to refuel and took off again for Teterboro Airport in northern New Jersey. From there a ground ambulance took Frank onto the interstate highway, cars and trucks assaulting the senses with noise and fumes, through heavy traffic at the toll booths, across the George Washington Bridge and down the Harlem River Drive toward The Mount Sinai Hospital. It was an exhausting trip for anyone, much less Frank in his weakened state. But Frank was home.

⊙⁊☉☉⁊☉⊙

At Mount Sinai, Frank's doctor was Dr. Arthur Weisenseel, who was a colleague of Arthur Soval, whom Frank knew from his student days. Dr. Weisenseel remembered:

> When he came to Mount Sinai he had multiple afflictions. He was a handsome man, and he very much resembled the pastor at a Catholic parish in Nyack, New York, and whose name also happened to be Netter. So I asked Frank where his family came from, and he told me Alsace. And I asked the priest at St. Ann's Parish where his family came from, and he also told me Alsace. So somehow, they had a common ancestry.[7]

One was Jewish, the other Roman Catholic. Somewhere along the line, one branch converted to Catholicism.

Dr. Weisenseel began to treat Frank and wanted to get him strong enough to leave the hospital environment. Cornelia began to talk of his getting an apartment. He would be wheelchair-bound, but it would allow him to get back to his life and pictures. If he could make pictures, she thought, that would give him a reason for living. She brought some pastels and a sketch pad to the hospital, and she even had a drawing board brought to his hospital room. But the pastels went unused and the drawing board sat folded in the corner of Frank's small private hospital room, with its institutional furniture—a far cry from the fancy furnishings at Methodist Hospital.

Professional companions stayed with Frank day and night—kind, gentle women who helped him and kept him company. Family, friends, and colleagues came to visit him at Mount Sinai. Richard Netter came. Gina Dingle visited him a couple of times.[8] Peter Som came to see him and ran into Francine briefly in Frank's room when she was visiting.[9]

Vera, escorted by her sister-in-law, Gladys Burrows, came once to New York to see Frank at Mount Sinai. They were in the city maybe four or five days and stayed in the luxury of the Sherry-Netherland hotel on Fifth Avenue overlooking Central Park. At the hospital, Vera walked to Frank's bedside and spoke so lovingly, softly calling to him, "My darling." She had her hair done and her makeup and wore a print shirtwaist dress with a white wool blazer. But the blazer was absolutely filthy, and she refused Gladys's offer to send it out to the cleaners. It is difficult to say whether the problem was that she could not see or instead could not comprehend, because both her eyesight and cognitive abilities were failing.

James Carlson was not quite 7 years old that summer when he went to see his grandfather at Mount Sinai. Francine held her son's hand and led him through the hospital corridor to Frank's room. The small child unabashedly walked right up to Frank's bedside, stepped up on the footstool by the bed, and gently patted Frank on the hand. "Hello, Grandpa," he said. Frank looked into the innocent green eyes of this buoyant grandchild he barely knew.

At that time, the latest toy craze for young children was a set of four plastic figures called the Teenage Mutant Ninja Turtles. Each of the four cartoon-like characters bore the name of one of the grand masters of the Italian Renaissance, although great art was in no way part of the lore of these toys or of their appeal to children.

James was completely beguiled by the Teenage Mutant Ninja Turtles. He never went anywhere without at least one of the toy figures, and they were his favorite topic of conversation. On each visit to the hospital, he would bring one to show Frank and would tell the latest story of Ninja Turtle adventures. With crayons and paper, he would sit in the hospital room and occupy himself making pictures of them, his enthusiasm never waning. "What are their names?" Frank asked innocently. "Raphael," said James. "Leonardo." Frank looked squarely at his grandson. "Michelangelo." Frank opened his eyes wide. "And Donatello." Frank's jaw dropped open. After that introduction, Frank and James became fast friends. Frank took up his pastels, the ones that Cornelia had brought, and James took up his crayons, and throughout the summer months they spent their visits together drawing pictures of the Ninja Turtles and talking about the grand masters. And Annie, Frank's caregiver, hung the pictures on the wall in his hospital room.

He seemed to improve after that—a baby step forward—before there was a new setback: sepsis. During her next visit, Francine found Cornelia sitting in the hospital cafeteria, her eyes glazed over, unseeing, focused inward. Together, the sisters visited Frank in the ICU. He had been in the hospital first in Texas and now in

New York for a total of 11 months. After their visit, as they rode down in the elevator, people who knew him, colleagues, and even Lina Popper, widow of Hans Popper, offered condolences.

"I visited Daddy again on September 16," remembered Francine. "He seemed glad to see me and asked about James. I stayed with him for a time and held his hand. 'This, too, shall pass,' he told me. He was so serene. I kissed him good night and went home to my children."[10]

Frank Henry Netter died in the ICU at The Mount Sinai Hospital on September 17, 1991. Cornelia was by his side.

ᘓᘏᘓᘏᘓᘏᘓ

In the casket at the Frank E. Campbell funeral home in New York was a shell of the man, small and shriveled. Jonathan came from Germany. John Stetson came from Florida and took photos of Frank in the coffin to show his mother, who did not come. With Frank's passing, Richard Netter assumed the role of family patriarch. At the funeral he spoke of Jacob Mordecai Netter's journey around the world, about how Charles and Abraham Netter had come to New York and married two sisters and how his grandparents and Frank's parents had a stationery store and raised six children—three lawyers, two doctors, and an accountant. He thanked Jacob Mordecai Netter for his family and particularly for Frank Henry Netter.

When his children spoke, they talked about what they most remembered of their father, about how Frank had taught them to strive for excellence, about how they went to the studio as children, about Frank's art and his integrity. Caroline Carlson played a song on a piano, which was terribly out of tune. Phil Flagler spoke, as Richard had asked him to do. "I felt very inadequate doing that," Phil said later, "but I was flattered to be asked."[11] Fred Kaplan spoke eloquently of his experiences working with his dear friend. Afterward, the body was cremated and the ashes sent to Florida.

The following week, on September 28, the family gathered in Florida for a memorial service at the Episcopal Church of Bethesda-by-the-Sea, where as a child Francine had sung in the choir. Frank's ashes were subsequently interred at the nondenominational Royal Poinciana Chapel in the newly built columbarium in a garden overlooking Lake Worth.

Epilogue

W HEN FRANK'S CHILDREN RETURNED to Florida for his memorial service there, they found the studio untouched since the day their father had left for Texas one year before. The smell of his cigars still permeated the room. His golf trophies sat on his library bookshelf beside the caduceus from New York University, together with family photos and one of Max Som. Amid his sable brushes in the drawer of his taboret was a small photo of Francine as a young child standing at the front portico of Folly Farm.

Vera continued to live in The Breakers Row apartment, spending most of her time in a chair by the television and suffering from a bout with shingles that nearly killed her with pain. At her request, John came to stay with her in the apartment. He was frail, and his face was terribly disfigured from successive cancer operations. He slept on one of the chesterfield sofas in the living room, so that the flamingo-colored Ultrasuede upholstery became stained and shabby. The Aubusson rug on the floor, neglected and torn, waited for Vera to trip on it. The elderly cook was incapable of cleaning, and the kitchen grew ever more encrusted with grease.

Vera Netter died in 1992 at the age of 92. A memorial service for her was at the Episcopal Church of Bethesda-by-the-Sea and her ashes were interred with Frank's in Palm Beach. Frankie Netter died in 1993 at the Lexington Center residence for the developmentally disabled in Gloversville, New York. His ashes were interred with Mary's in Oyster Bay. John Stetson died from cancer in 1995. His ashes were interred in Palm Beach near his mother's. Richard Netter died in New York in 2009 at the age of 90.

The *Life of a Doctor* paintings, which during his lifetime Frank had given to his alma mater, New York University Medical College, were transferred to that institution, where they are periodically exhibited.[1] The sketch of the Spinners, which Frank was never able to authenticate as a Velázquez study, went to auction along with the furnishings of The Breakers Row apartment.

Musculoskeletal System, Part III,[2] the final tome in *The Ciba Collection*, was published posthumously in 1993. It contained 201 plates, 37 of which were attributed jointly to Frank Netter and either David Mascaro or Craig Luce. For seven of the illustrations, John Craig developed the concept and created detailed sketches and Dave Mascaro did the painting. Two of Frank's unfinished sketches are in the forepart of the book.

Ciba-Geigy merged with Sandoz in 1996 to become Novartis. Novartis continues to own the portfolio of illustrations Frank made for Ciba and Ciba-Geigy, but it sold the publication rights, which are now owned by Elsevier. *The Ciba Collection of Medical Illustrations* was renamed *The Netter Collection of Medical Illustrations*, now in a second edition. Publication of *Clinical Symposia* ended in 1998. *Atlas of Human Anatomy* is in its seventh edition.[3] Drs. John Craig and Carlos Machado, as medical illustrators, provide updates of clinical advancements for the Netter publications, although neither had ever worked with Frank Netter on any illustrations or publications.

Phil Flagler and Gina Dingle are retired.

Carol Orzel visited the University of Pennsylvania several times to talk to the medical school class about living with a terrible genetic disease. She brought her copy of *Musculoskeletal System*, Part I, and told the students, "My picture is in every medical school library in the world. I knew Dr. Netter, and Dr. Netter painted my picture."[4] In 2006, Dr. Frederick Kaplan and his research associates at the University of Pennsylvania reported in *Nature Genetics*[5] that they had pinpointed the gene that causes the excessive bone growth of FOP, and in 2011 in *Nature*[6] reported finding a potential drug treatment for the disease.

Cornelia Netter died in New York in 2011. James Netter lives in Pennsylvania with his wife, Carol. His oldest daughter, Nancy, is a physician in South Carolina. Francine Netter lives with her husband, Ralph Roberson, in North Carolina. Jonathan Netter lives in Florida and Germany with his wife, Christina.

Caroline Carlson recovered fully from her hip click to become an intercollegiate athlete and run marathons. James Carlson no longer draws pictures of Teenage Mutant Ninja Turtles.

In 2013, the Frank H. Netter MD School of Medicine at Quinnipiac University welcomed its first class of medical students.

Medical Pictures and Publications

THE ITEMS HERE DO not include *Clinical Symposia* issues, which are listed in Appendix II.

Medical Education Booklets
Armour Atlas of Hematology, softcover, illustrated by Frank H. Netter, Armour Laboratories, Armour and Co., 1939, Chicago

The Pituitary Gland, hardcover, illustrated by Frank H. Netter, Armour Laboratories, Armour and Co., 1940, Chicago

The Thyroid Gland and Clinical Application of Medicinal Thyroid, hardcover, illustrated by Frank H. Netter, Armour Laboratories, Armour and Co., 1943, Chicago

Function and Malfunction of the Biliary System, softcover, illustrated by Frank H. Netter, Armour Laboratories, Armour and Co., 1946, Chicago

Walton, J.H., *Control of Pain with Saddle Block and Higher Anesthesia* (52-page monograph), Ciba, Summit, New Jersey, 1948

Novocain (44-page monograph), Winthrop Chemical Company, New York, 1936

Portfolios, Ciba Pharmaceuticals, Summit, New Jersey, 1940–1947
Endocrine Physiology in the Female
Major Pathology of the Heart and Aorta
Major Pathology of the Testicle and Prostate
Major Pathology of the Lungs

Major Pathology of the Stomach
War Injuries of the Chest (folder of color plates), 1943
Major Pathology of the Esophagus
Major Pathology of the Nose and Accessory Sinuses
Major Pathology of the Duodenum
War Injuries of the Abdomen
War Injuries of the Extremities (black-and-white bound pamphlet),
     1945
Major Pathology of the Small Intestine
Major Pathology of the Large Intestine, Series I and Series II
Major Anatomy and Pathology of the Breast, Series I and
     Series II

Portraits of Pioneers in Endocrinology, Armour Laboratories, Chicago, 1949

Dr. Oscar Riddle at Cold Spring Harbor, isolated prolactin,
     contributed to understanding of quantitative sexuality
     in submammalian animals and endocrine constitutional
     factors
Dr. Robert James Graves, after whom Graves' disease was named,
     advocate of "feed a fever"
Dr. Frederic Fenger, a pioneering researcher in enzymes, the
     thyroid, and the pituitary
Dr. John Jacob Abel, first professor of pharmacology at Johns
     Hopkins School of Medicine, gave epinephrine its name and
     was the first to isolate crystalline insulin
Dr. David Marine, who demonstrated the relation of iodine to the
     structure of the thyroid gland
Dr. Thomas Addison, after whom Addison's disease was named,
     made extensive studies of pernicious anemia
Dr. Herbert M. Evans, who discovered and charted human
     chromosomes, detected a sign of vitamin A deficiency and
     discovered vitamin E, and conducted extensive research on
     the hormones of the anterior pituitary, including purification
     of the growth hormone

Dr. George H. Whipple, who shared the 1934 Nobel Prize in
medicine (with Drs. George Richards Minot and William
Parry Murphy) for his part in the discovery that a diet of
liver is effective in blood regeneration

Dr. George R. Minot, who shared the 1934 Nobel prize in
medicine (with Drs. William Parry Murphy and George
H. Whipple) for his part in the discovery with Dr. Murphy
that a diet containing liver is effective in treating pernicious
anemia, up until then fatal

Dr. Edward C. Kendall, a biochemist who first isolated thyroxin
from the thyroid gland, also isolated glutathione and
hormones from the adrenal cortex, determined their
chemical structures and partial synthesis, and shed light on
their relation to metabolism

Dr. Edwin Joseph Cohen, a physical chemist who investigated the
specificity of proteins that led to liver extract for pernicious
anemia and fractionation of the blood to yield serum
albumins, gamma globulins, and other plasma proteins

Sir Frederick Grant Banting, recipient of the 1923 Nobel Prize in
Physiology or Medicine, shared with Charles H. Best, for the
isolation of insulin

Dr. Harvey W. Cushing, noted surgeon who published "The
Pituitary Gland and its Disorders"

Dr. Edward A. Doisy, who received the 1943 Nobel Prize in
Physiology or Medicine and extracted and isolated estrone,
estriol and estradiol, along with synthetic substitutes for
vitamin K

Sir Henry Hallett Dale, who discovered the oxytocic action
of pituitary extracts and identified acetylcholine as a
constituent of certain ergot extracts; together with Otto
Loewi, he won the Nobel Prize for 1936 for discoveries
relating to chemical transmission of nerve impulses

Dr. William B. Castle, who discovered gastric intrinsic factor, the
absence of which is the proximal cause of pernicious anemia,
and identified vitamin B_{12}

Life of a Doctor, **Armour Laboratories, Chicago, 1948**
Osteology Cram
Anatomy Lab
Fourth-Year Obstetrics
Ambulance Call
Catastrophe
Emergency Ward
Clinic
Pediatric Ward—Convalescent
Gyn Examining Room
Country Night Call
Reconversion
Class Reunion

Pfizer Series of Anatomical and Pathological Transparencies, Chas. Pfizer Antibiotic Division, Pfizer & Co., Brooklyn, New York, 1953–1957
No. 1: *Chronic Pulmonary Tuberculosis*
No. 2: *Segmental Anatomy of the Lung*
No. 3: *Clinical Anatomy of the Abdomen and Inguinal Region*
No. 4: *The Pregnant Uterus*
No. 5: *The Adrenal Glands and Kidneys*
No. 6: *The Head and Neck*

The **Ciba Collection of Medical Illustrations** and *Atlas of Human Anatomy,* **Ciba Pharmaceuticals, Summit, New Jersey**
Netter, Frank H., *Ciba Collection of Medical Illustrations: A Compilation of Pathological and Anatomical Paintings,* Ciba, Summit, New Jersey, 1948
———, *Ciba Collection of Medical Illustrations,* volume 1, *Nervous System,* Ciba, Summit, New Jersey, 1953
———, *Ciba Collection of Medical Illustrations,* volume 2, *Reproductive System,* Ciba, Summit, New Jersey, 1954
———, *Ciba Collection of Medical Illustrations,* volume 3, *Digestive System Part III,* Ciba, Summit, New Jersey, 1957

————, *Ciba Collection of Medical Illustrations*, volume 3, *Digestive System Part I*, Ciba, Summit, New Jersey, 1959

————, *Ciba Collection of Medical Illustrations*, volume 3, *Digestive System Part II*, Ciba, Summit, New Jersey, 1962.

————, *Ciba Collection of Medical Illustrations*, volume 4, *Endocrine System*, Ciba, Summit, New Jersey, 1965

————, *Ciba Collection of Medical Illustrations*, volume 5, *Heart*, Ciba, Summit, New Jersey, 1969

————, *Ciba Collection of Medical Illustrations*, volume 6, *Kidney*, Ciba, Summit, New Jersey, 1973

————, *Ciba Collection of Medical Illustrations*, volume 7, *Respiratory System*, Ciba, Summit, New Jersey, 1979

————, *Ciba Collection of Medical Illustrations*, volume 1, *Nervous System Part I*, 2nd edition, Ciba, Summit, New Jersey, 1983

————, *Ciba Collection of Medical Illustrations*, volume 1, *Nervous System Part II*, 2nd edition, Ciba, Summit, New Jersey, 1986

————, *Ciba Collection of Medical Illustrations*, volume 8, *Musculoskeletal System Part I*, Ciba-Geigy, Summit, New Jersey, 1987

————, *Atlas of Human Anatomy*, Ciba-Geigy, Summit, New Jersey, 1989

————, *Ciba Collection of Medical Illustrations*, volume 8, *Musculoskeletal System Part II*, Ciba-Geigy, Summit, New Jersey, 1990

————, *Ciba Collection of Medical Illustrations*, volume 8, *Musculoskeletal System Part III*, Ciba-Geigy, Summit, New Jersey, 1993

Clinical Symposia

"Diagnosing Uterine Cancer by Vaginal Smear," *Clin. Symp.* vol. 1, no. 1, 1948

"The Hormonal Control of Menstruation," *Clin. Symp.* vol. 1, no. 1, 1948

"Endocrinologic Aspects of Menopause," *Clin. Symp.* vol. 1, no. 1, 1948

"Venus Catheterization of the Heart," *Clin. Symp.* vol. 1, no. 1, 1948

"How Effective Is Influenza Vaccine?" *Clin. Symp.* vol. 1, no. 1, 1948

Netter FH, "Anatomical Plates on the Nervous System," *Clin. Symp.* vol. 1, no. 1, 1948

"Infectious Hepatitis," *Clin. Symp.* vol. 1, no. 2, 1948

"Plantar Warts," *Clin. Symp.* vol. 1, no. 2, 1948

"Office Examination of Semen," *Clin. Symp.* vol. 1, no. 2, 1948

"The Male Climacteric," *Clin. Symp.* vol. 1, no. 2, 1948

Netter FH, "Anatomical Plates on the Nervous System," *Clin. Symp.* vol. 1, no. 2, 1948

"Peripheral Vascular Disease," *Clin. Symp.* vol. 1, no. 3, 1949

"Amebiasis," *Clin. Symp.* vol. 1, no. 3, 1949

"Ringworm of the Scalp," *Clin. Symp.* vol. 1, no. 3, 1949

Netter FH, "A New Series of Anatomical Plates on the Nervous System—the Basal Ganglia," *Clin. Symp.* vol. 1, no. 3, 1949

"The Vaginal Smear," *Clin. Symp.* vol. 1, no. 4, 1949

"Functional Uterine Bleeding," *Clin. Symp.* vol. 1, no. 5, 1949

"Prefrontal Lobotomy," *Clin. Symp.* vol. 1, no. 5, 1949

"A New Frog Test for Pregnancy," *Clin. Symp.* vol. 1, no. 5, 1949

Netter FH, "Anatomical Plates on the Nervous System—the Basal Ganglia," *Clin. Symp.* vol. 1, no. 5, 1949

Netter FH, "The Brain and Spinal Cord," *Clin. Symp.* vol. 1, no. 6, 1949

Heyd CG, "Colostomy," *Clin. Symp.* vol. 1, no. 7, 1949

Gordon WH, "Heart Disease Complicating Pregnancy," *Clin. Symp.* vol. 1, no. 7, 1949

Miller SE, "Some Newer Concepts in the Laboratory Diagnosis of Tuberculosis," *Clin. Symp.* vol. 1, no. 7, 1949

Netter FH, "Anatomic Plates—The Spinal Column," *Clin. Symp.* vol. 1, no. 7, 1949

Talbott JH, Lockie LM, "Gouty Arthritis," *Clin. Symp.* vol. 2, no. 1, 1950

Netter FH, Kuntz A, "The Autonomic Nervous System," *Clin. Symp.* vol. 2, no. 1, 1950

DeCourcy JL, "Steroid Hormones in Inoperable Breast Cancer," *Clin. Symp.* vol. 2, no. 1, 1949–1950

Netter FH, "Anatomy of the Spinal Column," *Clin. Symp.* vol. 2, no. 1, 1949–1950

Glaser J, "The Eczematoid Dermatoses of Infancy and Childhood," *Clin. Symp.* vol. 2, no. 2, 1950

Cortes GH, "Pilonidal Disease," *Clin. Symp.* vol. 2, no. 2, 1950

Netter FH, "Anatomy of the Spinal Column," *Clin. Symp.* vol. 2, no. 2, 1950

Netter FH, von Bonin G, "Functional Neuro-Anatomy," *Clin. Symp.* vol. 2, no. 3, 1950

Mandel EE, Lehmann EB, Paris DA, "Simple Blood Tests Available to the General Practitioner," *Clin. Symp.* vol. 2, no. 3, 1950

Hochberg LA, Mackles A, "The Early Diagnosis of Bronchogenic Carcinoma," *Clin. Symp.* vol. 2, no. 4, 1950

Netter FH, von Bonin G, "Functional Neuro-Anatomy," *Clin. Symp.* vol. 2, no. 4, 1950

White CJ, "Diseases of the Nails," *Clin. Symp.* vol. 2, no. 5, 1950

Netter FH, von Bonin G, "Functional Neuro-Anatomy," *Clin. Symp.* vol. 2, no. 5, 1950

Netter FH, Gaines JA, "Diseases of the Vulva," *Clin. Symp.* vol. 2, no. 6, 1950

Jegheris H, McKusick VA, Katz KH, "Syndrome of Generalized Intestinal Polyposis," *Clin. Symp.* vol. 2, no. 6, 1950

Netter FH, von Bonin G, "Functional Neuro-Anatomy," *Clin. Symp.* vol. 2, no. 6, 1950

Netter FH, Kuntz A, "The Autonomic Nervous System," *Clin. Symp.* vol. 2, no. 7, 1950

Al Akl FM, "Circumcision," *Clin. Symp.* vol. 2, no. 7, 1950

Moseley HF, "Disorders of the Shoulder," *Clin. Symp.* vol. 2, no. 8, 1950

Netter FH, Kuntz A, "The Autonomic Nervous System," *Clin. Symp.* vol. 2, no. 8, 1950

Lippman RW, "Significance of the Urinary Sediment," *Clin. Symp.* vol. 2, no. 9, 1950

Prudente A, "Androgens in Postoperative Prophylaxis and Treatment of Breast Cancer," *Clin. Symp.* vol. 2, no. 9, 1950

Netter FH, Kuntz A, "The Autonomic Nervous System," *Clin. Symp.* vol. 2, no. 9, 1950

"Present Status of Percorten and Ascorbic Acid in Rheumatoid Arthritis," *Clin. Symp.* vol. 2, no. 10 suppl., 1950

Netter FH, Kaplan A, "Pathology of the Brain and Spinal Cord," *Clin. Symp.* vol. 3, no. 1, 1951

Greenblatt RB, "Kraurosis Vulvae," *Clin. Symp.* vol. 3, no. 1, 1951

Lisser H, "Symposium on Sublingual or Buccal Administration of Steroid Hormones," *Clin. Symp.* vol. 3, no. 2, 1951

Goldberg MB, "Technique and Rationale," *Clin. Symp.* vol. 3, no. 2, 1951

Gordan GS, "Sublingual Methyltestosterone for Weight Gain," *Clin. Symp.* vol. 3, no. 2, 1951

Lisser H, Gordan GS, "Sublingual Administration of Methyltestosterone in Short, Slender, Sexually Retarded Boys," *Clin. Symp.* vol. 3, no. 2, 1951

Craig LS, "Sublingual Administration of Desoxycorticosterone Acetate in Addison's Disease," *Clin. Symp.* vol. 3, no. 2, 1951

Arick MS, "Sublingual Administration of Progestational Substances," *Clin. Symp.* vol. 3, no. 2, 1951

Escamilla RF, Gordan GS, "Sublingual Administration of Testosterone Compounds in Male Hypogonadism," *Clin. Symp.* vol. 3, no. 2, 1951

Gordan GS, Aird RB, "Sublingual Desoxycorticosterone for the Control of Convulsive Seizures," *Clin. Symp.* vol. 3, no. 2, 1951

Netter FH, Kaplan A, "Pathology of the Brain and Spinal Cord," *Clin. Symp.* vol. 3, no. 2, 1951

Arena JM, "Accidental Poisoning in Children," *Clin. Symp.* vol. 3, no. 3, 1951

Kaplan A, "Pathology of the Brain and Spinal Cord," *Clin. Symp.* vol. 3, no. 3, 1951

Ayre JE, "Cyto-Diagnosis in Uterine Cancer," *Clin. Symp.* vol. 3, no. 4, 1951

Netter FH, Kaplan A, "Pathology of the Brain and Spinal Cord," *Clin. Symp.* vol. 3, no. 4, 1951

Sulzberger MB, Baer RL, Jessner M, "Selected Dermatoses Seen in General Practice," *Clin. Symp.* vol. 3, no. 5, 1951

Netter FH, Kaplan A, "Pathology of the Brain and Spinal Cord," *Clin. Symp.* vol. 3, no. 5, 1951

Kost Shelton E, Skeels RF, "Growth and Development," *Clin. Symp.* vol. 3, no. 6, 1951

Netter FH, Kaplan A, "Pathology of the Brain and Spinal Cord," *Clin. Symp.* vol. 3, no. 7, 1951

Meyer E, "The Spinal Fluid," *Clin. Symp.* vol. 3, no. 7, 1951

Lampe EW, "Surgical Anatomy of the Hand," *Clin. Symp.* vol. 3, no. 8, 1951

Sturgis SH, "Diseases of the Uterus," *Clin. Symp.* vol. 4, no. 1, 1952

Doyle JB, "Culdotomy; a Procedure for Direct Visualization and Palpation of the Pelvic Contents," *Clin. Symp.* vol. 4, no. 1, 1952

Kegel AH, "Stress Incontinence and Genital Relaxation; a Nonsurgical Method of Increasing the Tone of Sphincters and Their Supporting Structures," *Clin. Symp.* vol. 4, no. 2, 1952

Berkow SG, "Orthostatic Incontinence of Urine in Women; the Theory and Technique of Para-Urethral Fixation," *Clin. Symp.* vol. 4, no. 2, 1952

Kugelmass IN, "Hemorrhagic Problems in Infants and Children," *Clin. Symp.* vol. 4, no. 3, 1952

Sturgis SH, "Diseases of the Uterus," *Clin. Symp.* vol. 4, no. 3, 1952

Goldman HM, "The Mucous Membranes of the Oral Cavity," *Clin. Symp.* vol. 4, no. 4, 1952

Sturgis SH, "Diseases of the Uterus," *Clin. Symp.* vol. 4, no. 4, 1952

Bedell AJ, "The Fundus of the Eye," *Clin. Symp.* vol. 4, no. 5, 1952

Novak J, Rubin IC, "Anatomy and Pathology of the Fallopian Tubes," *Clin. Symp.* vol. 4, no. 6, 1952

Decker A, "Culdoscopy: A Method for Visual Diagnosis of Gynecologic Disease," *Clin. Symp.* vol. 4, no. 6, 1952

Whitacre FE, "The Use of Obstetric Forceps," *Clin. Symp.* vol. 4, no. 7, 1952

Bedell AJ, "The Fundus of the Eye," *Clin. Symp.* vol. 4, no. 7, 1952

Vest SA, "The Anatomy of the Male Genito-Urinary Tract," *Clin. Symp.* vol. 4, no. 8, 4 1952

Sulzberger MB, Baer RL, Jessner M, "Selected Dermatoses Seen in General Practice. II," *Clin. Symp.* vol. 5, no. 1, 1953

Moseley HF, "Disorders of the Hip," *Clin. Symp.* vol. 5, no. 2, 1953

Stern L Jr, "Pathology of the Mouth and Jaws," *Clin. Symp.* vol. 5, no. 3, 1953

Luke JC, "Venous Disorders of the Lower Extremity," *Clin. Symp.* vol. 5, no. 4, 1953

Scannell JG, Robbins LL, "X-Ray Examination of the Chest and Its Surgical Significance," *Clin. Symp.* vol. 5, no. 5, 1953

Moseley HF, "Disorders of the Knee," *Clin. Symp.* vol. 5, no. 6, 1953

Assali NS, "Toxemia of Pregnancy," *Clin. Symp.* vol. 6, no. 1, 1954

Gaunt R, Renzi AA, "Prevention of an Experimental Eclampsia-like Syndrome by Apresoline," *Clin. Symp.* vol. 6, no. 1, 1954

Vest SA, "The Prostate," *Clin. Symp.* vol. 6, no. 2, 1954

Silbert NE, "Nasal Allergy," *Clin. Symp.* vol. 6, no. 3, 1954

Vest SA, "Prostatic Malignancy," *Clin. Symp.* vol. 6, no. 3, 1954

Gaines JA, "Ovarian Neoplasms; Thumbnail Sketches of Tumors of the Ovary with Emphasis on Clinical Recognition, Pathology and Management," *Clin. Symp.* vol. 6, no. 4, 1954

Burnham PJ, "Amputation of the Lower Extremity," *Clin. Symp.* vol. 6, no. 5, 1954

Prandoni AG, Moser M, "Intra-Arterial Priscoline," *Clin. Symp.* vol. 6, no. 5, 1954

Rubin IC, "Myomectomy in the Treatment of Infertility," *Clin. Symp.* vol. 6, no. 6, 1954

Gaines JA, "Ovarian Neoplasms; Thumbnail Sketches of Tumors of the Ovary with Emphasis on Clinical Recognition, Pathology and Management," *Clin. Symp.* vol. 6, no. 6, 1954

Goldman HM, "Dental Abnormalities of Importance to the Medical Practitioner," *Clin. Symp.* vol. 7, no. 1, 1955

Eller JJ, "Acne and Acne Scars; Management of Disease and Removal of Scars by High Speed Rotary Abrasives," *Clin. Symp.* vol. 7, no. 1, 1955

Iason AH, "Inguinal and Femoral Hernias," *Clin. Symp.* vol. 7, no. 2, 1955

Cuono JD, "Chest Surgery in Tuberculosis," *Clin. Symp.* vol. 7, no. 3, 1955

Bachrach WH, "Medical Treatment of Ulcerative Colitis," *Clin. Symp.* vol. 7, no. 4, 1955

Rankin FW, "Surgical Treatment of Chronic Ulcerative Colitis," *Clin. Symp.* vol. 7, no. 4, 1955

Popper H, "Jaundice; Important Anatomic and Functional Considerations," *Clin. Symp.* vol. 7, no. 5, 1955

Moseley HF, "Traumatic Disorders of the Ankle and Foot," *Clin. Symp.* vol. 7, no. 6, 1955

Craig GE, "Shaving / a Cause of Skin Disorders," *Clin. Symp.* vol. 7, no. 6, 1955

Woodward FD, "Diseases of the Esophagus," *Clin. Symp.* vol. 8, no. 1, 1956

Zaino C, Poppel MH, "The Lower Esophagus," *Clin. Symp.* vol. 8, no. 1, 1956

Miller ER, "The First Stages of Swallowing," *Clin. Symp.* vol. 8, no. 1, 1956

DeBakey ME, Cooley DA, Creech O Jr, "Surgery of the Aorta," *Clin. Symp.* vol. 8, no. 2, 1956

Popper H, "Hepatitis and Hepatic Tests," *Clin. Symp.* vol. 8, no. 3, 1956

Ingram WR, "The Hypothalamus," *Clin. Symp.* vol. 8, no. 4, 1956

Hampton AO, Schumacher FV, "Radiographic Differentiation of Benign and Malignant Gastric Ulcers," *Clin. Symp.* vol. 8, no. 5, 1956

Benedict EB, "Gastroscopic Diagnosis of Malignant Disease," *Clin. Symp.* vol. 8, no. 5, 1956

Ayre JE, "A Rotating Gastric Brush for Rapid Cancer Detection," *Clin. Symp.* vol. 8, no. 5, 1956

Popper H, "Cirrhosis," *Clin. Symp.* vol. 8, no. 6, 1956

Lampe EW, "Surgical Anatomy of the Hand," *Clin. Symp.* vol. 9, no. 1, 1957

Cliffton EE, "Diseases of the Pancreas," *Clin. Symp.* vol. 9, no. 2, 1957

Moseley HF, "Static Disorders of the Ankle and Foot," *Clin. Symp.* vol. 9, no. 3, 1957

Wilkins RW, "The Treatment of Hypertension," *Clin. Symp.* vol. 9, no. 4, 1957

Bedell AJ, "The Fundus in Hypertension," *Clin. Symp.* vol. 9, no. 4, 1957

Green HD, "Pharmacology of Antihypertensive Drugs," *Clin. Symp.* vol. 9, no. 4, 1957

Ayd FJ Jr, "Treatment of the Office Neurotic," *Clin. Symp.* vol. 9, no. 5, 1957

Brown WL, "Psycho-Iconography of the Office Neurotic," *Clin. Symp.* vol. 9, no. 5, 1957

Pruce AM, Miller JA Jr, Berger IR, "Anatomic Landmarks in Joint Paracentesis," *Clin. Symp.* vol. 10, no. 1, 1958

Hoagland RJ, "Infectious Mononucleosis," *Clin. Symp.* vol. 10, no. 1, 1958

Lord JW Jr, Rosati LM, "Neurovascular Compression Syndromes of the Upper Extremity," *Clin. Symp.* vol. 10, no. 2, 1958

Huber JF, "Anatomy of the Mouth," *Clin. Symp.* vol. 10, no. 3, 1958

Duffner GJ, "Medical Problems Involved in Underwater Compression and Decompression," *Clin. Symp.* vol. 10, no. 4, 1958

Huber JF, "Anatomy of the Pharynx," *Clin. Symp.* vol. 10, no. 4, 1958

Bailey CP, "Surgery of the Heart," *Clin. Symp.* vol. 10, no. 5, 1958

Farber SM, Wilson RH, "Pulmonary Emphysema," *Clin. Symp.* vol. 10, no. 6, 1958

Bachrach WH, "Physiology and Pathologic Physiology of the Stomach," *Clin. Symp.* vol. 11, no. 1, 1959

Koop CE, "Emergency Surgery of the Newborn," *Clin. Symp.* vol. 11, no. 2, 1959

Moseley HF, "Disorders of the Shoulder," *Clin. Symp.* vol. 11, no. 3, 1959

Burnham PJ, "Amputation of the Upper Extremity," *Clin. Symp.* vol. 11, no. 4, 1959

Mitchell GA, "Nerve Supply of the Gastrointestinal Tract," *Clin. Symp.* vol. 11, no. 5, 1959

Arena JM, "Diagnosis and Treatment of Poisoning," *Clin. Symp.* vol. 12, no. 1, 1960

Gorsch RV, "The Sigmoid, Rectum, and Anal Canal: Relations, Attachments, and Pelvic Spaces," *Clin. Symp.* vol. 12, no. 2, 1960

Michele AA, "The Iliopsoas Muscle," *Clin. Symp.* vol. 12, no. 3, 1960

Pontes JF, Polak M, "Disorders of the Small Intestine," *Clin. Symp.* vol. 12, no. 4, 1960

Chamberlain JW, Welch K, Morse TS, "The Management of Burns in Children," *Clin. Symp.* vol. 13, no. 1, 1961

Polak M, "Benign Tumors of Small Intestine," *Clin. Symp.* vol. 13, no. 1, 1961

Schreiner GE, "The Urinary Sediment," *Clin. Symp.* vol. 13, no. 2, 1961

Kevorkian J, "The Eye in Death," *Clin. Symp.* vol. 13, no. 2, 1961

Crelin, ES, "Development of Gastrointestinal Tract," *Clin. Symp.* vol. 13, no. 3, 1961

Lockhart-Mummery HE, "Diseases of the Large Intestine," *Clin. Symp.* vol. 13, no. 3, 1961

Martin H, "Radical Neck Dissection," *Clin. Symp.* vol. 13, no. 4, 1961

Martin H, "Surgical Removal of Parotid Tumors," *Clin. Symp.* vol. 13, no. 4, 1961

King ER, "Survival in Nuclear Warfare," *Clin. Symp.* vol. 14, no. 1, 1962

Meyers D, Schlosser WD, Winchester RA, "Otologic Diagnosis and the Treatment of Deafness," *Clin. Symp.* vol. 14, no. 2, 1962

Myers D, Schlosser WD, Winchester RA, "Otologic Diagnosis and the Treatment of Deafness," *Clin. Symp.* vol. 14, no. 2, 1962

Reich C, "The Cellular Elements of the Blood," *Clin. Symp.* vol. 14, no. 3, 1962

Gordon DM, "Diseases of the Eye," *Clin. Symp.* vol. 14, no. 4, 1962

Forsham PH, "The Adrenal Gland," *Clin. Symp.* vol. 15, no. 1, 1963

Biglieri EG, "Aldosterone," *Clin. Symp.* vol. 15, no. 1, 1963

Forsham PH, "Abnormalities of the Adrenal Cortex," *Clin. Symp.* vol. 15, no. 2, 1963

Ezrin C, "The Pituitary Gland," *Clin. Symp.* vol. 15, no. 3, 1963

Levine R, "Diabetes Mellitus," *Clin. Symp.* vol. 15, no. 4, 1963

Burnham PJ, "Amputation of the Lower Extremity," *Clin. Symp.* vol. 16, no. 1, 1964

Pruce AM, Miller JA Jr, Berger IR, "Anatomic Landmarks in Joint Paracentesis," *Clin. Symp.* vol. 16, no. 1, 1964

Pack GT, Islami AH, "Operative Treatment of Hepatic Tumors," *Clin. Symp.* vol. 16, no. 2, 1964

Saunders WH, "The Larynx," *Clin. Symp.* vol. 16, no. 3, 1964

Hopping RA, "Common Disorders Of Anus, Rectum, and Sigmoid," *Clin. Symp.* vol. 16, no. 4, 1964

Moseley HF, "Traumatic Disorders of the Ankle and Foot," *Clin. Symp.* vol. 17, no. 1, 1965

Rawson RW, "The Thyroid Gland," *Clin. Symp.* vol. 17, no. 2, 1965

Van Mierop LH, "Anatomy of the Heart," *Clin. Symp.* vol. 17, no. 3, 1965

Baron MG, "Angiocardiography," *Clin. Symp.* vol. 17, no. 3, 1965

Wolfson RJ, Myers D, Schlosser WD, Winchester RA, "Vertigo," *Clin. Symp.* vol. 17, no. 4, 1965

Arena JM, "The Treatment of Poisoning," *Clin. Symp.* vol. 18, no. 1, 1966

Iason AH, "Inguinal and Femoral Hernias," *Clin. Symp.* vol. 18, no. 2, 1966

Jackson FE, "The Pathophysiology of Head Injuries," *Clin. Symp.* vol. 18, no. 3, 1966

Jackson FE, "The Treatment of Head Injuries," *Clin. Symp.* vol. 19, no. 1, 1967

James AP, "Common Dermatologic Disorders," *Clin. Symp.* vol. 19, no. 2, 1967

Pickrell KL, "Reconstructive Plastic Surgery of the Face," *Clin. Symp.* vol. 19, no. 3, 1967

Luisada AA, "The Signs and Symptoms of Valvular Disease and Heart Failure," *Clin. Symp.* vol. 20, no. 1, 1968

Farber SM, Wilson RH, "Chronic Obstructive Emphysema," *Clin. Symp.* vol. 20, no. 2, 1968

Frazier CA, "Diagnosis and Treatment of Insect Bites," *Clin. Symp.* vol. 20, no. 3, 1968

Winsor T, "The Electrocardiogram in Myocardial Infarction," *Clin. Symp.* vol. 20, no. 4, 1968

Effler DB, "The Surgical Treatment of Myocardial Ischemia," *Clin. Symp.* vol. 21, no. 1, 1969

Castaneda AR, "Surgical Treatment of Cardiac Valvular Disease," *Clin. Symp.* vol. 21, no. 1, 1969

Conwell HE, "Injuries to the Elbow," *Clin. Symp.* vol. 21, no. 2, 1969

Lampe EW, "Surgical Anatomy of the Hand with Special Reference to Infections and Trauma," *Clin. Symp.* vol. 21, no. 3, 1969

Conwell HE, "Injuries to the Wrist," *Clin. Symp.* vol. 22, no. 1, 1970

Myers D, Schlosser WD, Wolfson RJ, Winchester RA, Carmel NH, "Otologic Diagnosis and the Treatment of Deafness," *Clin. Symp.* vol. 22, no. 2, 1970

Naclerio EA, "Chest Trauma," *Clin. Symp.* vol. 22, no. 3, 1970

Calabro JJ, "Rheumatoid Arthritis: A Potentially Crippling Disease That May Attack at Any Age," *Clin. Symp.* vol. 23, no. 1, 1971

Lord JW Jr, Rosati LM, "Thoracic-Outlet Syndromes," *Clin. Symp.* vol. 23, no. 2, 1971

[No authors listed.] "Syphilis," *Clin. Symp.* vol. 23, no. 3, 1971

Keim HA, "Scoliosis," *Clin. Symp.* vol. 24, no. 1, 1972

Wilkins RW, Hollander W, Chobanian AV, "Evaluation of Hypertensive Patients," *Clin. Symp.* vol. 24, no. 2, 1972

Horton CE, Devine CJ, "Hypospadias and Epispadias," *Clin. Symp.* vol. 24, no. 3, 1972

Pullman TN, Coe FL, "Chronic Renal Failure," *Clin. Symp.* vol. 25, no. 1, 1973

Krull EA, Fellman AC, Fabian LA, "White Lesions of the Mouth," *Clin. Symp.* vol. 25, no. 2, 1973

Keim HA, "Low Back Pain," *Clin. Symp.* vol. 25, no. 3, 1973

Lawrence MR, "The Cell," *Clin. Symp.* vol. 25, no. 4, 1973

Berman LB, Vertes V, "The Pathophysiology of Renin," *Clin. Symp.* vol. 25, no. 5, 1973

Jaffe BF, "Diseases and Surgery of the Nose," *Clin. Symp.* vol. 26, no. 1, 1974

Crelin ES, "Development of the Nervous System. A Logical Approach to Neuroanatomy," *Clin. Symp.* vol. 26, no. 2, 1974

Paton D, Craig J, "Cataracts," *Clin. Symp.* vol. 26, no. 3, 1974

Fields WS, "Aortocranial Occlusive Vascular Disease (Stroke)," *Clin. Symp.* vol. 26, no. 4, 1974

Shapter RK, Katz HJ, Cobb LA, Grace WJ, Nagel EL, Schwartz ML, Uhley HN, Warren JV, "Cardiopulmonary Resuscitation: Basic Life Support," *Clin. Symp.* vol. 26, no. 5, 1974

Weiss EB, "Bronchial Asthma," *Clin. Symp.* vol. 27, no. 1–2, 1975

Tyson KR, "Congenital Heart Disease in Infants," *Clin. Symp.* vol. 27, no. 3, 1975

Crelin ES, "Development of the lower Respiratory System," *Clin. Symp.* vol. 27, no. 4, 1975

Duvoisin R, "Parkinsonism," *Clin. Symp.* vol. 28, no. 1, 1976

Paton D, Craig JA, "Glaucomas. Diagnosis and Management," *Clin. Symp.* vol. 28, no. 2, 1976

Crelin ES, "Development of the Upper Respiratory System," *Clin. Symp.* vol. 28, no. 3, 1976

Abston S, "Burns in Children," *Clin. Symp.* vol. 28, no. 4, 1976

Shane JM, Schiff I, Wilson EA, "The Infertile Couple: Evaluation and Treatment," *Clin. Symp.* vol. 28, no. 5, 1976

Ellison AE, "Skiing Injuries," *Clin. Symp.* vol. 29, no. 1, 1977

Winsor T, "The Electrocardiogram in Myocardial Infarction," *Clin. Symp.* vol. 29, no. 2, 1977

Bryant WM, "Wound Healing," *Clin. Symp.* vol. 29, no. 3, 1977

Rhoton AL, Jackson FE, Gleave J, Rumbaugh CT, "Congenital and Traumatic Intracranial Aneurysms," *Clin. Symp.* vol. 29, no. 4, 1977

McNeese MC, Hebeler JR, "The Abused Child," *Clin. Symp.* vol. 29, no. 5, 1977

Weintraub MI, "Hysteria," *Clin. Symp.* vol. 29, no. 6, 1977

Keim HA, "Scoliosis," *Clin. Symp.* vol. 30, no. 1, 1978

Arena JM, "The Treatment of Poisoning," *Clin. Symp.* vol. 30, no. 2, 1978

Lieberman E, "Hypertension in Childhood and Adolescence," *Clin. Symp.* vol. 30, no. 3, 1978

Ziskind MM, "Occupational Pulmonary Disease," *Clin. Symp.* vol. 30, no. 4, 1978

Kodner IJ, "Colostomy and Ileostomy," *Clin. Symp.* vol. 30, no. 5, 1978

Hensinger RN, "Congenital Dislocation of the Hip," *Clin. Symp.* vol. 31, no. 1, 1979

Altose MD, "The Physiological Basis of Pulmonary Function Testing," *Clin. Symp.* vol. 31, no. 2, 1979

Heimlich HJ, Uhley MH, Netter FH, "The Heimlich Maneuver," *Clin. Symp.* vol. 31, no. 3, 1979

Koffler D, "The Immunology of Rheumatoid Diseases," *Clin. Symp.* vol. 31, no. 4, 1979

Agris J, Spira M, "Pressure Ulcers Prevention and Treatment," *Clin. Symp.* vol. 31, no. 5, 1979

Swanson AB, "Reconstructive Surgery in the Arthritic Hand and Foot," *Clin. Symp.* vol. 31, no. 6, 1979

Cloward RB, "Acute Cervical Spine Injuries," *Clin. Symp.* vol. 32, no. 1, 1980

Townsend CM Jr, "Breast Lumps," *Clin. Symp.* vol. 32, no. 2, 1980

Grossman MB, "Gastrointestinal Endoscopy," *Clin. Symp.* vol. 32, no. 3, 1980

Brody DM, "Running Injuries," *Clin. Symp.* vol. 32, no. 4, 1980

Nyham WL, "Understanding Inherited Metabolic Disease," *Clin. Symp.* vol. 32, no. 5, 1980

Keim HA, Kirkaldy-Willis WH, "Low Back Pain," *Clin. Symp.* vol. 32, no. 6, 1980

Crelin ES, "Development of the Musculoskeletal System," *Clin. Symp.* vol. 33, no. 1, 1981

Diamond S, Medina JL, "Headaches," *Clin. Symp.* vol. 33, no. 2, 1981

Swanson AB, "Congenital Limb Defects Classification and Treatment," *Clin. Symp.* vol. 33, no. 3, 1981

Bertz JE, "Maxillofacial Injuries," *Clin. Symp.* vol. 33, no. 4, 1981

Sheldon JJ, "Blood Vessels of the Scalp and Brain," *Clin. Symp.* vol. 33, no. 5, 1981

Wolfson RJ, Silverstein H, Marlowe F, Keels EW, "Vertigo," *Clin. Symp.* vol. 33, no. 6, 1981

Kodner IJ, Fry RD, "Inflammatory Bowel Disease," *Clin. Symp.* vol. 34, no. 1, 1981

Donovan WH, Bedbrook G., "Comprehensive Management of Spinal Cord Injury," *Clin. Symp.* vol. 34, no. 2, 1982

Johnson LL, "Diagnostic and Surgical Arthroscopy," *Clin. Symp.* vol. 34, no. 3, 1982

Schoenfield LJ, "Gallstones and Other Biliary Diseases," *Clin. Symp.* vol. 34, no. 4, 1982

Chobanian AV, "Hypertension," *Clin. Symp.* vol. 34, no. 5, 1982

White RD, "CPR: Basic Life Support," *Clin. Symp.* vol. 34, no. 6, 1982

Nyhan WL, "Cytogenic Diseases," *Clin. Symp.* vol. 35, no. 1, 1983

Scheidt S, "Basic Electrocardiography: Leads, Axes, Arrhythmias," *Clin. Symp.* vol. 35, no. 2, 1983

Friedman WA, "Head Injuries," *Clin. Symp.* vol. 35, no. 4, 1983

Kaplan FS, "Osteoporosis," *Clin. Symp.* vol. 35, no. 5, 1983

Devries WC, Joyce LD, "The Artificial Heart," *Clin. Symp.* vol. 35, no. 6, 1983

Romanowski B, Harris JRW, "Sexually Transmitted Diseases," *Clin. Symp.* vol. 36, no. 1, 1984

Wolfe MS, "Diseases of Travelers," *Clin. Symp.* vol. 36, no. 2, 1984

Pullman TN, Coe FL, "Pathophysiology of Chronic Renal Failure," *Clin. Symp.* vol. 36, no. 3, 1984

Garcia CA, Ruiz RS, "Diabetes and the Eye," *Clin. Symp.* vol. 36, no. 4, 1984

McGuigan MA, "Treatment of Poisoning," *Clin. Symp.* vol. 36, no. 5, 1984

Scheidt S, "Basic Electrocardiography: Abnormalities of Electrocardiographic Patterns," *Clin. Symp.* vol. 36, no. 6, 1984

Berman RL, "Current Perspectives in Gynecology," *Clin. Symp.* vol. 36, no. 1, 1985

Jones HR Jr, "Diseases of the Peripheral Motor-Sensory Unit,"
    Clin. Symp. vol. 37, no. 2, 1985

Hamilton WG, "Surgical Anatomy of the Foot and Ankle," *Clin.
    Symp.* vol. 37, no. 3, 1985

Moake JL, Levine JD, "Thromboplastic Disorders," *Clin. Symp.*
    vol. 37, no. 4, 1985

Epstein M, "Renal Complications of Liver Disease," *Clin. Symp.*
    vol. 37, no. 5, 1985

Fry RD, Kodner IJ, "Anorectal Disorders," *Clin. Symp.* vol. 37,
    no. 6, 1985

Thompson GH, Salter RB, "Legg-Calvé-Perthes Disease," *Clin.
    Symp.* vol. 38, no. 1, 1986

Calabro JJ, "Rheumatoid Arthritis: Diagnosis and Management,"
    Clin. Symp. vol. 38, no. 2, 1986

Andriani RT, Carson CC III, "Urolithiasis," *Clin. Symp.* vol. 38,
    no. 3, 1986

Freidberg SR, "Tumors of the Brain," *Clin. Symp.* vol. 38, no. 4,
    1986

Ellis FH, "Hiatus Hernia," *Clin. Symp.* vol. 38, no. 5, 1985

Wolfson RJ, Silverstein H, Marlowe FI, Keels EW, "Vertigo," *Clin.
    Symp.* vol. 38, no. 6, 1986

Kaplan FS, "Osteoporosis. Pathophysiology and Prevention," *Clin.
    Symp.* vol. 39, no. 1, 1987

Koffler D, "Immunology of Systemic Lupus Erythematosus and
    Related Rheumatic Diseases," *Clin. Symp.* vol. 39, no. 2,
    1987

Brody DM, "Running Injuries. Prevention and Management,"
    Clin. Symp. vol. 39, no. 3, 1987

Townsend CM Jr, "Management of Breast Cancer, Surgery and
    Adjuvant Therapy," *Clin. Symp.* vol. 39, no. 4, 1987

Kozinn SC, Wilson PD Jr, "Adult Hip Disease and Total Hip
    Replacement," *Clin. Symp.* vol. 39, no. 5, 1987

Keim HA, Kirkaldy-Willis WH, "Low Back Pain," *Clin. Symp.*
    vol. 39, no. 6, 1987

Scott CI Jr, "Dwarfism," *Clin. Symp.* vol. 40, no. 1, 1988

Choefield, LJ, "Gallstones," *Clin. Symp.* vol. 40, no. 2, 1988, revision of vol. 34, no. 4, 1982

Lampe EW, "Surgical Anatomy of the Hand. With Special Reference to Infections and Trauma," *Clin. Symp.* vol. 40, no. 3, 1988

Caplan LR, "Stroke," *Clin. Symp.* vol. 40, no. 4, 1988

Friedman G, "Peptic Ulcer Disease," *Clin. Symp.* vol. 40, no. 5, 1988

Diamond S, Medina JL, "Headaches," *Clin. Symp.* vol. 41, no. 1, 1989

Paulson D, "Diseases of the Prostate," *Clin. Symp.* vol. 41, no. 2, 1989

Enneking WF, Conrad EU III, "Common Bone Tumors," *Clin. Symp.* vol. 41, no. 3, 1989

Keim HA, Hensinger RN, "Spinal Deformities. Scoliosis and Kyphosis," *Clin. Symp.* vol. 41, no. 4, 1989

Fry RD, Fleshman JW, Kodner IJ, "Cancer of the Colon and Rectum," *Clin. Symp.* vol. 41, no. 5, 1989

Conrad EU III, Enneking WF, "Common Soft Tissue Tumors," *Clin. Symp.* vol. 42, no. 1, 1990

Nyhan WL, "Structural Abnormalities," *Clin. Symp.* vol. 42, no. 2, 1990

Sheldon JJ, "Blood Vessels of the Scalp and Brain," *Clin. Symp.* vol. 42, no. 3, 1990

Paton D, Craig JA, "Management of Cataracts," *Clin. Symp.* vol. 42, no. 4, 1990

Chobanian AV, Gavras H, "Hypertension," *Clin. Symp.* vol. 42, no. 5, 1990

Kessler DB, Hyden P, "Physical, Sexual, and Emotional Abuse of Children," *Clin. Symp.* vol. 43, no. 1, 1991

Kleinert HE, Kleinert JM, McCabe SJ, Berger AC, "Replantation," *Clin. Symp.* vol. 43, no. 2, 1991

Heckman JD, "Fractures," *Clin. Symp.* vol. 43, no. 3, 1991

Danyluk AW, Paton F, "Diagnosis and Management of Glaucoma," *Clin. Symp.* vol. 43, no. 4, 1991

Garcia CA, Ruiz RS, "Ocular Complications of Diabetes," *Clin. Symp.* vol. 44, no. 1, 1992

[No authors listed.] "A Tribute to Frank H. Netter, 1906–1991," *Clin. Symp.* vol. 44, no. 2, 1992

Silverstein H, Wolfson RJ, Rosenberg, S, "Diagnosis and Management of Hearing Loss," *Clin. Symp.* vol. 44, no. 3, 1992

Schenck RC Jr, Heckman JD, "Injuries of the Knee," *Clin. Symp.* vol. 45, no. 1, 1993

Shane JM, "Evaluation and Treatment of Infertility," *Clin. Symp.* vol. 45, no. 2, 1993

Harvey JC, Beattie EJ, "Lung Cancer," *Clin. Symp.* vol. 45, no. 3, 1993

Devinsky O, "Seizure Disorders," *Clin. Symp.* vol. 46, no. 1, 1994

Josephson JS, Rosenberg SI, "Sinusitis," *Clin. Symp.* vol. 46, no. 2, 1994

Diamond S, "Head Pain: Diagnosis and Management," *Clin. Symp.* vol. 46, no. 3, 1994

Blumfeld JD, "Renal and Cardiac Complications of Hypertension," *Clin. Symp.* vol. 46, no. 4, 1994

Kaplan FS, "Prevention and Management of Osteoporosis," *Clin. Symp.* vol. 47, no. 1, 1995

Buckwalter JA, Martin J, "Degenerative Joint Disease," *Clin. Symp.* vol. 47, no. 2, 1995

Retzky SS, Rogers RM Jr, "Urinary Incontinence in Women," *Clin. Symp.* vol. 47, no. 3, 1995

Geller A, "Common Addictions," *Clin. Symp.* vol. 48, no. 1, 1996

Jacobs A, "Ovarian Cancer," *Clin. Symp.* vol. 48, no. 2, 1996

Pendlebury WW, Solomon PR, "Alzheimer's Disease," *Clin. Symp.* vol. 48, no. 3, 1996

Mooney V, Saal JA, Saal J, "Evaluation and Treatment of Low Back Pain," *Clin. Symp.* vol. 48, no. 4, 1996

Townsend CM Jr, "Treatment of Breast Cancer," *Clin. Symp.* vol. 49, no. 1, 1997

Rayan GM, "Compression Neuropathies, Including Carpal Tunnel Syndrome," *Clin. Symp.* vol. 48, no. 2, 1997

Williams PV, "Management of Asthma," *Clin. Symp.* vol. 48, no. 3, 1997

Grundy SM, "Lipid Abnormalities and Coronary Heart Disease," *Clin. Symp.* vol. 48, no. 4, 1997

HONORS AND AWARDS

Year	Honor	Grantor
1939	Artist membership	Society of Illustrators
1940	Fellow	New York Academy of Medicine
1965	For contributions to medical education through graphic art	New York University School of Medicine
1966	Townsend Harris Medal	College of the City of New York
1966	Award for Distinctive Achievement	Modern Medicine
1968	Life member	Society of Illustrators
1969	The Harold Swanberg Distinguished Service Award	American Medical Writers Association
1973	Distinguished Service Award	National Kidney Foundation
1974	Award for Excellence	Art Directors Club of New Jersey
1979	Resolution of commendation	Florida State Legislation
1981	Distinguished Service Award	American College of Cardiology
1981	Honorary degree, doctor of science	New Jersey College of Medicine and Dentistry
1981	Dell' Ippocrate D'oro Honorary Academic	Academia Medicorum Litteratorum—Medicine, Literature, Arts, Venice, Italy
1985	Honorary degree, doctor of science	Georgetown University
1986	Lifetime Achievement Award	Society of Illustrators
1986	The Solomon A. Berson Medical Alumni Achievement Award	New York University School of Medicine

Year	Honor	Grantor
1986	Honorary degree, doctor of science	University of Sherbrooke, Canada
1986	Lifetime Achievement Award	Association of Medical Illustrators
1986	Dedication of the Frank H. Netter Library	Ciba-Geigy Corporation
1986	Honorary fellowship	American Academy of Neurological and Orthopaedic Surgeons
1987	Honorary member	American Academy of Neurologists
1988	Honorary Award for Contribution to Knowledge of Musculoskeletal System	American Academy of Orthopaedic Surgeons
1988	Award for Contributions to Medicine	American Laryngological Association
1988	Honorary fellowship	American Medical Artists Association of Great Britain
1988	Illustrated Medical Book Award, *Musculoskeletal System Part I*	Association of Medical Illustrators
1989	Honorary alumnus	University of Pennsylvania School of Medicine
1989	Trustee	Vesalius Trust for Visual Communication in the Health Sciences
1990	Book of the Year for *Atlas of Human Anatomy*	New York Book Show
1990	Award of Special Recognition	American Otological Society
1990	First recipient of the Frank Netter Award	Vesalius Trust for Visual Communication in the Health Sciences
1990	Award of Special Recognition	Association of Medical Illustrators
1990	Honorary Member Award	American Association of Clinical Anatomists

Year	Honor	Grantor
1990	Honorary degree, doctor of arts	The Ohio State University
1990	Award of Special Recognition	American Otological Society
1991	Honorary member	American Orthopaedic Association
2006	Illustrators Hall of Fame	Society of Illustrators
2013	Dedication of the Frank H. Netter, MD School of Medicine	Quinnipiac University

NOTES

All page numbers given for *Quails from the Sea* are those from the 1987 translation by Rabbi Joan Friedman.

Abbreviations Used
CCMI: *Ciba Collection of Medical Illustrations*
CCNY: College of the City of New York
Clin. Symp.: *Clinical Symposia*
FHN: Frank H. Netter
FMN: Francine Mary Netter
GWU: George Washington University
NA: National Academy of Design
NYU: New York University
RN: Richard Netter
UNC: University of North Carolina.

Introduction
1   Interview, Frederick S. Kaplan, December 18, 2005.
2   Agreement between Ciba-Geigy Corporation and Frank H. Netter, MD, effective July 5, 1960.
3   FHN, *Atlas of Human Anatomy*, Ciba-Geigy, Summit, NJ, 1989.

Chapter 1: New York City
1   Letter, RN to Gideon Katz, Mikveh Israel Agricultural School, November 19, 1991.
2   Email, Magistrat der Stadt Wien, Helmut Kretschmer/Katharina Smola, October 18, 2005.
3   Netter JM, *Quails from the Sea* (title also translated as *Seagulls from the Sea*), Vienna, 1860, translated by Rabbi Joan Friedman, 1987, p. 39.
4   Netter JM, op. cit., p. 112, ref.: The Taiping Rebellion (1851–1864).
5   Netter JM, op. cit., p. 39.
6   Albo Yosef, *The Book of Principles*, Castile, 1425.
7   Netter JM, op. cit., p. 69.

8   Netter JM, op. cit., p. 114. The translation has the Sermon of Repentance delivered in Utica in 1860. But because the manuscript was published in 1860 and he left San Francisco for Utica in the spring of 1859 (p. 69), the date is given here as 1859.

9   Netter JM, op. cit., p. 34.

10 Netter JM, op. cit., p. 48. Also, letter, RN to Gideon Katz, Mikveh Israel Agricultural School, November 19, 1991: In 1859, during Jacob's absence, Solomon Netter published a rabbinic bible with his own commentary on Ibn Ezra, an important Jewish scholar and poet in twelfth-century Muslim Spain.

11 Netter JM, op. cit., p. 112.

12 Netter JM, *Quails from the Sea* (title also translated as *Seagulls from the Sea*), Vienna, 1860.

13 Interview, RN, April 7, 2004.

14 Passenger list, *Bohemia*, Arrival New York, June 25, 1888.

15 Passenger list, *Celtic*, Arrival New York, May 20, 1889.

16 *Soundex Index to Petitions for Naturalizations Filed in Federal, State, and Local Courts in New York City, 1792–1906*. NARA microfilm publication M1674, 295 rolls. Records of District Courts of the United States. National Archives, Washington, DC. Naturalization papers filed in US District Court, New York, August 13, 1894.

17 *Soundex*, op. cit., naturalization papers filed in US District Court NY, May 31, 1895.

18 Three sisters came: Eva, Esther Adel, and Annie Slutsky, 20, 21, and 25 years old. United States Census records, 1900 and 1920.

19 United States Census, 1900–1930; naturalization documents, op. cit.

20 United States Census, 1900: Charles and Esther at 768 Washington Street and Abraham and Eva at 53 Horatio Street, a three-block walk.

21 State of New York certificate and record of birth no. 22064.

22 Cigar-cutter story: FHN to FMN, c. 1964.

23 RN, eulogy for FHN, delivered September 22, 1991.

24 United States Census, 1910: Charles and Esther lived in an apartment on 8th Avenue with George, Rose and Frank (ages 10, 7, and 4). Abraham and Eva lived two blocks away (202 West 54th Street) with their three sons, 2-year-old Emile and the teenage boys, Bill and Bob.

25 RN, eulogy for FHN, delivered September 22, 1991.

26 Interview, RN, April 4, 2004.

27 Wood G, "Nanny Speaks" interview of Gertrude Netter, November 1984.

28 Interview, RN, April 4, 2004.

29 FHN, autobiographical notes.

30 New York City Archives, Death Certificate Index #21794: He died on July 17, 1919, and was buried the following day at Mount Carmel Cemetery.

31 New York City Archives Death Certificate Index #2641: He died within four days of first seeing a doctor. The influenza virus might have been the

cause of the pneumonia, and the death record is consistent with the rapid progress of an influenza infection. The following day, Abraham was buried at Mount Carmel.

32 Wood, op. cit.
33 United States Census, 1920.

Chapter 2: Art Student

1   In 1929 the school moved to 100 W. Mosholu Parkway in the South Bronx.
2   One of the student editors was Harold B. Clemenko, who would go on to become an editor of *Look* magazine and manager of Dell Publishing.
3   FHN, autobiographical notes.
4   Email, Gerard J. Pelisson, archivist for DeWitt Clinton High School, to FMN, April 13, 2006.
5   FHN, autobiographical notes.
6   FHN, autobiographical notes.
7   *Magpie*: October 1922, *Miser*, p. 21; November 1922, *On Second Music Shops*, by Imre V. Klein, illus. by FHN, pp. 24–25; November 1922, *Methinks*, p. 21; December 1922, *McCarthy*, by David Blum, illus. by FHN; February 1923, *Makaava*, p. 11; March 1923, *Battle of Wits*, a play by Imre V. Klein, illus. by FHN, pp. 16 & 18; March 1923, *Candy*, by Stanley Rosenthal, illus. by FHN, pp. 10–13; March 1923, *Rambler*, pp. 22, 23, and 30; April 1923, *Oriental Justice*, by Imre V. Klein, illus. by FHN, pp. 10 and 12.
8   *Magpie*, March 1923, *Battle of Wits*, a play by Imre V. Klein, illus. by FHN, p. 16.
9   *Magpie*, March 1923, *Candy*, by Stanley Rosenthal, illus. by FHN, p. 10.
10 *Magpie*, October 1922, *Miser*, p. 21.
11 *Magpie*, March 1923, *Rambler*, pp. 22, 23 & 30.
12 *Magpie*, April 1923, cover.
13 *Magpie*, January 1923, p. 19.
14 Ibid., p. 9.
15 Ibid., p. 37.
16 *Clintonian* yearbook, 1922.
17 FHN, "Frank H. Netter, MD, Artist, Physician, Teacher," Ciba-Geigy, Summit, NJ, 1988.
18 Ibid.
19 CCNY limited enrollment to male students until the 1950s. Hunter College's Manhattan campus was limited to female students until 1964.
20 FHN, autobiographical notes.
21 FHN's NA records and dates from email of Peter Hasting Falk to FMN, June 12, 2004.
22 Letter, Ruth Reininghaus, Salmagundi Club, to FMN, April 20, 2004.
23 Henri R, *The Art Spirit*, Lippincott, first published 1923, then 1930, then 1939.
24 FHN, autobiographical notes.

25 In his notes Frank failed to identify who the teacher was. The NA records indicate that he took a Life Class with Ivan Olinsky in April 1924. However, Frank wrote in his notes that this teacher was not thought to be as great an artist as some of the others but was a better teacher. Both Olinsky and Charles Courtney Curran had excellent reputations as painters, but George Elmer Browne had a reputation as an excellent teacher, as did Charles Louis Hinton.

26 FHN, autobiographical notes.

27 Ibid.

28 Ibid.

29 Ibid.

30 Students at the College of the City of New York, later renamed City College of New York, paid no tuition, and admission was extremely competitive. In 1970, CCNY began charging tuition and opened enrollment to all high school graduates in New York City.

31 Transcript for FHN, CCNY.

32 3028 Ivy Court, per NA records, email, Peter Falk to FMN, June 12, 2004.

33 Wood G, "Nanny Speaks" interview of Gertrude Netter, November 1984.

34 Frederick Banting and Charles Best isolated insulin in 1922, and Eli Lilly and Company introduced a purified insulin product in 1923.

35 Interview, RN, April 7, 2004.

36 FHN, told to FMN, c. 1980.

37 Story of George and Gertie's courtship and the visit to Brighton Beach per Wood, G, "Nanny Speaks" interview of Gertrude Netter, November 1984.

38 Wood G, "Nanny Speaks" interview of Gertrude Netter, November 1984.

39 City of New York Archives, death certificate no. 19878.

40 Interview, RN, April 7, 2004.

41 FHN, told to FMN, c. 1980.

42 That they went to live with Eva per Wood, G, "Nanny Speaks" interview of Gertrude Netter, November 1984; 311 West 94th Street: FHN address, CCNY *Microcosm*, 1927, p. 108; Rose Netter address, NYU Medical College *Bellevue Violet*, 1927(?), p. 122.

43 Transcript for FHN, CCNY.

44 FHN, autobiographical notes.

45 Ibid.

46 Ibid.

47 Ibid.

48 Ibid.

49 Ibid.

50 In his autobiographical notes Frank did not mention Hunt, known for his etchings.

51 *Mercury*, May 1926, p. 8.

52 *Mercury*, October 1926, p. 13.

53 *Mercury*, December 1926, p. 17.

54 FHN, autobiographical notes.
55 *Microcosm*, 1927, p. 19.
56 *Microcosm*, 1927, p. 17.
57 *Microcosm*, 1927, p. 8.
58 Isidore Seidler, Julius Raskin, and David W. Kanstoren, *Microcosm*, 1927, p. 55.
59 Letter, Leon Bankoff to FHN, August 22, 1984.
60 FHN, autobiographical notes.
61 Ibid.

Chapter 3: Medical Student

1 New York University Medical College is now known as New York University School of Medicine.
2 *NYU Medical College Bulletin*, 1930–1931. Information in this and subsequent paragraphs about the history of NYU Medical College and Bellevue are based on information published in the bulletin and the *Bellevue Violet*, unless otherwise noted.
3 Holden Frederick C, Opening Address, *Bellevue Violet*, 1927.
4 The University Heights campus was sold to the City University of New York in 1973.
5 Wyckoff John, "Medical Teaching in Bellevue Hospital," *Bellevue Violet*, 1927.
6 Cooper Page, *The Bellevue Story*, Thomas Y. Crowell, New York, 1948.
7 *New York University Bulletin*, 1930–31, pp. 50–51.
8 *Bellevue Violet*, vol. 6, 1930, pp. 142–148.
9 Ibid., p. 36.
10 Interview, Frederick S. Kaplan, December 18, 2005.
11 FHN, autobiographical notes.
12 Ibid.
13 FHN, told to FMN, c. 1960.
14 Blitzer Andrew, *Bulletin of the New York Academy of Medicine*, vol. 62, no. 8, October 1986.
15 Interview, Peter Som, March 24, 2006.
16 *Bellevue Violet*, vol. 5, 1929, p. 6.
17 Ibid., pp. 236–238. Oscar Drexler, editor-in-chief; Joseph Hillel, business manager; Joseph A. Rube, art editor.
18 Ibid., pp. 13–23.
19 Forerunner of Con Edison.
20 FHN, told to FMN, c. 1963.
21 Interview, RN, April 7, 2004.
22 Wood G, "Nanny Speaks" interview of Gertrude Netter, November 1984.
23 By permission of Robert Marrazzi.
24 United States Census, 1930: 1 Marble Hill Avenue.
25 *Bellevue Violet*, 1930, p. 156.
26 Mary MacFadyen, told to FMN, c. 1950–1960.

27   *Bellevue Violet*, 1930, p. 158.

28   *Bellevue Violet*, 1931, p. 156.

29   Email, Colleen Bradley-Sanders, archivist, NYU Medical Center, per annual catalogues, July 27, 2004.

30   FHN, told to FMN, c. 1965.

31   *Bellevue Violet*, 1931, p. 139.

32   *Bellevue Violet*, 1931, p. 126.

33   *Bellevue Violet*, 1931, p. 130.

34   New York State license to marry, June 17, 1931.

35   Knights Edwin M Jr, "The Tumultuous Past of Bellevue Hospital," *History Magazine*, December 2000.

36   Family gravestones, Fayetteville, NC. Oscar McFadyen died in July 1932, and Katie McFadyen, in February 1933. They are buried side by side in a family plot in Fayetteville.

37   New York City Archives, Death Certificate Index #20525. She died in September 1933 and was buried at Mount Lebanon Cemetery.

Chapter 4: Mary

1   The spelling she used was *Rene*, but in writing the pronunciation is often confused with that of the French name *René*. To preserve the pronunciation of her name, the spelling used here is *Renie*.

2   Family history is from Mary MacFadyen's autobiographical notes and various United States Census records. That Mary's maternal great-grandfathers had owned slaves is well documented in the United States Census of 1850 [United States Census, 1850, Slave Schedules: Enoch Robbins, eleven slaves ages 1–35; Samuel Musgrave Sr., 1 slave].

3   Whyte Donald, *Dictionary of Scottish Emigrants to the U.S.A.*, vol. 2, with an appendix and corrections tovol. 1. Magna Carta Book Co., Baltimore, MD, 1986, p. 88. Note historical spelling.

4   Unites States Census, 1860.

5   *Musgrove* was the spelling used by Samuel Sr. The historical spelling is *Musgrave*, which Samuel Jr. adopted.

6   United States Civil War soldiers, 1861–1865, film M230, roll 28 [online database at www.ancestry.com].

7   Renie Robinson, told to FMN, c. 1985.

8   Interview, Oscar Lee McFadyen Jr, Fayetteville, NC, July 3, 2004.

9   Mary MacFadyen, told to FMN, c. 1960.

10   Mary MacFadyen, autobiographical notes.

11   Renamed the Women's College of the University of North Carolina in 1932 and again renamed the University of North Carolina at Greensboro in 1963.

12   Email, Marilyn Robinson, UNC—Greensboro Record Services, to FMN, June 15, 2004.

13   "Inventors Must Go Nature One Better," *The Washington Post*, February 20, 1927.

14 In her last year at GWU, she became ill and was forced to take a year
off from school. She began her studies at University of North Carolina
School of Medicine in the fall of 1926, without a bachelor of arts degree.
She earned that degree from GWU in June 1927 and returned to medical
school in the fall of 1928, completing the work there in June 1929.

15 Interview, Oscar Lee McFadyen Jr, July 3, 2004; United States Census, 1910.

16 Stationery: O. L. McFadyen, M.D., Anderson and Old Streets, Fayetteville,
NC.

17 Mary MacFadyen, told to FMN, c. 1970.

18 Mary McFadyen transcript, UNC.

19 *University of North Carolina Catalogue*, 1927–1928.

20 Mary MacFadyen, told to FMN, c. 1950–1970.

21 Records of the North Carolina College for Women show the *McFadyen*
spelling; GWU diploma has the *MacFadyen* spelling with the *a* added; at
UNC it was back to *Mc*; at NYU, it was *Mac*.

22 Diploma, GWU, 1927.

23 *Yackety Yack* (UNC yearbook), 1929.

24 *Bellevue Violet* (NYU Medical College yearbook), 1931.

25 Mary MacFadyen, told to FMN, c. 1950–1970.

26 Ibid.

27 Mary MacFadyen, autobiographical notes.

28 Ibid.

29 Woman's Hospital merged with St. Luke's Hospital in 1954.

30 504 West 110th Street. Prior to resigning from Mount Sinai, Frank moved
his office from the Park Avenue address to the W. 110th Street address.

Chapter 5: The Art of Medicine

1 Email correspondence, Barbara Niss (Mount Sinai School of Medicine) to
FMN, February 16, 2004, and October 28, 2011. The outpatient clinic was
on the corner of 100th Street and Madison Avenue.

2 Interview, Arthur H. Aufse Jr., March 13, 2006. Also, Aufses AH Jr and
Niss BJ, *This House of Noble Deeds: The Mount Sinai Hospital, 1852–2002*, New
York University Press, New York, 2002. Arthur Aufses Sr. was on the staff
of Mount Sinai 10 years ahead of Frank. Arthur Aufses Jr. joined the staff
of Mount Sinai later. Within the Department of Surgery at that time, there
were four services. Edwin Beer was chief of urology; Richard Lewisohn,
chief of general surgery, had in 1915 introduced the citrate method of
preserving blood; A.A. Berg was chief of gastrointestinal and, at the urging
of his colleague Richard Lewisohn, had performed the first gastrectomy in
the United States in 1922; Harold Neuhof was chief of thoracic, succeeding
the distinguished Howard Lilienthal, who stepped down in 1922. Among
his many noted accomplishments during his lifelong career at Mount
Sinai, Dr. Lilienthal published the first book in English on thoracic surgery
in 1925. Frank made a pencil-sketch portrait of him. It is not dated, but
he signed the picture in the same cursive script, *Frank H. Netter*, as on

the pictures he made while a medical student at NYU, except that the signature is more mature with the *N* in block lettering.

3   Ibid. Also, email, Barbara Niss (Mount Sinai School of Medicine) to FMN, July 18, 2006.

4   Email, Colleen Bracley-Sanders (NYU Medical College) to FMN, July 21, 2008.

5   Interview, Frederick S. Kaplan, December 18, 2005.

6   Bernake Ben S., "Money, Gold and the Great Depression," H. Parker Willis Lecture in Economic Policy, Washington and Lee University, Lexington, Virginia, March 2, 2004.

7   Interview, Arthur H. Aufses, Jr., March 13, 2006.

8   Monroe Mayer, told to FMN, c. 1976.

9   FHN, autobiographical notes.

10 FHN student transcript, Art Students League.

11 *Novocain*, Winthrop Chemical Company, New York, 1936.

12 The revised twelfth edition of *Cunningham's Textbook of Anatomy* was printed by Oxford University Press in January 1981. The heart flyer used text from an earlier edition, available in 1938.

13 Gray H, *Anatomy, Descriptive and Surgical*, Lea Brothers & Co., Philadelphia, 1901.

14 Suprarenalin, Armour Laboratories, 1938.

15 *Armour Atlas of Hematology*, Armour Laboratories, 1939.

16 FHN, letter to FMN, February 14, 1980.

17 *The Pituitary Gland*, Armour Laboratories, 1940.

18 *The Thyroid Gland*, Armour Laboratories, 1943.

19 Letter, Fred Bradley to Jim Weber, April 4, 1942.

20 MacFadyen M, *Beauty Plus*, Emerson Books, Inc., New York, 1938.

21 The first edition went to three printings by 1946: *Books Published Today*, *The New York Times*, December 3, 1957; a second edition in 1947 was widely quoted between 1947 and 1951 by Alicia Hart, NEA Service Inc. staff writer, in her columns.

22 *Evening Bulletin*, Philadelphia, October 1, 1940; *The Cleveland Press*, February 6, 1941.

23 "Club Events," *Miami Herald*, page 3-B, c. 1940, exact date unknown.

24 *Miami Herald*, March 29, 1940.

25 "Club Events," *Miami Herald*, p. 9-A, c. 1940, exact date unknown.

26 *St. Louis Post-Dispatch*, November 3, 1940.

27 Letter, Ruth Reninghaus, chairman, Curators' Committee, Salmagundi Club, to FMN, April 20, 2004.

28 Email, Terrence Brown, director, Society of Illustrators, to FMN, January 12, 2006. Frank was elected a life member in 1968.

29 *Post* illustration for *The Posthumous Papers of the Pickwick Club*, December 23, 1935, per Montgomery, E.M., *Norman Rockwell*, JG Press, reprinted World Publications Group, North Dighton, MA, 2003.

30 Cather W, *Death Comes for the Archbishop*, A.A. Knopf, New York, 1927.
31 Interview, Dave Mascaro and William Stenstrom, 1986, by permission of S. Harrison, Medical College of Georgia; the same story is also related in Malloni, B., "Frank Netter Dean of Medical Illustrators," *Visual Medicine*, vol. 6, no. 4, December 1966.
32 FHN, autobiographical notes. Frank heard Flanagan speak at a meeting of the Society of Illustrators.
33 Mary MacFadyen, told to FMN, c. 1970.
34 FHN, "Frank H. Netter, MD, Artist, Physician, Teacher," Ciba-Geigy, Summit, NJ, 1988.
35 Dellie Bendes, told to FMN, August 5, 2006.
36 FHN 1136 Fifth Avenue: stationery advertising his availability for work on projects for the New York World's Fair.

Chapter 6: Transparent Woman

1   Nelson GL, *Pharmaceutical Company Histories*, vol. I, Bismarck, ND: Woodbine Publishing, 1983, p. 142.
2   FHN, autobiographical notes, *Transparent Woman*, p. II.
3   Ibid., p. III.
4   Ibid., p. II.
5   Ibid., p. III.
6   Ibid.
7   Ibid., p. IV.
8   Ibid.
9   Ibid.
10 Ibid., p. V.
11 FHN to FMN, c. 1982.
12 Burman BL, *Steamboat Round the Bend*, Grosset & Dunlap, New York, 1933.
13 *Steamboat Round the Bend*, 20th Century Fox, 1935.
14 Burman BL, *Blow for a Landing*, Houghton Mifflin, Boston, MA, 1938.
15 Ben Lucien Burman and Alice Caddy Burman Papers, Manuscripts Collection 529, Manuscripts Department, Howard-Tilton Memorial Library, Tulane University, New Orleans, LA.
16 FHN, op. cit., p. VI.
17 Nelson, op. cit., p. 142.
18 FHN, op. cit., p. VI.
19 Pratt R, "The Enchanted Isle," *Ladies' Home Journal*, July 1939, p. 15.
20 FHN, op. cit., p. VI.

Chapter 7: World War II

1   127 East 80th Street.
2   Lowry C, "Successful Woman MD Switches to Antiques," *Syracuse Herald American*, November 29, 1953.

3   Interview, RN, April 7, 2004.

4   Mary MacFadyen, told to FMN, c. 1950–1970.

5   Leo Kanner, the psychologist who coined the term, reported case histories in 1943; the American Psychiatric Association first defined autism in the 1980 publication *Diagnostic and Statistical Manual of Mental Disorders*, 3rd edition.

6   After February 16, 1942, men between the ages of 20 and 44 were eligible to be drafted; after June 30, 1942, men between 18 and 20 were also eligible.

7   MacFadyen M, "Good Health, Good Posture and the Bust-line," Jones Syndicate, March 23, 1942.

8   Email, Merrilee Mose (Sanford School), August 1, 2006, and school reports, July 1943.

9   The museum was at Independence Avenue and 7th Street, SW. After World War II, it evolved into the Armed Forces Institute of Pathology and the National Museum of Health and Medicine and relocated to Walter Reed Army Medical Center in 1949. In September 2011 the National Museum of Health and Medicine moved to Silver Spring and the Armed Forces Institute of Pathology closed.

10 Records of Frank Netter's military service were destroyed in a fire at the National Personnel Records Center on July 12, 1973, per a letter from Hatti M. Robertson, archives technician, National Personnel Records Center, August 2, 2004.

11 Interview film of FHN by David Mascaro and David Stenstrom, 1986, by permission of S. Harrison, Medical College of Georgia.

12 FHN, autobiographical notes, Army, p. II.

13 Email, Sharon Colacinio Oberg to FMN, November 25, 2006.

14 FHN, op. cit., p. III.

15 Ibid., p. IV.

16 Ibid., p. V.

17 Ibid.

18 Ibid.

19 Ibid.

20 Ibid., p. VI.

21 Ibid., p. VII.

22 Ibid., pp. VII–VIII.

23 Nationwide gasoline rationing was imposed December 1, 1942. It was designed to reduce driving and thereby save rubber tires—rubber, not gasoline, being the commodity in scarce supply. Rationing continued until August 15, 1945. Speed limits were 35 miles per hour for the duration. Brownout laws forbade headlight use, and only parking lights were permitted for night driving.

24 FHN, op. cit., p. X.

25 Ibid.

26 Frank left no notes as to who the artists were who did the painting.

27 "Combat First Aid, How to Save Life in Battle," *Infantry Journal*, 1944.

28 Interview, Ray Olivere to FMN, November 28, 2005.
29 Teleconference, Ray Olivere with FMN, June 2006.
30 Email, Ray Olivere to FMN, November 29, 2005.
31 Email, Ray Olivere to FMN, November 1, 2005.
32 FHN, autobiographical notes.
33 This was the concept that years later led the military to create mobile army surgical hospital (MASH) units.
34 These centers became the Veterans Administration Medical Center system, now known as the US Department of Veterans Affairs.
35 Email, Ray Olivere to FMN, November 29, 2005.

Chapter 8: The Studio

1 The oil brushes were from a variety of manufacturers, including Robert Simmons, M. Grumbacher, Universal Artline, and Favor Ruhl.
2 Gray H, *Anatomy Descriptive and Surgical*, Lea Brothers & Co., Philadelphia, 1901.
3 Rabelais François, *The Complete Works of Rabelais*, Bibliophilist Society, London, no date.
4 Defoe Daniel, *Moll Flanders*, Hogarth Press, New York, 1931.
5 Goldberg R, *Rube Goldberg's Guide to Europe*, Vanguard Press, New York, 1954.
6 *World Book*, Quarrie Corporation, Chicago, 1947.
7 *Who's Who in American Art*, American Federation of Arts, Washington, DC, 1947.
8 FHN, autobiographical notes.
9 FHN, "A Medical Illustrator at Work," *Ciba Symposia*, vol. 10, no. 6, pp. 1090–1091, 1949.
10 Ibid., p. 1091.
11 Ibid.
12 Ibid., p. 1092.
13 FHN, "Medical Illustration, Its History and Present Day Practice", *Journal of the International College of Surgeons*, vol. XXVI, no. 4, p. 505, 1956.
14 FHN, autobiographical notes.
15 Ibid.
16 Ibid.
17 Ibid.
18 FHN, "A Picture Is Worth a Thousand Words," *Medical and Health Annual*, Encyclopedia Britannica, Chicago, 1989, p. 118.
19 FHN, autobiographical notes.
20 Ibid.
21 Hendrickson R.M., "Doctor at the Drawing Board," *Today's Health*, American Medical Association, May 1961, p. 32.
22 FHN, "A Picture Is Worth a Thousand Words," op. cit., p. 117.
23 Email, Arlene Shaner, assistant curator and reference librarian, New York Academy of Medicine, March 9, 2007.

Chapter 9: Diverse Interests

1   Divorce agreement dated June 15, 1956, by and between FHN and Mary Netter, pp. 1–2.

2   Forrest Laboratories, Inc. was at 246 East 44th Street; Forrest, Inc. was at that address until moving to 16 Bay Street in Oyster Bay, on Long Island. Forrest is not the same company as—and has no connection with—Forest Laboratories, Inc.

3   Theocabital, trademark 355881, US Patent Office, April 5, 1938.

4   Bi-Laticol, trademark 364436, US Patent Office, January 31, 1939.

5   Benzox, trademark 312266, US Patent Office, original registration April 24, 1934, renewed June 22, 1954.

6   Hembron, trademark 404429, US Patent Office, January 23, 1943, and Hembro, trademark 433944, US Patent Office, November 4,1947.

7   Serts, trademark 417511, US Patent Office, October 30, 1945.

8   Chasp, trademark 556559, US Patent Office, March 25, 1952.

9   John Hay Whitney (1905–1982).

10   Mary MacFadyen, autobiographical notes.

11   Ibid.

12   FHN, Autobiographical notes, proposal draft for *The Doctor Draws a Picture*, p. 5.

13   Letter to Norman Weisman from FHN, May 25, 1949.

14   Letter, Harry C. Folts to Norman (Bud) Weisman, April 15, 1949.

15   Letter, FHN to Norman Weisman, April 19, 1949.

16   Letter, Norman Weisman to FHN, May 13,1949.

17   Letter, FHN to Norman Weisman, May 25, 1949.

18   Letter, FHN to Peter Lasker, May 28, 1951.

19   Telegram, Peter Lasker to FHN, August 20, 1951.

20   Letter, H.P. Lasker to FHN, October 2, 1951.

21   The first edition went to three printings by 1946, according to "Books Published Today," *New York Times*, December 3, 1957; a second edition in 1947 was widely quoted between 1947 and 1951 by Alicia Hart, NEA Service Inc. staff writer, in her columns.

Chapter 10: Folly Farm

1   FMN, August 10, 2008.

2   Passenger lists, 1948–1956, show that they often traveled to Europe in the summer.

3   Bookmiller MM, Bowen GL, *Textbook of Obstetrics and Obstetrical Nursing*, WB Saunders, Philadelphia, 1949.

4   The name Royal Ballet was granted by royal charter in 1956.

5   It was then on Broadway at 40th Street.

6   Letter, FHN to Professor José López-Rey, New York University Institute of Art, October 20, 1971.

7   121 East 60th Street.

8   Email, Peter Som, September 11, 2006: After he numbed the mucosa, Max inserted a curved metal tube into the maxillary sinus and forced warm saline into the sinus to push out the infected secretions.

9   105 East 80th Street.

10 Not until 1963 did Easson and Russell publish "The Cure of Hodgkin's Disease," which reversed the belief that Hodgkin's was incurable: Easson EC, Russell MH, "The Cure of Hodgkin's Disease," *British Medical Journal*, vol. 1, pp. 1704–1707, June 29, 1963.

11 Interview, Kathryn Mills, April 21, 2006.

Chapter 11: The Life of a Doctor

1   FHN, *CCMI*, vol. 3, *Lower Digestive Tract Part II, Digestive System*, Ciba, Summit, NJ, 1962, p. vii: *War Injuries of the Chest, War Injuries of the Abdomen* and *War Injuries of the Extremities* were intended to be of assistance to physicians treating wounded soldiers returning from World War II.

2   FHN, *CCMI*, Ciba, Summit, NJ, 1948. This book of 210 plates is divided into four sections: "Lungs and Chest," "Gastrointestinal Tract," "Male Reproductive Organs and Male and Female Mammary Glands" and "Heart and Aorta," with a brief introductory text prepared by FHN preceding each section. Jacob Buckstein, Michael E. DeBakey, Charles F. Geschickter, Reuben A. MacBrayer, Henry H. Ritter, Eli H. Rubin, and Samuel A. Vest were responsible for the explanatory texts that accompanied the plates.

3   *Ciba Symposia*, Summit, NJ: Ciba Pharmaceutical Products, April 1939–October 1951.

4   *Ciba Symposia*, vol. 1, no. 1, 1939.

5   Gebhard B, "Health and Hygiene at International Expositions," *Ciba Symposia*, vol. 8, no. 12, 1947, p. 599.

6   Vesalius A, *De Humani Corporis Fabrica*, Basel, 1543.

7   *Clin. Symp.*, spring, vol. 1, no. 1, 1948.

8   New York Polyclinic Medical School and Hospital, as the postgraduate medical school of Columbia University was then called.

9   FHN, *CCMI*, vol. 1, *Nervous System*, Ciba, Summit, NJ, 1953, Introduction, p. viii.

10 *Clinical Symposia* had an ambitious production schedule—two issues in 1948, seven in 1949, ten in 1950, eight in 1951 and 1952 and six per year for the remainder of the decade. From 1960 until 1973 it averaged four issues per year, and then increased again to generally six per year.

11 Walton JH, *Control of Pain with Saddle Block and Higher Anesthesia*, Ciba, Summit, NJ, 1948.

12 *Clin. Symp.*, vol. 3, no. 3, 1951.

13 *The Biliary System*, Armour Laboratories, Chicago, 1946.

14 "Flair Personified," *Flair*, February 1950, pp. 20–25.

15 "Medicine," *Life*, August 15, 1949, pp. 47–47.

16 Lear J, "Polio Losing Its Punch," *Colliers*, August 4, 1951, pp. 13–15.

17 Jonas Salk was also developing a vaccine, but Frank's allegiance was with his classmate, Albert Sabin. When the Salk vaccine appeared in 1952, Frank was displeased that it had preempted the glory that belonged to Sabin, whose more effective vaccine did not appear until 1957.

18 *Pfizer Series of Anatomical and Pathological Transparencies*, Pfizer, Brooklyn, NY, 1950–1954.

19 FHN, CCMI, vol. 4, *Endocrine System and Selected Metabolic Diseases*, Ciba, Summit, NJ, 1965, p. vi.

20 Agreement between Ciba-Geigy Corporation and FHN, effective January 1, 1991.

21 FHN, CCMI, vol. 4, *Endocrine System and Selected Metabolic Diseases*, Ciba, Summit, NJ, 1965, p. vi.

22 FHN, CCMI, vol. 1, *Nervous System*, Ciba, Summit, NJ, 1953.

23 FHN, "Anatomical Plates on the Nervous System," *Clin. Symp.*, vol. 1, no. 1, 1948; FHN, "Anatomical Plates on the Nervous System," *Clin. Symp.*, vol. 1, no. 2, 1948; FHN, "A New Series of Anatomical Plates on the Nervous System—The Basal Ganglia" *Clin. Symp.*, vol. 1, no. 3, 1949; FHN, "Anatomical Plates on the Nervous System—The Basal Ganglia," *Clin. Symp.*, vol. 1, no. 5, 1949; FHN, "The Brain and Spinal Cord," *Clin. Symp.*, vol. 1, no. 6, 1949; FHN, "Anatomic Plates—The Spinal Column," *Clin. Symp.*, vol. 1, no. 7, 1949; FHN, Kuntz A, "The Autonomic Nervous System," *Clin. Symp.*, vol. 2, no. 1, 1950; FHN, "Anatomy of the Spinal Column," (plates 4–6), *Clin. Symp.*, vol. 2, no. 1, 1949–1950; FHN, "Anatomy of the Spinal Column," (plates 7–11), *Clin. Symp.*, vol. 2, no. 2, 1950; FHN, von Bonin G, "Functional Neuro-Anatomy," *Clin. Symp.*, vol. 2, no. 3, 1950; FHN, von Bonin, G, "Functional Neuro-Anatomy," (plates 11, 12, 13), *Clin. Symp.*, vol. 2, no. 4, 1950; FHN, von Bonin G, "Functional Neuro-Anatomy," (plates 14, 15, 16), *Clin. Symp.*, vol. 2, no. 5, 1950; FHN, von Bonin G, "Functional Neuro-Anatomy," *Clin. Symp.*, vol. 2, no. 6, 1950; FHN, Kuntz A, "The Autonomic Nervous System," *Clin. Symp.*, vol. 2, no. 7, 1950; FHN, Kuntz A, "The Autonomic Nervous System," *Clin. Symp.*, vol. 2, no. 8, 1950; FHN, Kuntz A, "The Autonomic Nervous System," *Clin. Symp.*, vol. 2, no. 9, 1950; FHN, Kaplan A, "Pathology of the Brain and Spinal Cord," *Clin. Symp.*, vol. 3, no. 1, 1951; FHN, Kaplan A, "Pathology of the Brain and Spinal Cord," *Clin. Symp.*, vol. 3, no. 2, 1951; Kaplan A, "Pathology of the Brain and Spinal Cord," *Clin. Symp.*, vol. 3, no. 3, 1951; FHN, Kaplan A, "Pathology of the Brain and Spinal Cord," *Clin. Symp.*, vol. 3, no. 4, 1951; FHN, Kaplan A, "Pathology of the Brain and Spinal Cord," *Clin. Symp.*, vol. 3, no. 5, 1951; FHN, Kaplan A, "Pathology of the Brain and Spinal Cord," *Clin. Symp.*, vol. 3, no. 7, 1951.

24 FHN, op. cit. *Nervous System*, Sec. I. "Anatomy of the Spine," plates 1–10; Sec. II. "The Central Nervous System," plates 11–32; Sec. V. "Pathology of the Brain and Spinal Cord," plates 73–104.

25 Ibid., Sec. III. "Functional Neuro-Anatomy," plates 33–52.

26 Ibid., Sec. IV. "The Autonomic Nervous System," plates 53–72.

27 Ibid., "Preface to the Fourth Printing."

28 Mary MacFadyen to FMN, c. 1955.

29 Doodle died the following year and was buried at Arlington National Cemetery in July 1954.

30 FHN, *CCMI*, vol. 2, *Reproductive System*, Ciba, Summit, NJ, 1954.

31 Joe Gaines wrote two *Clinical Symposia* articles on ovarian neoplasms and one on diseases of the vulva [FHN, Gaines JA, "Diseases of the Vulva," *Clin. Symp.*, vol. 2, no. 6, 1950; Gaines JA, "Ovarian Neoplasms; Thumbnail Sketches of Tumors of the Ovary with Emphasis on Clinical Recognition, Pathology and Management," *Clin. Symp.*, vol. 6, no. 4, 1954; Gaines JA, "Ovarian Neoplasms; Thumbnail Sketches of Tumors of the Ovary with Emphasis on Clinical Recognition, Pathology and Management" [a continuation], *Clin. Symp.*, vol. 6, no. 6, 1954], and 44 plates from those were in the *Reproductive* volume [FHN, op. cit. *Reproductive System*, Sec. VI. "Anatomy of the Female Genital Tract," plates 1–2, 4, 6–7, 9–16; Sec. VII. "Diseases of the Vulva," plates 1–10; Sec. XI. "Diseases of the Ovary," plates 1–21]. N. S. Assali had prepared an article in an issue of *Clinical Symposia* on toxemia [Assali NS, "Toxemia of Pregnancy," *Clin. Symp.*, vol. 6, no. 1, 1954]. He collaborated with Pearl M. Zeek and, in addition to the 24 older pictures on pregnancy, worked with Frank to develop a new plate on hormonal fluctuations [FHN, op. cit. *Reproductive System*, Sec. XII. "Pregnancy and Its Diseases," plates 1–25]. Isidor C. Rubin wrote two *Clinical Symposia* articles, one on infertility and one with Josef Novak on the fallopian tubes [Novak J., Rubin I.C., "Anatomy and Pathology of the Fallopian Tubes," *Clin. Symp.*, vol. 4, no. 6, 1952; Rubin IC., "Myomectomy in the Treatment of Infertility," *Clin. Symp.*, vol. 6, no. 6, 1954]. Twelve plates from those publications were included in the *Reproductive System*, and they developed one new plate on cysts [FHN, op. cit. *Reproductive System*, Sec. VI. "Anatomy of the Female Genital Tract," plate 24; Sec. X. "Diseases of the Fallopian Tubes," plates 1–12]. Samuel Vest at the University of Virginia wrote *Clinical Symposia* articles on the male genitourinary tract [Vest, S.A., "The Anatomy of the Male Genito-Urinary Tract," *Clin. Symp.*, vol. 4, no. 8, 1952; Vest S.A., "The Prostate," *Clin. Symp.*, vol. 6, no. 2, 1954; Vest S.A., "Prostatic Malignancy," *Clin. Symp.*, vol. 6, no. 3, 1954], from which they reused 63 plates. He consulted with Frank on 14 new plates [FHN, op. cit. *Reproductive System*, Sec. I. "Development of the Genital Tracts," plates 1, 2; Sec. II. "Anatomy of the Male Genital Tract," plates 1–18; Sec. III. "Diseases of the Penis and Urethra," plates 1–16; Sec. IV. "Diseases of the Prostate and the Seminal Tract," plates 1–16; Sec. V. "Diseases of the Scrotum and Testis," 1–23; Sec. XIV. "Intersexes," plates 1–4]. Albert Decker at New York Medical College wrote an article in a *Clinical Symposia* issue on gynecologic diseases [Decker A., "Culdoscopy: A Method for Visual

Diagnosis of Gynecologic Disease," *Clin. Symp.*, vol. 4, no. 6, 1952], and one plate [FHN, op. cit. *Reproductive System*, Sec. VI. "Anatomy of the Female Genital Tract," plate 31] from that was included in the volume. Other plates were from the series of portfolios Frank had done for Ciba in the 1940s, for which Charles F. Geschickter, at Georgetown University School of Medicine, wrote the text for the 19 plates on the mammary gland [FHN, op. cit. *Reproductive System*, Sec. XIII. "Anatomy and Pathology of the Mammary Gland," plates 1–19]. Robert A. Hingson, at Western Reserve School of Medicine, wrote the text for one plate on neuropathways [FHN, op. cit. *Reproductive System*, Sec. VI. "Anatomy of the Female Genital Tract," plate 17].

32 FHN, op. cit. *Reproductive System*, Sec. VI. "Anatomy of the Female Genital Tract," plates 21–21, 25–29; Sec. IX. "Diseases of the Uterus," plates 1–19. Ciba also reused 20 older ones from the three *Clinical Symposia* articles Dr. Sturgis had written: Sturgis SH, "Diseases of the Uterus," *Clin. Symp.*, vol. 4, no. 1, 1952; Sturgis S.H., "Diseases of the Uterus," *Clin. Symp.*, vol. 4, no. 3, 1952; Sturgis SH, "Diseases of the Uterus," *Clin. Symp.*, vol. 4, no. 4, 1952.

33 FHN, op. cit. *Reproductive System*, Sec. VI. "Anatomy of the Female Genital Tract," plates 3, 5, 8, 18–20, 30; Sec. VIII. "Diseases of the Vagina," plates 1–16.

34 Interview, George Mitchell, November 14, 2005.

35 Ibid.

36 FHN, op. cit. *Reproductive System*, Sec. I. "Development of the Genital Tracts," plate 3.

Chapter 12: Palm Beach

1 Oleg Cassini obituary, *New York Times*, March 19, 2006.

2 560 South Ocean Boulevard.

3 Jim (15), Francine (10), and Jonathan (8).

4 417 East 57th Street.

5 Email, Elliot Kleinberg, *Palm Beach Post*, to FMN, June 6, 2006, from an article in the *Post*, Wednesday, January 14, 2004, section "Neighborhood Post," p. 14.

6 Interview, Marvin Moser, March 16, 2006.

7 FHN, *CCMI*, vol. 3, *Digestive System Part III*, Ciba, Summit, NJ, 1957.

8 Ibid., p. vi.

9 www.mssm.edu/departments-and-institutes/pathology/about-us /hall-of-fame, January 4, 2012.

10 FHN, op. cit., *Digestive System*, Sec. XV. "Anatomy of the Liver, Biliary Tract and Pancreas," plates 1–24; Sec. XVI. "Physiology and Pathophysiology of the Liver, Biliary Tract, and Pancreas," plates 1–19; Sec. VII. "Diseases of the Liver," plates 1–8, 10–12, 15–56, Sec. XVIII. "Diseases of

the Gallbladder and Bile Ducts," plates 9–12, 16; supplement, 2nd ed., 1964, "New Aspects," plates 1–12.

11 Popper H, "Jaundice; Important Anatomic and Functional Considerations," *Clin. Symp.*, vol. 7, no. 5, 1955.

12 Popper H, "Hepatitis and Hepatic Tests," *Clin. Symp.*, vol. 8, no. 3, 1956.

13 Popper H, "Cirrhosis," *Clin. Symp.*, vol. 8, no. 6, 1956.

14 Popper H, Schaffner F., *Liver Structure and Function*, Blakiston Division, New York 1957.

15 Popper did 12 more plates with Frank as a supplement to the second edition of *Digestive System Part III* in 1964. George Pack at Memorial Cancer Center also did a supplement—FHN, op. cit., *Digestive System*, 2nd ed. 1964, supplement; New Aspects 1–12; "Surgical Treatment of Tumors," plates 13–21—for that second edition. Frank did an issue of *Clinical Symposia*— Pack G.T., Islami A.H., "Operative Treatment of Hepatic Tumors," *Clin. Symp.*, vol. 16, no. 2, 1964—with Dr. Pack and his colleague, Abdol H. Islami, that was incorporated into supplement in the second edition.

16 In addition to working with Hans Popper and his colleague Donald Kozoll [FHN, op. cit., *Digestive System*, Sec. XVIII. "Diseases of the Gallbladder and Bile Ducts," plates 9–12, 16] in Chicago, Frank consulted with two physicians at Cornell in New York, Oscar Bodansky [ibid., Sec. XVI. "Physiology and Pathophysiology of the Liver, Biliary Tract and Pancreas," plates 20–23] and Eugene Cliffton [ibid., Sec. XV. "Normal Anatomy of the Liver, Biliary Tract and Pancreas," 25–29; and Sec. XIX, "Diseases of the Pancreas," plates 1–9], the latter being the author of an issue of *Clinical Symposia* on the pancreas [Cliffton E.E., *Diseases of the Pancreas*, *Clin. Symp.*, vol. 9, no. 2, 1957], and with Victor Sborov [FHN, op. cit., *Digestive System*, Sec. XVII. "Diseases of the Liver," plates 9, 13–14] at the University of California Medical School in San Francisco.

17 Bowen C, *The Curse of the Misbegotten*, McGraw-Hill, New York, 1959, p. 354.

18 Interview, Rudolph E. Drosd, May 17, 2007.

19 Ibid. Dr. Drosd recalled that Frank gave him a set of pictures, but did not recall if it was books or loose pictures. Of *The Ciba Collection*, at that time only the *Nervous System* and *Reproductive System* had been published.

20 FMN, February 12, 2006.

Chapter 13: Back to Folly Farm

1 Letter, Katie Mills to Mrs. Frank Netter, October 16, 1955.

2 Ibid.

3 Letter, Aubrey McFadyen to Mary Netter, November 14, 1955.

4 Interview, RN, April 7, 2004.

5 Subsequently renamed the Section on the History of Medicine and Public Health, per email, Arlene Shaner, curator, New York Academy of Medicine, to FMN, July 24, 2008.

6   The papers were FHN, "History of Medical Illustration and
      Demonstration of Techniques"; Meyer M. Melikow, MD, "The
      Interrelationship of Medicine and Art"; William Stanley Wyatt, MA,
      "Expression vs. Illustration in Visual Art." Email, Arlene Shaner to FMN,
      July 24, 2008.
7   FHN, "Medical Illustration, Its History, Significance and Practice" *Bull. N
      Y Acad. Med.*, vol. 33, no. 5, May 1957; Dr. Melikow's paper also appeared in
      that publication.
8   Ibid., p. 364.
9   Interview, Michael DeBakey, June 30, 2004.
10   Ibid.
11   Ibid.
12   DeBakey ME, Dooley DA, Creech O Jr, "Surgery of the Aorta," *Clin. Symp.*,
      vol. 8, no. 2, 1956.
13   Popper H, "Hepatitis and Hepatic Tests," *Clin. Symp.*, vol. 8, no. 3, 1956; also
      FHN, CCMI, vol. 3, *Digestive System Part III*, Ciba, Summit, NJ, 1957.
14   Agreement between FHN and Mary Netter, dated June 15, 1956.
15   Bowen C, *The Curse of the Misbegotten*, McGraw-Hill, New York, 1959, p. 318.
16   Madison Square Garden moved to 34th Street and 7th Avenue in 1968.
17   FMN, July 24, 2008.
18   The Hyde Park Hotel on East 77th Street and Madison Avenue later
      became the Mark Hotel.
19   Handwritten note, FHN to Mary Netter, June 26, 1956.
20   FMN, July 24, 2008.
21   FHN, CCMI, vol. 3, *Digestive System Part III*, Ciba, Summit, NJ, 1957. A
      second edition was published in 1964, with revisions and the addition of
      two supplemental sections, one on new aspects of liver metabolism and
      structure and another on the management of liver tumors, in association
      with Hans Popper and with George Pack in New York.
22   Ibid., introduction, p. vii.

Chapter 14: Vera

1   Unites States Census, 1900.
2   Ibid.
3   Ibid.
4   United States Census, 1910.
5   Death certificate, Henry Burrows, 1943.
6   United States Census, 1910.
7   Unites States Census, 1930.
8   Marriage license, Frank Netter—Vera Burrows, December 26, 1956.
9   Ibid. Record of the marriage not located in New York State. Record of
      passenger list, SS *Siboney*, sailing from Vera Cruz, Mexico, arriving New
      York June 15, 1933, lists James Stetson and his wife, Mary.
10   Death certificate, John Stetson, Palm Beach FL no. 6095-5649.

11 Death certificate, New York City, no. 156-53-103322, James Stetson, February 8, 1953; there was no estate in Nassau County Surrogate's Court for James D. Stetson, but there was a guardianship for his son, John P. Stetson. The petition for guardianship was filed May 22, 1956, and says, "That the infant's father is James D. Stetson that he died a resident of New York State County of Nassau . . ." John was almost 20 and asked that his mother be assigned guardian. The asset of interest was an insurance policy on the life of his father, payable to John (the policy was $2505, and interest was $225). After Vera was appointed guardian, she petitioned for money to be used for John's college expenses. He was by then attending Bucknell University.

12 John Stetson to FMN, c. 1993.

13 The address was 66 Perry Avenue, Bayville, New York; Henrietta had died in 1934. She was buried where her sister Rebecca lived in Bayville. Harry Burrows lived in Brooklyn with Vera's sister, Beatrice, who was retired from a career on the stage. Harry died in 1943, and sometime after that Beatrice, widowed and childless, had moved from Brooklyn to Bayville to live with Rebecca.

14 "Mrs. Stetson Rewed," *New York Times*, December 31, 1956, p. 10.

15 FHN, *CCMI*, vol. 3, *Digestive System Part I*, Ciba, Summit, NJ, 1959, Sec. II. "Anatomy of the Esophagus," 11–13; Sec. III. "Anatomy of the Stomach and Duodenum," 16–17.

16 Ibid., Sec. VII. "Diseases of the Stomach and Duodenum," 1–32.

17 Ibid., Sec. III. "Anatomy of the Stomach and Duodenum," 1–7, 15.

18 *Las Hilanderas* measures 220 × 289 centimeters. www.museodelprado.es /coleccion/galeria-on-line/galeria-on-line/obra /la-fabula-de-aracne-o-las-hilanderas/, January 30, 2012.

19 Letter, FHN to Professor José López-Rey, New York University Institute of Fine Arts, October 20, 1971.

20 "Planning May 23 Event for Long Island Orchestra," *New York Times*, May 9, 1958, p. 20.

21 Nassau County property card. Apportionment in 1956 in preparation for the sale.

22 FHN, told to FMN, c. 1980.

23 The approach to the main house at Folly Farm was used as a movie location for two Hollywood films. It can be seen in *An Affair to Remember* (Twentieth Century Fox), the 1957 film starring Deborah Kerr and Cary Grant. For the 1960 film *From the Terrace* (Twentieth Century Fox), starring Paul Newman and Joanne Woodward, Hollywood again came to Folly Farm to film the long drive and the portico. The Newmans came to the location for the shooting and had lunch at Folly Farm with Frank and Vera.

24 Lampe EW, "Surgical Anatomy of the Hand," *Clin. Symp.*, vol. 9, no. 2, 1957. This article is highly regarded by hand surgeons; it was first issued as

Lampe EW, "Surgical Anatomy of the Hand," *Clin. Symp.*, vol. 3, no. 8, 1951, and again as Lampe EW, "Surgical Anatomy of the Hand With Special Reference to Infections and Trauma," *Clin. Symp.*, vol. 21, no. 3, 1969 and Lampe EW, "Surgical Anatomy of the Hand With Special Reference to Infections and Trauma," *Clin. Symp.*, vol. 40, no. 3, 1988.

25 Ayd FJ Jr, "Treatment of the Office Neurotic," *Clin. Symp.*, vol. 9, no. 5, 1957.

26 Huber JF, "Anatomy of the Mouth," *Clin. Symp.*, vol. 10, no. 3, 1958.

27 Huber JF, "Anatomy of the Pharynx," *Clin. Symp.*, vol. 10, no. 4, 1958.

28 Huber JF, "Anatomy of the Mouth," *Clin. Symp.*, vol. 10, no. 3, 1958, plates VIII, X and XI, "Arterial Supply of the Mouth and Pharynx," "Venous Drainage of the Mouth and Pharynx" and "Nerve Supply of the Mouth and Pharynx."

29 Huber JF, "Anatomy of the Pharynx," *Clin. Symp.*, vol. 10, no. 4, 1958, plate II, "Interior of the Pharynx."

30 FHN, CCMI, vol. 1, *Nervous System*, Ciba, Summit, NJ, April 1957 printing.

31 Ingram WR, "The Hypothalamus," *Clin. Symp.*, vol. 8, no. 4, 1956.

32 FHN, CCMI, *Nervous System*, Ciba, Summit, NJ; 3rd printing, 1957; 7th printing, 1967.

33 In that same year, Frank did a *Clinical Symposia* issue with H.F. Moseley on the ankle and foot (Moseley HF, "Static Disorders of the Ankle and Foot," *Clin. Symp.*, vol. 9, no. 2, 1957; they subsequently did another together: Moseley H.F., "Traumatic Disorders of the Ankle and Foot," *Clin. Symp.*, vol. 17, no. 1, 1965). Frank had worked with him a decade earlier, in 1945, on Dr. Moseley's book *Shoulder Lesions* (Moseley H.F., *Shoulder Lesions*, Charles C. Thomas, Chicago, 1945), which had 11 color plates by Frank Netter and other illustrations by Helen MacArthur Moseley. In 1958, Frank worked again with Dr. Moseley on an issue of *Clinical Symposia*, this time on the shoulder (Moseley H.F., "Disorders of the Shoulder," *Clin. Symp.*, vol. 11, no. 3, 1959).

34 Interview, C. Everett Koop, August 19, 2004.

35 Koop CE, "Emergency Surgery of the Newborn," *Clin. Symp.*, vol. 11, no. 4, 1959.

36 Interview, C. Everett Koop, August 19, 2004.

37 FHN, op. cit. *Digestive System Part I.*

38 Ibid., Sec. IV, plate 28.

39 Ibid., Sec. V, plate 16.

40 Ibid., Sec. IV, plates 2, 11 and 15.

41 Ibid., Sec. I, "Anatomy of the Mouth and Pharynx," plates 1–29.

42 Ibid., Sec. II, "Anatomy of the Esophagus," plates 1–7, 10; Sec. IV, "Functional and Diagnostic Aspects," plate 23; Sec. V, "Diseases of the Mouth and Pharynx," plates 27–33; Sec. VI, "Diseases of the Esophagus," plates 1–6, 8–19.

43 Ibid., Sec. IV. "Functional and Diagnostic Aspects," plates 1–5, 8–22, 24–29.

44 Ibid., p. vi.

45 Frank worked also with Nicholas Michels (*Digestive System Part I*, Sec. II, "Anatomy of the Esophagus," plates 8–9, and Sec. III, "Anatomy of the Stomach and Duodenum," plates 8–14); Rudolph Nissen (*Digestive System Part I*, Sec. VII, "Diseases of the Stomach and Duodenum," plates 1–32); Leo Stern (*Digestive System Part I*, Sec. V, "Diseases of the Mouth and Pharynx," plates 1–26), with whom Frank also published an issue of *Clinical Symposia* (Stern L., Jr. "Pathology of the Mouth and Jaws," *Clin. Symp.*, vol. 5, no. 3, 1953); Bernard S. Wolf (*Digestive System Part I*, Sec. IV, "Functional and Diagnostic Aspects," plates 6–7; Sec. VI, "Diseases of the Esophagus," plate 7); and with Professor Gerhard Wolf-Heideggers (*Digestive System Part I*, Sec. III, "Anatomy of the Stomach and Duodenum," plates 1–7, 15).

46 In addition to working together on this and subsequent volumes of the *Ciba Collection* atlases, Frank and Professor G.A.G. Mitchell prepared an issue of *Clinical Symposia* that was published later in 1959: Mitchell GAG., "Nerve Supply of the Gastrointestinal Tract," *Clin. Symp.*, vol. 11, no. 5, 1959.

47 FHN, autobiographical notes.

48 FHN, op. cit. *Digestive System Part I*, p. vi.

Chapter 15: The East Side

1 48 East 65th Street.

2 FHN, CCMI, *Digestive System Part II: Lower Digestive Tract*, Ciba, Summit, NJ, 1962.

3 Ibid., Sec. IX, "Anatomy of the Abdomen," plates 30–34; Sec. X, "Anatomy of the Lower Digestive Tract," plates 30–34.

4 Ibid., Sec. IX, "Anatomy of the Abdomen," plates 25–28; Sec. X, "Anatomy of the Lower Digestive Tract," plates 18–27.

5 Ibid., Sec. IX, "Anatomy of the Abdomen," plate 29; Sec. X, "Anatomy of the Lower Digestive Tract," plates 1–9, 28–29.

6 Ibid., Sec. XI, "Functional and Diagnostic Aspects," plates 1–25.

7 Ibid., Sec. IX, "Anatomy of the Abdomen," plates 1–20.

8 Ibid., Sec. VIII, "Development of the Digestive Tract," plates 1–6.

9 Frank Netter did two issues of *Clinical Symposia* with William H. Bachrach (Bachrach WH, "Medical Treatment of Ulcerative Colitis," *Clin. Symp.*, vol. 7, no. 4, 1955, and Bachrach WH, "Physiology and Pathologic Physiology of the Stomach," *Clin. Symp.*, vol. 11, no. 1, 1959). R.V. Gorsch contributed to 18 plates on anatomy for *Volume 3, Part II of CCMI* (Sec. IX, "Anatomy of the Abdomen," plates 21–24; Sec. X, "Anatomy of the Lower Digestive Tract," 10–17), and Frank also did an issue of *Clinical Symposia* with him (Gorsch RV, "The Sigmoid, Rectum, and Anal Canal. Relations, Attachments, and Pelvic Spaces," *Clin. Symp.*, vol. 12, no. 2,1960). Frank did issues of *Clinical Symposia* with Alfred H. Iason (Iason AH, "Inguinal and Femoral Hernias," *Clin. Symp.*, vol. 7, no. 2, 1955, later reprinted as Iason AH, "Inguinal and Femoral Hernias," *Clin. Symp.*, vol. 18, no. 2, 1966),

Professor H.E. Lockhart-Mummery (Lockhart-Mummery HE, "Diseases of the Large Intestine," *Clin Symp.*, vol. 13, no. 3, 1961), Professor G.A.G. Mitchell (Mitchell GAG, "Nerve Supply of the Gastrointestinal Tract," *Clin. Symp.*, vol. 11, no. 5, 1959), and Drs. José Fernandes Pontes and Mitja Polak, of the São Paulo University Group (Pontes JF, Polak M, "Disorders of the Small Intestine," *Clin Symp.*, vol. 12, no. 4, 1960, and Polak M, "Benign Tumors of Small Intestine," *Clin. Symp.*, vol. 13, no. 1, 1961).

10 Crelin ES, "Development of Gastrointestinal Tract," *Clin. Symp.*, vol. 13, no. 3, 1961. They also did an issue of *Clinical Symposia* a decade later on topics incorporated into subsequent atlases: Crelin ES, "Development of the Nervous System. A Logical Approach to Neuroanatomy," *Clin. Symp.*, vol. 26, no. 2, 1974, and Crelin ES, "Development of the Lower Respiratory System," *Clin. Symp.*, vol. 27, no. 4, 1975.

11 Koop CE, "Emergency Surgery of the Newborn," *Clin. Symp.*, vol. 11, no. 4, 1959.

12 FHN, op. cit., *Digestive System Part II*, Sec. XII, "Diseases of the Lower Digestive Tract," plates 1–14.

13 Ibid., Sec. XIII, "Diseases and Injuries of the Abdominal Cavity," plates 9–14.

14 FHN, *War Injuries of the Abdomen*, Ciba Pharmaceuticals, Summit, NJ, 1945.

15 José Fernandes Pontes, José Thiago Pontes, Mitja Polak, Daher E. Cutait and Virgilio Carvalho Pinto: FHN, op. cit. *Digestive System Part II*, Sec. XII, "Diseases of the Lower Digestive Tract," plates 15–18, 23–29, 31, 35–71; Sec. XIII, "Diseases and Injuries of the Abdominal Cavity," plates 5–7.

16 FHN, op. cit., *Digestive System Part II*.

17 Ibid., Sec. XIII, "Diseases and Injuries of the Abdominal Cavity," plates 1–4.

18 Interview, Arthur H. Aufses, Jr., March 13, 2006.

19 Iason AH, "Inguinal and Femoral Hernias," *Clin. Symp.*, vol. 7, no. 2, 1955, and subsequently, Iason AH, "Inguinal and Femoral Hernias," *Clin. Symp.*, vol. 18, no. 2, 1966.

20 Iason AH, *Hernia*, Blakiston Co., Philadelphia, 1941.

21 FHN, op. cit., *Digestive System Part II*, Sec. XIV, "Hernias," plates 1–15.

22 House EL, Pansky B, *A Functional Approach to Neuroanatomy*, McGraw-Hill, New York, 1960 (three editions); Pansky B, House EL, *A Review of Gross Anatomy*, Collier-Macmillan, New York, 1964 (seven editions).

23 Email, B. Pansky to FMN, December 21, 2005.

24 FHN, *CCMI*, Vol. 4, *Endocrine System*, Ciba, Summit, NJ, 1965.

25 Now the Brigham and Women's Hospital.

26 Now the University of California, San Francisco School of Medicine.

27 FHN, op. cit., *Endocrine System*, Sec. III, "The Adrenal Glands," plates 6–10, 12–15, 21–28; Sec. IV, "Sex Differentiation and the Gonads," plate 7; Sec. VII, "Lipid Metabolism, Lipidoses, Atherosclerosis, Obesity," plates

1–4, 9; Sec. VIII, "Protein Metabolism, Genetics, Growth, Hormones and Cancer," plate 7.

28   Edward Biglieri (*Vol. 4, Endocrine System,* Sec. III, plates 16–18, 20), Maurice Galante (*Vol. 4, Endocrine System,* Sec. III, plates 2–3), Lloyd Smith (*Vol. 4, Endocrine System,* Sec. IX, plates 6–7), Howard Steinbach (*Vol. 4, Endocrine System,* Sec. VIII, plates 8–9) and Felix Kolb.

29   FHN, op. cit., *Endocrine System,* Sec. II, plates 2–6, 8–19.

30   Interview, Felix O. Kolb, February 14, 2006.

31   S.J. Thannhauser at New England Medical Center in Boston did five plates in the section on lipid metabolism (*Vol. 4, Endocrine System,* Sec. VII, plates 5–8, 10, 11). Alexander Bearn at Rockefeller University did four plates on genetics (*Vol. 4, Endocrine System,* Sec. VIII, plates 3–6). Judson J. Van Wyk, recipient of the United States Public Health Services Career Research Award and professor of pediatrics at the University of North Carolina, contributed to 17 plates in two sections, one on the gonads and another on growth and dwarfism (*Vol. 4, Endocrine System,* Sec. IV, plates 1, 4–6, 8–19; Sec. VIII, plates 10–12). Frank did two beautiful plates with Oliver Cope at Harvard on the anatomy of the thyroid and the parathyroid glands (*Vol. 4, Endocrine System,* Sec. II, plates 1–2), and with Rulon Rawson at Sloan-Kettering Institute, he did the plates on thyroid disease (*Vol. 4, Endocrine System,* Sec. II, plates 5–3).

32   FHN, op. cit., *Endocrine System,* Sec. V, plates 1–31.

33   Ibid., Sec. VII, plates 1–4, 9.

34   Ibid., Sec. II, plates 3–4; Sec. III, plate 1.

35   Ibid., Sec. III, plate 4.

36   Ibid., Sec. I, plates 34–35.

37   Email, Aaron Lerner to FMN, November 2, 2005.

38   Interview, Robert E. Olson, November 28, 2005.

39   FHN, op. cit., *Endocrine System,* Sec. VII, plates 12–15.

40   Ibid., Sec. X, plates 1–7.

41   Interview, Robert E. Olson, November 28, 2005.

42   Interview, Calvin Ezrin, November 3, 2005.

43   Now the Biomedical Communications at the University of Toronto.

44   Interview, Calvin Ezrin, November 3, 2005.

45   FHN, op. cit., *Endocrine System,* Sec. I, plates 1–6.

46   Ibid., plate 7.

47   Ibid., Sec. I, "The Pituitary Gland," plates 1–33; Sec. III, "The Adrenal Glands," plate 11.

48   Ibid., Sec. I, plate 26.

49   Interview, Calvin Ezrin, November 3, 2005.

50   FHN, autobiographical notes; Ciba film.

51   Forsham PH, "The Adrenal Gland," *Clin. Symp.,* vol. 15, no. 1, 1963; Biglieri EG, "Aldosterone," *Clin. Symp.,* vol. 15, no. 1, 1963; Forsham PH, "Abnormalities of the Adrenal Cortex," *Clin. Symp.,* vol. 15, no. 2, 1963;

Ezrin C., "The Pituitary Gland," *Clin. Symp.*, vol. 15, no. 3, 1963; Levine R, "Diabetes Mellitus," *Clin. Symp.*, vol. 15, no. 4, 1963; Rawson RW, "The Thyroid Gland," *Clin. Symp.*, vol. 17, no. 2, 1965.

52   FHN, op. cit., *Endocrine System*.
53   Interview, Felix O. Kolb, February 14, 2006.
54   FHN, op. cit., *Endocrine System*, p. vi.

Chapter 16: Heart

1   FHN, CCMI, vol. 5, *Heart*, Ciba, Summit, NJ, 1969.
2   FHN, op. cit., *Heart*, Introduction by Frederick Yonkman, p. xiii.
3   Letter, I. Page to FHN, December 1965, informing Frank that he was to receive the 1966 Modern Medicine Award for Distinguished Achievement.
4   Ibid., Sec. I. Anatomy, plates 17–18.
5   Email, Barbara Niss, archivist, Mount Sinai, to FMN, July 18, 2006.
6   FHN, op. cit., *Digestive System*, Part I, Sec. IV. "Functional and Diagnostic Aspects," plates 6 and 7; Sec. VI. "Diseases of the Esophagus," plates 7.
7   FHN, op. cit., *Heart*, Sec. I. "Anatomy," plates 21–28.
8   FHN, op. cit., *Heart*, Sec. II. "Physiology and Pathophysiology," plates 33 and 34.
9   Interview, Robert S. Litwak, January 4, 2006.
10   FHN, op. cit., *Heart*, Sec. I. "Anatomy," plates 19 and 20.
11   Letter, John Abel to FMN, undated but circa December 2005.
12   Interview, Abel Lazzarini Robertson, Jr., November 28, 2005.
13   FHN, op. cit., *Heart*, Sec. V. "Diseases—Acquired," plates 69–75.
14   Ibid., Sec. I. "Anatomy," plates 29–31.
15   Ibid. Lawrence McCormack consulted on Vol. 5, Sec. V. "Diseases—Acquired," plates 49, 52–56, and 61–63.
16   Ibid. Richard Westcott consulted on Sec. V. "Diseases—Acquired," plates 64–68.
17   Ibid., Sec. V. "Diseases—Acquired," plates 47 and 48.
18   Interview, Abel Lazzarini Robertson, Jr., November 28, 2005.
19   Interview, Lodewyk H.S. Van Mierop, December 2, 2005.
20   FHN, op. cit., *Heart*, Sec. I. "Anatomy," plates 1–11, 15–16; Sec. III. "Embryology," plates 1–17; Sec. IV. "Diseases—Congenital Anomalies," plates 1–32.
21   FHN, op. cit., *Heart*, Sec. I. "Anatomy," plate 9.
22   Van Mierop LH, *Anatomy of the Heart. Clin. Symp.*, vol. 17, no. 3, 1965. Murray G. Baron subsequently did an article on angiocardiography that appeared in the same 1965 *Clinical Symposia* issues (Baron MG, "Angiocardiography" *Clin. Symp.*, vol. 17, no. 3, 1965) as the article by Bob Van Mierop, but for that, no Netter illustrations accompanied Dr. Baron's angiocardiograms.
23   FHN, op. cit., *Heart*, Sec. V. "Diseases—Acquired," plate 57.

24 FHN, op. cit., *Heart*, Sec. II. "Physiology and Pathophysiology," plates 12–31.

25 Ibid., Sec. II. "Physiology and Pathophysiology," plate 55.

26 Ibid., Sec. V. "Diseases—Acquired," plates 80–81.

27 FHN, *CCMI*, Vol. 6, *Kidney*, Ciba, Summit, NJ, 1973, Sec. VI. Diseases of the Urinary System, plate 13.

28 Letter, M. Schwarts, Associate National Director, Albert Einstein College of Medicine, to FHN, November 4, 1966.

29 Drs. Marvin B. Bacaner, Aldo Castaneda, Jesse E. Edwards, Richard L. Varco, and Maurice B. Visscher.

30 Letter, Brooks S. Edwards, son of Jesse E. Edwards, to FMN, December 16, 2005, with materials and correspondence from Netter, Edwards and Yonkman.

31 FHN, op. cit., *Heart*, Sec. V. "Diseases—Acquired," plates 4–14, 16–25.

32 FHN, op. cit., *Heart*, Sec. II. "Physiology and Pathophysiology," plates 1–4.

33 Interview, Marvin B. Bacaner, April 19, 2006.

34 Cyclosporine was isolated from a soil fungus in 1972, and approved for use in 1983.

35 FHN, op. cit., *Heart*, Sec. V. "Diseases—Acquired," pp. 94–97.

36 Letter, Norman E. Shumway, November 14, 2005, by permission of his daughter, Sara Shumway.

37 In addition to the one by Ludwig Van Mierop and the one by Murray Baron, there were others. Aldo Luisada at Chicago Medical School consulted on 20 plates (FHN, op. cit., *Heart*, Sec. II. "Physiology and Pathophysiology," plates 35–52) for *Heart*, and he also wrote a *Clinical Symposia* issue on valvular disease (Luisada AA, "The Signs and Symptoms of Valvular Disease and Heart Failure," *Clin. Symp.*, vol. 20, no. 1, 1968). Travis Winsor consulted on 19 plates (FHN, op. cit., *Heart*, Sec. II. "Physiology and Pathophysiology," plates 12–31), and he prepared a *Clinical Symposia* issue on electrocardiography (Winsor T, "The Electrocardiogram in Myocardial Infarction," *Clin. Symp.*, vol. 20, no. 4, 1968). Dr. Effler prepared a *Clinical Symposia* issue on surgery for myocardial ischemia (Effler DB, "The Surgical Treatment of Myocardial Ischemia," *Clin. Symp.*, vol. 21, no. 1, 1969). And Aldo Castaneda, who consulted on valve-replacement surgery (FHN, op. cit., *Heart*, Sec. V. "Diseases—Acquired," plates 26–31), prepared a *Clinical Symposia* issue on that topic (Castaneda AR, "Surgical Treatment of Cardiac Valvular Disease," *Clin. Symp.*, vol. 21, no. 1, 1969).

38 FHN, op. cit., *Heart*, Introduction, p. xiii.

39 FHN, autobiographical notes.

40 Letter, Frederick Yonkman to Jesse Edwards, May 19, 1969.

Chapter 17: Ciba-Geigy

1 Interview, Earle B. Weiss, December 1, 2005.

2 Ibid.

3   Weiss EB, "Bronchial Asthma," *Clin. Symp.*, vol. 27, no. 1–2, 1975.

4   FHN, *CCMI*, vol. 6, *Kidneys, Ureters and Urinary Bladder*, Ciba, Summit, NJ, 1973.

5   Becker: ibid., Sec. IV. "Diseases of the Kidney," plates 12–15; Churg: ibid., Sec. IV. "Diseases of the Kidney," plates 19–25; Sec. V. "The Kidney and Systemic Diseases," plates 10 and 11.

6   FHN, *CCMI*, vol. 6, *Heart*, Ciba, Summit, NJ, 1969, Sec. I. "Anatomy," plates 19 and 20.

7   FHN, op. cit., *Kidneys, Ureters and Urinary Bladder*, Sec. I. "Anatomy, Structure and Embryology," plates 1–24.

8   Ibid., Sec. I. "Anatomy, Structure and Embryology," plates 25–27.

9   Ibid., Sec. III. "Diagnostic Techniques," plates 1–15, 36–37.

10   Email, Suresh Patel to FMN, November 18, 2005. Frank also made pictures of the pathology and clinical aspects of amyloidosis, a rare illness that Alan S. Cohen at Boston University studied most of his medical career (Letter, Alan S. Cohen to FMN, December 10, 2005). Between 1970 and 1971 Frank went twice to Paul J. Cannon's laboratory at Columbia (email, Paul J. Cannon, April 23, 2006) and subsequently made four schematic diagrams for the therapeutics section, depicting the various ion transport pumps located along the renal tubules, and a tabulation of the effects of diuretic drugs (FHN, op. cit., *Kidneys, Ureters and Urinary Bladder*, Sec. VIII. "Therapeutics," plates 1–4).

11   FHN op. cit., *Kidneys, Ureters and Urinary Bladder*, Sec. VIII. "Therapeutics," plates 12–15.

12   Ibid., Sec. VIII. "Therapeutics," plates 16–17.

13   Frederic L. Coe and Theodore N. Pullman, both at the University of Chicago, contributed to nine plates on renal failure (*Kidneys, Ureters and Urinary Bladder*, Sec. IV. "Diseases of the Kidney," plates 3–11). Those plates, supplemented with six more plates and in-depth text, were published in an issue of *Clinical Symposia* (Pullman TN, Coe FL, "Chronic Renal Failure," *Clin. Symp.*, vol. 25, no. 1, 1973) in early 1973. Victor Vertes consulted for six plates (*Kidneys, Ureters and Urinary Bladder*, Sec. V. "The Kidney and Systemic Diseases," 4–9) on renovascular hypertension in the kidney and also prepared an issue of *Clinical Symposia* (Berman LB, Vertes V, "The Pathophysiology of Renin," *Clin. Symp.*, vol. 25, no. 5, 1973) with his colleague at Mount Sinai Hospital in Cleveland, Leonard B. Berman. While the topic was related, that booklet required all new plates. Frank reused some of his pencil sketches, however. The woman's torso for the *Kidneys, Ureters and Urinary Bladder*, Sec. V, plate 9, was painted from the same sketch as the torso he painted for plate 21 in issue 2 of the 1973 *Clinical Symposia*—two separate plates from the same sketch.

14   Interview, Gina Dingle, February 15, 2006.

15   FHN, op. cit., *Kidneys, Ureters and Urinary Bladder*, Introduction, p. xi.

16   Ibid.

17   Horton CE, Devine CJ, "Hypospadias and Epispadias," *Clin. Symp.*, vol. 24, no. 3, 1972.

18   Interview, Charles Horton, March 6, 2006.

Chapter 18: China

1   FHN, autobiographical notes.

2   "Now, About My Operation in Peking," *New York Times*, July 26, 1971, p. 1.

3   "Medical Group Here from China," *New York Times*, October 13, 1972, p. 8.

4   FHN, *CCMI*, vol. 5, *Heart*, Sec. V. "Diseases—Acquired," plate 57, Ciba, Summit, NJ, 1969.

5   Dimond EG, "Acupuncture Anesthesia. Western Medicine and Chinese Traditional Medicine," *JAMA*, vol. 218, no. 10, 1971, pp. 1558–1563.

6   FHN, autobiographical notes.

7   Ibid.

8   *New York Times*, October 13, 1972, p. 8.

9   FHN, autobiographical notes.

10   Ibid.

11   In 1971 the Chinese Mission had replaced Taiwan at the United Nations. Diplomatic relations with the United States were not established until January 1, 1979.

12   FHN, autobiographical notes.

13   Ibid.

14   Frank failed to include in his notes the name of this doctor.

15   Interview, Sharon Colacino Oberg, October 13, 2004. Frank told Sharon that during his trip to China he thought about his grandfather.

16   FHN, autobiographical notes.

17   Ibid.

18   Ibid.

19   Ibid.

20   Ibid.

21   Ibid.

22   Dimond EG, op. cit.

23   Aggressive campaigns to control schistosomiasis among the residents of Hunan Province and elsewhere in South China were a cornerstone of Chairman Mao's "patriotic health campaigns." During the 1950s and 1960s, entire populations in schistosomiasis-endemic areas were mobilized against *Oncomelania* snails and recruited to drain rivers and ditches; millions of people were treated with anthelminthics. As a result, the number of infections was reduced from 10 million in 1955 to 1.52 million in 1989. In consultation with J. Stauffer Lehman at the Harvard School of Public Health, Frank had done two plates on schistosomiasis for the *Kidneys, Ureters and Urinary Bladder* (FHN, *CCMI*, vol. 6, *Kidneys, Ureters and Urinary Bladder*, Ciba, Summit, NJ, 1973, Sec. VI. "Diseases of the Urinary System," plates 14 and 15).

24   Abrams Herbert K, "The Resurgence of Sexually Transmitted Disease in China," *Journal of Public Health Policy*, January 1, 2001.

25   FHN, *Frank H. Netter, MD film*, Ciba-Geigy, 1985.

26   Birmingham Frederic A, "Dr. Frank H. Netter, Michelangelo of Medicine," *Saturday Evening Post*, May/June 1976.

27   FHN, autobiographical notes.

28   Ibid.

29   Ibid.

30   Ibid.

31   Ibid.

32   Ibid.

33   Ibid.

34   Ibid.

35   Netter JM, *Quails from the Sea* (title also translated as *Seagulls from the Sea*), Vienna, 1860, translated by Rabbi Joan Friedman, 1987, p. 39.

36   FHN, autobiographical notes.

Chapter 19: Point Manalapan

1   FHN, letter to Professor José López-Rey, October 20, 1971.

2   Keim HA, "Scoliosis," *Clin. Symp.*, vol. 24, no. 1, 1972.

3   Interview, Hugo Keim, February 8, 2006.

4   Keim HA, "Low Back Pain" *Clin. Symp.*, vol. 25, no. 3, 1973.

5   Interview, Hugo Keim, February 8, 2006.

6   Email, Hugo Keim to FMN, December 13, 2005.

7   Interview, Hugo Keim, February 8, 2006.

8   Interview, Gina Dingle, February 15, 2006.

9   Baron MG, "Angiocardiography," *Clin. Symp.*, vol. 17, no. 3, 1965.

10   Krull EA, Fellman AC, Fabian LA, "White Lesions of the Mouth," *Clin. Symp.*, vol. 25, no. 2, 1973.

11   Lawrence MR, "The Cell," *Clin. Symp.*, vol. 25, no. 4, 1973.

12   Student American Medical Association—Eaton Laboratories Medical Art Contest.

13   Interview, John Craig, March 16, 2006.

14   FHN, *Fad Diets Can Be Deadly*, Exposition Press, Hicksville, NY, 1975, p. 12.

15   Ibid.

16   Ibid., p. 26.

17   FHN, *CCMI*, vol. 1, *Nervous System*, Ciba, Summit, NJ, 1962, *Hypothalamus Supplement*, plate 15.

18   FHN, *Fad Diets*, op. cit., p. 28.

19   FHN, *CCMI*, vol. 4, *Endocrine System*, Ciba, Summit, NJ, 1959, Sec. I, plate 14.

20   FHN, *Fad Diets*, op. cit., pp. 30–31.

21   FHN, *CCMI*, vol. 3, *Digestive System Part I*, Ciba, Summit, NJ, 1959, Sec. IV, plate 1.

22 FHN, *Fad Diets*, op. cit., pp. 43, 49, 58.

23 FHN, *CCMI*, vol. 3, *Digestive System Part II*, Ciba, Summit, NJ, 1962, Sec. XI, plates 7 and 8.

24 Keim HA, op. cit., plates 12 and 15.

25 Birmingham FA, "Michelangelo of Medicine," *Saturday Evening Post*, vol. 248, no. 4, May/June 1976.

26 FHN passport stamps.

27 Interview, Peter Som, March 23, 2006.

28 FMN, January 15, 2008.

29 Hip dysplasia.

30 Interview, Peter Som, March 23, 2006.

31 Hensinger RN, "Congenital Dislocation of the Hip," *Clin. Symp.*, vol. 31, no. 1, 1979.

32 Interview, Robert Hensinger, December 8, 2005.

33 Interview, Dean MacEwen, November 1, 2006.

34 Interview, Robert Hensinger, December 8, 2005.

35 Ibid.

36 Ibid.

37 Ibid.

38 Interview, Gina Dingle, February 15, 2006.

39 Interview, Phil Flagler, December 2, 2005.

40 Interview, Gina Dingle, February 15, 2006.

41 Ibid.

Chapter 20: Team Leader

1 Interview, Phil Flagler, December 2, 2005.

2 Interview, Gina Dingle, February 15, 2006.

3 Between 1976 and 1979, there were five editors for *Clinical Symposia*. Richard H. Roberts did two, Anne H. Trench did eight, Irene A. Estler did three, Barbara Bekiesz did four and Kristine J. Bean did four.

4 Interview, Robert Hensinger, December 8, 2005.

5 John Craig had authored and illustrated an article (Paton D, Craig J, "Cataracts," *Clin. Symp.*, vol. 26, no. 3, 1974) in 1974, illustrated an article (Tyson KR, "Congenital Heart Disease in Infants," *Clin. Symp.*, vol. 27, no. 3, 1975) in 1975, and by mid-1976 authored and illustrated another article (Paton D, Craig JA, "Glaucomas: Diagnosis and Management," *Clin. Symp.*, vol. 28, no. 2, 1976). He illustrated two more articles (Abston S, "Burns in Children," *Clin. Symp.*, vol. 28, no. 4, 1976; Shane JM, Schiff I, Wilson EA, "The Infertile Couple: Evaluation and Treatment," *Clin. Symp.*, vol. 28 no. 5, 1976) in 1976 and three (Bryant WM, "Wound Healing," *Clin. Symp.*, vol. 29, no. 3, 1977; McNeese MC, Hebeler JR, "The Abused Child," *Clin. Symp.*, vol. 29, no. 5, 1977; Weintraub M.I., "Hysteria," *Clin. Symp.*, vol. 29, no. 6, 1977) in 1977.

6 Interview, Phil Flagler, December 2, 2005.

7   Letter, Alister Brass to Sigurd C. Sandzen, Jr. January 25, 1980.

8   Letter, Alister Brass to James Hardy, September 2, 1980.

9   Memo, Mary McKinsey to FHN, c. January 1982.

10 Arena JM, "Accidental Poisoning in Children," *Clin. Symp.*, vol. 3, no. 3, 1951.

11 Arena JM, "Diagnosis and Treatment of Poisoning," *Clin. Symp.*, vol. 12, no. 1, 1960; Arena JM, "The Treatment of Poisoning," *Clin. Symp.*, vol. 18, no. 1, 1966.

12 Arena JM, "The Treatment of Poisoning," *Clin. Symp.*, vol. 30, no. 2, 1978.

13 Letter, William Futrell to FHN, September 15, 1977.

14 Letter, James R. Ubaniak to Alister Brass, January 3, 1980.

15 Letter, FHN to Alister Brass, November 15, 1980.

16 Email, James R. Urbaniak to FMN, September 25, 2006.

17 Letter, FHN to Alister Brass, November 25, 1980.

18 Johnson L.L., "Diagnostic and Surgical Arthroscopy," *Clin. Symp.*, vol. 34, no. 3, 1982.

19 Interview, Phil Flagler, December 2, 2005.

20 FHN, *CCMI*, vol. 7, *Respiratory System*, Ciba, Summit, NJ, 1979.

21 Ibid., Sec. IV. "Diseases and Pathology," plates 2, 3, 114–120, 124–125.

22 Ibid., Sec. I. "Anatomy and Embryology," plates 32–41.

23 Crelin ES, "Development of the Lower Respiratory System," *Clin. Symp.*, vol. 27, no. 4, 1975; Crelin E.S., "Development of the Upper Respiratory System," *Clin. Symp.*, vol. 28, no. 3, 1976.

24 Ibid., Sec. I. "Anatomy and Embryology," plate 20; Sec. IV. "Diseases and Pathology," plates 13–27.

25 FHN, op. cit. *Respiratory System*, Sec. I. "Anatomy and Embryology," plates 1–19.

26 Ibid., Sec. III. "Radiology," plates 1–17; Sec. IV. "Diseases and Pathology, plates 60, 110.

27 FHN, op. cit., *Respiratory System*, Sec. II. "Physiology," plates 1–21; Sec. V. "Diagnostic and Therapeutic Procedures," plates 1–2.

28 Interview, Murray D. Altose, November 29, 2005.

29 Altose MD, "The Physiological Basis of Pulmonary Function Testing," *Clin. Symp.*, vol. 31, no. 2, 1979.

30 FHN, op. cit. *Respiratory System*, Sec. II. "Physiology," plates 22–24.

31 Letter, James W. Ryan to FMN, January 25, 2004.

32 Interview, Una S. Ryan, December 2, 2005.

33 Ibid.

34 Ibid.

35 FHN, op. cit. *Respiratory System*, Sec. I. "Anatomy and Embryology," plates 27–29.

36 Interview, Una S. Ryan, December 2, 2005.

37 Max Som consulted on FHN, op. cit. *Respiratory System*, Sec. IV. "Diseases and Pathology," plates 10–12. Alvin Teirstein and Jacob Churg consulted

on FHN, op. cit. *Respiratory System*, Sec. IV. "Diseases and Pathology," plates 140–149.

38   Letter, Alvin S. Teirstein to FMN, November 18, 2005.

39   FHN, op. cit., *Respiratory System*, Sec. IV. "Diseases and Pathology," plates 66–76.

40   Interview, Morton N. Swartz, April 5, 2006.

41   Ibid., Sec. V. "Diagnostic and Therapeutic Procedures," plates 3–4, 12, 22.

42   Dr. Michaelson consulted on oxygen therapy and mechanical ventilation (ibid., plates 10, 23–26), and Dr. Landa, on intubation and bronchofibroscopic lavage (ibid., plates 8, 11). In 1977 or 1978 Frank drove down to Miami Beach to meet with them and go over the sketches, and Dr. Landa sensed that Frank immediately understood the concepts (interview, José F. Landa, March 15, 2006). Also Victor J. Marder, at the University of Rochester, consulted on a plate (Sec. V. "Diagnostic and Therapeutic Procedures," plates 111) on labeled fibrinogen to detect a thrombus, and he recalled that he spent only about an hour talking about his research with Frank but that the resulting plate captured the essence of Dr. Marda's work (teleconference, Victor J. Marder, January 30, 2005).

43   Ibid., plate 22.

44   Additionally, with Morton Ziskind, director of the Pulmonary Disease Section at Tulane University, Frank made highly detailed pictures of diseased lung specimens for a *Clinical Symposia* on occupational pulmonary disease (Ziskind, M.M., "Occupational Pulmonary Disease," *Clin. Symp.*, vol. 30, no. 4, 1978). The monograph came out in 1978, but the following year those plates appeared in *Respiratory System*, but with the text modified to fit the format of the book (FHN, op. cit., *Respiratory System*, Sec. IV. "Diseases and Pathology," plates 97–104).

45   FHN, op. cit., *Respiratory System*, Sec. V. "Diagnostic and Therapeutic Procedures," plates 5, 6.

46   Heimlich HZ, Uhley MH, Netter FH, "The Heimlich Maneuver," *Clin. Symp.*, vol. 31, no. 3, 1979.

47   Ibid. pp. 3–23.

48   Ibid. pp. 24–31.

49   Interview, Henry J. Heimlich, April 4, 2006.

50   Ibid.

51   FHN, op. cit., *Respiratory System*, Introduction, p. vii.

52   Interview, Gina Dingle, February 15, 2006.

53   Ibid.

Chapter 21: Revising Nervous System

1   Swanson AB, "Reconstructive Surgery in the Arthritic Hand and Foot," *Clin. Symp.*, vol. 31, no. 6, 1979.

2   Swanson AB, "Congenital Limb Defects Classification and Treatment," *Clin. Symp.*, vol. 33, no. 3, 1981.

3   A. Swanson, Hogden Memorial Lecture, introduction of FHN, 1989.

4   Swanson AB, "Congenital Limb Defects," op. cit., p. 13.

5   Noted in the foreword of the January 1979 issue (Hensinger R.N., "Congenital Dislocation of the Hip," *Clin. Symp.*, vol. 31, no. 1, 1979, foreword).

6   Interview, Gina Dingle, February 15, 2006.

7   FHN, *CCMI*, vol. 1, *Nervous System*, 2nd ed., Part I, Ciba, Summit, NJ, 1983.

8   FHN, *CCMI*, vol. 1, *Nervous System*, 2nd ed., Part II, Ciba, Summit, NJ, 1986.

9   FHN, op. cit. *Nervous System* Part I.

10 Ibid., Sec. I. "Bony Coverings of the Brain and Spinal Cord," plates 1–18; Sec. II. "Gross Anatomy of the Brain and Spinal Cord," plates 1–16; Sec. IV. "Autonomic Nervous System," plates 1–21; Sec. V. "Cranial Nerves," plates 1–13; Sec. VI. "Nerve Plexuses and Peripheral Nerves," plates 1–16.

11 Ibid. Sec I., plate 1.

12 Ibid., Sec. VII. "Embryology," plates 1–15.

13 Crelin ES, "Development of the Nervous System. A Logical Approach to Neuroanatomy," *Clin. Symp.*, vol. 26, no. 2, 1974.

14 Also, Joe G. Wood was a neuroanatomist at the University of Texas Health Sciences Center at Houston, and in that section he contributed to two plates on the cerebral cortex (FHN, op. cit., *Nervous System Part I*, 2nd Ed., Sec. VIII. "Physiology and Functional Neuroanatomy," plates 40, 43).

15 Interview, Barry W. Peterson, March 16, 2006.

16 FHN, op. cit., *Nervous System* Part I, 2nd ed., Sec. VIII, 38.

17 Interview, Barry W. Peterson, March 16, 2006.

18 FHN, op. cit., *Nervous System* Part I, 2nd ed., Sec. II. "Gross Anatomy of the Brain and Spinal Cord," plate 17; Sec. IV. "Autonomic Nervous System," plate 22; Sec. VIII. "Physiology and Functional Neuroanatomy," plates 1–39, 41, 42, 44–50, 65, 66.

19 Ibid., Sec. IV. "Autonomic Nervous System," plate 22; Sec. VIII. "Physiology and Functional Neuroanatomy," plates 3–9, 11, 12, 65, 66.

20 Grossman MB, "Gastrointestinal Endoscopy," *Clin. Symp.*, vol. 32, no. 3, 1980.

21 Letter, Jerome J. Sheldon, November 9, 2005.

22 Sheldon JJ, "Blood Vessels of the Scalp and Brain," *Clin. Symp.*, vol. 33, no. 5, 1981.

23 FHN, op. cit., *Nervous System* Part I, 2nd ed., Sec. III. "Blood Vessels of the Brain and Spinal Cord," plates 1–21.

24 Email, Jerome Sheldon to FMN, November 26, 2005.

25 Interview, John Craig, March 16, 2006.

26 FHN, *CCMI*, vol. 4, *Endocrine System*, Ciba, Summit, NJ, 1959, Sec. I, "Pituitary Gland," plates 3, 7.

27 FHN, op. cit., *Nervous System* Part I, 2nd ed., Sec. VIII. "Physiology and Functional Neuroanatomy," plates 51–64.

28 Letter, Jay B. Angevine, Jr, to FMN, January 16, 2006.

29 Interview, Jay B. Angevine, Jr, January 16, 2006.
30 Film: *FHN, Physician, Artist Teacher*, Ciba-Geigy, 1985.
31 Letter, Jay B. Angevine, Jr, to FMN, January 16, 2006.
32 1979, Resolution of Commendation, Florida State Legislature.
33 Interview, L.H.S. Van Mierop, December 2, 2005.
34 In addition, from Venice, Italy, he received honors when the Academia Medicorum Litteratorum named Frank an honorary academic.
35 Interview, Phil Flagler, December 2, 2005.
36 FHN, autobiographical notes.

Chapter 22: The Breakers

1   Caduceus inscribed "Presented to Frank H. Netter, M.D. '31 by New York University School of Medicine for his contributions to medical education through graphic art. April 5, 1965." Note: New York University Medical College was renamed New York University School of Medicine in 1960.
2   FHN, *CCMI*, Vol. 1, *Nervous System*, Ciba, Summit, NJ, 1953.
3   Interview, Royden Jones, December 9, 2005.
4   Jones HR Jr, "Diseases of the Peripheral Motor-Sensory Unit," *Clin. Symp.*, vol. 37, no. 2, 1985.
5   Interview, Seymour Diamond, March 15, 2006.
6   Diamond S, Medina JL, "Headaches," *Clin. Symp.*, vol. 33, no. 2, 1981.
7   With Roger Dean White, professor of anesthesiology at Mayo Medical School, Frank revised the *Clinical Symposia* issue on basic life support (Shapter RK, Katz HJ, Cobb LA, Grace WJ, Nagel EL, Schwartz ML, Uhley HN, Warren JV, "Cardiopulmonary Resuscitation: Basic Life Support," *Clin. Symp.*, vol. 26, no. 5, 1974) to bring it in line with the updated standards (White RD, "CPR: Basic Life Support," *Clin. Symp.*, vol. 34, no. 6, 1982).
8   Wilkins RW, Hollander W, Chobanian AV, "Evaluation of Hypertensive Patients," *Clin. Symp.*, vol. 24, no. 2, 1972; Chobanian AV, "Hypertension," *Clin. Symp.*, vol. 34, no. 5, 1982.
9   Interview, Aram Chobanian, March 27, 2006.
10 Chobanian AV, Gavras H, "Hypertension," *Clin. Symp.*, vol. 42, no. 4, 1990.
11 Letter, FHN to Alister Brass, November 25, 1980.
12 Interview, Stephen S. Scheidt, March 16, 2006.
13 Ibid. In 1987 Ciba published a booklet (Scheidt S, Erlebacher JA, Netter FH, *Basic Electrocardiography: ECG*, Ciba, Summit, NJ, 1987) in which an appendix was added with 50 or 60 examples of real electrocardiographs keyed back to the chapters. Frank's drawings are throughout the book and are the main teaching tool, but the learner can go to the back of the book and see the tracings.
14 Scheidt S, "Basic Electrocardiography: Leads, Axes, Arrhythmias," *Clin. Symp.*, vol. 35, no. 2, 1983.

15 Scheidt S, "Electrocardiography: Abnormalities of Electrocardiographic Patterns," *Clin. Symp.*, vol. 36, no. 6, 1984.

16 Letter, Robert Hensinger to Carl Brighton, November 30, 1981.

17 Letter, FHN to Carl Brighton, April 21, 1982.

18 Interview, Frederick S. Kaplan, December 18, 2005.

19 Letter, FHN to Frederick Kaplan, July 13, 1982.

20 Kaplan FS, "Osteoporosis," *Clin Symp.*, vol. 35, no. 5, 1983.

21 Interview, Frederick S. Kaplan, December 18, 2005.

22 Ibid.

23 Interview, Harold Kleinert, February 7, 2006.

24 Interview, Frederick Kaplan, December 18, 2005.

25 Kaplan F.S., op. cit., plate 5.

26 Frederick S. Kaplan, Eulogy for FHN delivered September 22, 1991.

Chapter 23: The Artificial Heart

1   FHN, autobiographical notes.

2   DeVries WC., Joyce LD, "The Artificial Heart" *Clin. Symp.*, vol. 35, no. 6, 1983. Blood oxygenation had been demonstrated by as early as 1882 by Waldemar von Schröder. In 1927, Charles Lindbergh, the aviator, began collaborating with Nobel laureate Alexis Carrel on an oxygen exchanger and pump used on organs outside the body. In 1928, two researchers in the United Kingdom, H.H. Dale and E.H.J. Schuster, devised a diaphragm pump intended specifically for providing blood circulation.

3   FHN, CCMI, vol. 5, *Heart*, Ciba, Summit, NJ, 1969, Sec. V, plates 94–97.

4   FHN, CCMI, vol. 6, *Kidneys, Ureters and Urinary Bladder*, Ciba, Summit, NJ, 1973, Sec. VIII, plates 12–15.

5   President's Commission for the Study of Ethical Problems in Medicine and Biomedical and Behavioral Research, "Defining Death: A Report on the Medical, Legal and Ethical Issues in the Determination of Death," Washington, DC, 1981. https://scholarworks.iupui.edu/handle/1805/707.

6   Interview, William DeVries, September 7, 2004.

7   FHN, op. cit., *Kidneys, Ureters and Urinary Bladder*, Sec. VIII, "Therapeutics," plates 6–11. Frank illustrated renal dialysis in *Kidneys, Ureters and Urinary Bladder*, for which George E. Schreiner wrote text.

8   www.achievement.org/autodoc/page/koloint-5, September 19, 2006.

9   DeVries W.C., et al, op. cit.

10 Interview, William DeVries, September 7, 2004.

11 Ibid.

12 Ibid.

13 FHN, autobiographical notes.

14 Heart–lung bypass was developed in 1955 by Richard A. DeWall, Dr. Lillehei's student.

15 Bailey CP, "Surgery of the Heart," *Clin. Symp.*, vol. 10, no. 5, 1958, plate I.

16 At Dr. Lillehei's request, Earl Bakken, an electrical engineer, developed a wearable cardiac pacemaker.

17 FHN, autobiographical notes.
18 Robert Jarvik did not work with Frank on the monograph: email, Robert Jarvik to FMN, June 4, 2007.
19 Interview, William DeVries, September 7, 2004.
20 Interview, Lyle Joyce, October 3, 2006.
21 FHN, autobiographical notes.
22 Ibid.
23 Email, William DeVries, June 30, 2005.
24 Interview, William DeVries, September 7, 2004.
25 Ibid.
26 FHN, autobiographical notes.
27 Email, William DeVries, June 30, 2005.
28 Interview, Lyle Joyce, October 3, 2006.
29 DeVries WC, et al, op. cit., p. 3.
30 Interview, William DeVries, September 7, 2004.
31 FHN, autobiographical notes.
32 Ibid.
33 Letter, FHN to Frederick S. Kaplan, June 1, 1983.
34 Kaplan FS, "Osteoporosis," *Clin. Symp.*, vol. 35, no. 5, 1983.
35 DeVries W.C., et al, op. cit.
36 Interview, William DeVries, September 7, 2004.

Chapter 24: A Body of Work

1   Thompson GH, Salter RB, "Legg-Calvé-Perthes Disease," *Clin. Symp.*, vol. 38, no. 1, 1986.
2   Interview, George H. Thompson, April 5, 2006.
3   Ernest U. Conrad.
4   Enneking WF, Conrad EU III, "Common Bone Tumors," *Clin. Symp.*, vol. 41, no. 3, 1989; Conrad EU III, Enneking WF, "Common Soft Tissue Tumors," *Clin. Symp.*, vol. 42, no. 1, 1990.
5   Email, William F. Enneking to FMN, February 22, 2006.
6   Interview, Lodewyk H.S. Van Mierop, December 2, 2005.
7   Conrad E.U. III, Enneking W.F., op. cit.
8   Enneking W.F., Conrad E.U. III, op. cit.
9   Interview, Ernest U. Conrad, April 5, 2006.
10 10. Ibid.

Chapter 25: Making Pictures to Teach

1   University of Texas Medical School at Houston.
2   Fields WS, "Aortocranial Occlusive Vascular Disease (Stroke)," *Clin. Symp.*, vol. 26, no. 4, 1974. In addition to his editorial duties for the *Ciba Collection* volume, he worked with Frank on eight plates on cardiovascular disease for the volume (FHN, *CCMI, Nervous System Part II*, 2nd ed., Sec. III. "Cerebrovascular Disease," plates 2–3, 6–7, 10, 20–21; Sec. VIII. "Infectious Diseases," plate 6).

3   FHN, op. cit., *Nervous System Part II*, 2nd ed., Sec. I, "Primary Neurologic Disorders in Infancy and Childhood," plate 10. For the section of the volume on neurologic disorders in infants and children, Michael J. Bresnan contributed significantly (FHN, op. cit., *Nervous System Part II*, 2nd ed., Sec. I. "Primary Neurologic Disorders in Infancy and Childhood," plates 1–5, 10–12, 16, 18, 23).

4   Interview, Gina Dingle, December 15, 2006.

5   Interview, Royden Jones, December 9, 2005.

6   Jones HR Jr, "Diseases of the Peripheral Motor-Sensory Unit," *Clin. Symp.*, vol. 37, no. 2, 1985, plate 8; FHN, CCMI, Vol. 1, *Nervous System Part II*, 2nd ed., Ciba, Summit, NJ, 1986, Sec. XI, "Disorders of Motor Neuron. Peripheral Nerve Neuromuscular Junction and Skeletal Muscles," plate 9.

7   FHN, op. cit., *Nervous System Part II*, 2nd ed., Sec. II. "Common Problems in Neurology," plates 1–7, 15; Sec. III. "Cerebrovascular Disease," plates 1, 5, 8–9, 11–15, 26–28, 37; Sec. V. "Brain Tumors," plate 2; Sec. VII. "Degenerative Disorders of the Central Nervous System," plates 1–8. They did the pictures for the *Nervous System Part II*, but also the plates were used in a *Clinical Symposia* issue on stroke (Caplan L.R., "Stroke," *Clin. Symp.*, vol. 40, no. 4, 1988) that came out subsequently.

8   Interview, Louis Caplan, February 21, 2006.

9   Ibid.

10   Letter, Stephen Freidberg to FMN, undated.

11   FHN, op. cit., *Nervous System Part II*, Sec. V. "Brain Tumors," plates 3–10, 14–15; Sec. X. "Disorders of Spinal Cord, Nerve Root and Plexus," plates 5, 6, 14, 15, 17; Freidberg S.R., "Tumors of the Brain," *Clin. Symp.*, vol. 38, no. 4, 1986.

12   Ayd F.J. Jr., "Treatment of the Office Neurotic," *Clin Symp.*, vol. 9, no. 5, 1957.

13   Richard A. Baker was a neuroradiologist at the Lahey Clinic, and Roy Jones recruited him to provide the radiographs, including computed tomography and magnetic resonance images, for plates in the sections on cerebrovascular disease, brain tumors, spinal tumors and herniated discs (FHN, op. cit., *Nervous System Part II*, 2nd ed., Sec. III. "Cerebrovascular Disease," plates 18–19, 22, 23, 28, 29; Sec. V. "Brain Tumors," plate 16; Sec. X. "Disorders of Spinal Cord, Nerve Root and Plexus," plates 7, 12, 13). Barbara Westmoreland—she had been a fellow with Roy Jones at Mayo— looked over the plates on epilepsy (FHN, op. cit., *Nervous System Part II*, 2nd ed., Sec. II. "Common Problems in Neurology," plates 9–14). They also included four plates (FHN, op. cit., *Nervous System Part II*, 2nd ed., Sec. VII. "Degenerative Disorders of the Central Nervous System," plates 9–12) that Frank previously had done with Roger Duvoisin for a *Clinical Symposia* issue (Duvoisin R., "Parkinsonism," *Clin. Symp.*, vol. 28, no. 1, 1976).

14   FHN, op. cit., *Nervous System Part II*, 2nd ed., Sec. VIII. "Infectious Diseases," plates 9, 10.

15   FHN, op. cit., *Nervous System Part II*, 2nd ed., Sec. I. "Primary Neurologic Disorders in Infancy and Childhood," plates 19–20.

16 Letter, Thomas Kemper to FMN, December 20, 2005.

17 Rhoton AL, Jackson FE, Gleave J, Rumbaugh CT, "Congenital and Traumatic Intracranial Aneurysms," *Clin. Symp.*, vol. 29, no. 4, 1977.

18 FHN, op. cit., *Nervous System Part II*, 2nd ed., Sec. III. "Cerebrovascular Disease," plates 30–36.

19 Interview, William Friedman, January 30, 2005.

20 Friedman WA, "Head Injuries," *Clin. Symp.*, vol. 35, no. 4, 1983.

21 Jackson FE, "The Pathophysiology of Head Injuries," *Clin. Symp.*, vol. 18, no. 3, 1966; Jackson FE, "The Treatment of Head Injuries," *Clin. Symp.*, vol. 19, no. 1, 1967.

22 Friedman, op. cit., plates 3, 4, 8, 14 taken from Jackson, 1967, op. cit., plates XI, II, VI, VII; Friedman, op. cit., plate 13 taken from Jackson, 1966, op. cit., plate XI; the Jackson *Clin. Symp.* issue had in turn incorporated plates 11, 13, 15, from the CCMI, *Nervous System*, 1st ed. In 2007, Naval Hospital Charlston was renamed the Naval Health Clinic Charleston.

23 FHN, op. cit., *Nervous System Part II*, 2nd ed., Sec IV. "Central Nervous System Trauma," plates 1–24; Dr. Friedman also wrote text for the plate on cervical spine injury (FHN, op. cit., *Nervous System Part II*, 2nd ed., Sec X. "Disorders of Spinal Cord, Nerve Root and Plexus," plate 11), which they took from a *Clinical Symposia* issue that Frank had prepared in 1980 with Ralph B. Cloward (Cloward RB, "Acute Cervical Spine Injuries," *Clin. Symp.*, vol. 32, no. 1, 1980).

24 Interview, Marc A. Flitter, December 22, 2005.

25 FHN, op. cit., *Nervous System Part II*, 2nd ed., Sec. I. "Primary Neurologic Disorders in Infancy and Childhood," plates 6–9; Sec. V. "Brain Tumors," plate 1.

26 Interview, Marc A. Flitter, December 22, 2005.

27 FHN, op. cit., *Nervous System Part II*, 2nd ed., Sec. I. "Primary Neurologic Disorders in Infancy and Childhood," plates 11, 13–15, 17, 18; Sec. III. "Cerebrovascular Disease," plates 4, 16, 17, 24; Sec. IV. "Central Nervous System Trauma," plate 25; Sec. VIII. "Infectious Diseases," plates 8, 11; Sec. IX. "Demyelinating Disorders of Central Nervous System," plates 1, 4; Sec. X. "Disorders of Spinal Cord, Nerve Root and Plexus," plates 1–4, 8–10, 17–19; Sec. XI. "Disorders of Motor Neuron, Peripheral Nerve, Neuromuscular Junction and Skeletal Muscles," plates 1, 2, 5–18, 20–34.

28 Interview, Gina Dingle, February 15, 2006.

29 Interview, Milt Donin, September 1, 2005.

30 Interview, Gina Dingle, February 15, 2006.

31 FHN to FMN, c. 1982.

32 Interview, Milt Donin, September 1, 2005.

33 Ibid.

34 Epstein M, "Renal Complications of Liver Disease," *Clin. Symp.*, vol. 37, no. 5, 1985.

35 Ibid., plate 14.

36 Ibid., plate 5.

37 Ibid., plate 8.
38 Ibid., plate 6.
39 Ibid., plate 7.
40 Interview, Murray Epstein, March 20, 2006.
41 Letter, Timothy S. Healy to FHN, January 2, 1985.
42 Interview, Milt Donin, September 1, 2005.
43 Email, Steven Harrison to FMN, February 20, 2006.
44 Interview with FHN, Medical College of Georgia, c. 1986, used by permission of Steven Harrison, chair, Medical Illustration Graduate Program.
45 Ibid.
46 FHN, CCMI, *Nervous System Part II*, 2nd ed., pp. iii–iv.
47 Born March 26, 1928, and died April 1985; Social Security Death Index.
48 Interview, Gina Dingle, February 15, 2006.
49 Interview, Royden Jones, December 9, 2005.

Chapter 26: Musculoskeletal System

1   FHN, CCMI, vol. 8, *Musculoskeletal System Part I*, Ciba, Summit, NJ, 1987.
2   FHN, CCMI, vol. 8, *Musculoskeletal System Part II*, Ciba, Summit, NJ, 1990.
3   FHN, CCMI, vol. 8, *Musculoskeletal System Part III*, Ciba, Summit, NJ, 1993.
4   Other University of Pennsylvania contributors to FHN, op. cit. *Musculoskeletal System Part I*: Abass Alavi, Sec. IV, "Metabolic Disorders," plate 28; Charles S. August, Sec. IV. "Metabolic Disorders," plates 39–40; Jonathan Black, Sec. III. "Physiology," plates 22–23; Charles Clark, Sec. III. "Physiology," plates 24–25; Murray K. Dalinka, Sec. IV. "Metabolic Disorders," plates 25–27, 29; Michael Fallon, Sec. IV. "Metabolic Disorders," plates 21, 30; John G. Haddad, Sec. IV. "Metabolic Disorders," plates 32, 41–43; Joseph P. Ianotti, Sec. III. "Physiology," plate 19; Joel S. Karp, Sec. IV. "Metabolic Disorders," plate 28; Richard G. Schmidt, Sec. III. "Physiology," plate 39. Additional contributors from other institutions were Joseph A. Buckwalter, University of Iowa College of Medicine, Sec. III. "Physiology," plate 25; Edward A. Millar, Northwestern University Medical School, Sec. IV. "Metabolic Disorders," plates 34–36.
5   FHN, op. cit. *Musculoskeletal System Part I*, Sec. III. "Physiology," plates 16–18, 34, 36–38.
6   Ibid., Sec. IV. "Metabolic Disorders," plates 1–10.
7   Ibid., Sec. III. "Physiology," plates 1–15.
8   Louis Caplan to FMN, November 13, 2006.
9   FHN, op. cit. *Musculoskeletal System Part I*, 2nd ed., Sec. I. "Anatomy," 8–14, 18, 35, 36, 47–49, 75–77, 97–98.
10 Ibid., plates 8–14, 18.
11 FHN, CCMI, vol. 1, *Nervous System Part I*, Ciba, Summit, NJ, 1983, Sec. I. "Bony Coverings of the Brain and Spinal Cord," plates 9–15, 17.
12 FHN, op. cit. *Musculoskeletal System Part I*, Sec. II. "Embryology," plates 1–8, 10–21.

13 Crelin ES, "Development of the Musculoskeletal System," *Clin. Symp.*, vol. 33, no. 1, 1981.

14 FHN, op. cit. *Musculoskeletal System Part I*, Sec. II, "Embryology," plate 9.

15 Ibid., Sec. III. "Physiology," plate 32; Sec. IV. "Metabolic Disorders," plates 1–20 (one plate is on calcium and phosphate metabolism, and 10 are on rickets, osteomalacia and renal osteodystrophy).

16 Bruce M. Carlson at the University of Michigan contributed to five plates (ibid., Sec. III. "Physiology," plates 2, 3, 7, 21, 27) also in the physiology section.

17 Ibid., Sec. III. "Physiology," plates 16, 19–25, 28–31, 33–36, 39; Sec. IV. "Metabolic Disorders," plates 1–4, 2–23, 37–44.

18 Kaplan FS, "Osteoporosis," *Clin. Symp.*, vol. 35, no. 5, 1983.

19 FHN, op. cit. *Musculoskeletal System Part I*, Sec. III, "Physiology," plate 31.

20 Ibid., Sec. III, "Physiology," plate 35.

21 Interview, Frederick S. Kaplan, December, 18, 2005.

22 Ibid.

23 FHN, op. cit. *Musculoskeletal System Part I*, Sec. III, plate 16.

24 FHN, *CCMI*, vol. 1, *Nervous System Part II*, 2nd Ed., Ciba, Summit, NJ, 1986, Sec. XI, "Bell's Palsy," plate 8.

25 Interview, Frederick S. Kaplan, December, 18, 2005.

26 Kaplan FS, "A Life That Made a Difference," eulogy for Frank H. Netter, September 22, 1991.

27 FHN, op. cit. *Musculoskeletal System Part I*, Sec. IV, "Metabolic Disorders," plate 44.

28 Interview, Frederick S. Kaplan, December, 18, 2005.

29 Kaplan, "A Life That Made a Difference," op. cit.

30 Interview, Frederick S. Kaplan, December, 18, 2005.

31 Ibid.

32 Ibid. Conversation excerpted.

33 Ibid.

34 Interview, Gina Dingle, February 15, 2006.

35 Interview, Frederick S. Kaplan, December, 18, 2005.

36 Cole H, "Frank Netter, MD: 'command performance' in medical art," *JAMA*, vol. 255, no. 16, pp. 2121–2127, April 25, 1986.

37 Senghas RE, "Book Reviews," *Journal of Bone and Joint Surg*, vol. 70A, no. 9, 1988, p. 1438.

38 Swanson AB, "Reconstructive Surgery in the Arthritic Hand and Foot," *Clin. Symp.*, vol. 31, no. 6, 1979.

39 Email, Genevieve de Groot Swanson to FMN, July 8, 2007.

Chapter 27: Atlas of Human Anatomy

1 Interview, RN, April 7, 2004.

2 Wolfe MS, "Diseases of Travelers," *Clin. Symp.*, vol. 36, no. 2, 1984.

3 Interview, Martin Wolfe, March 16, 2006.

4 745 Fifth Avenue.

5   Interview, Phil Flagler, December 2, 2005.
6   Interview, Milt Donin, September 1, 2004.
7   Ibid.
8   Gray, Henry, *Anatomy, Descriptive and Surgical*, 1901 ed., Running Press, Philadelphia, 1974.
9   Email, Roy Ellis to FMN, March 10, 2006.
10 Letter, Roy Ellis to FMN, January 14, 2006.
11 FHN, *Atlas of Human Anatomy*, Ciba-Geigy, Summit, NJ, 1989.
12 Interview, Sharon Colacino Oberg, October 13, 2004.
13 Interview, Gina Dingle, February 15, 2006.
14 Interview, Sharon Colacino Oberg, October 13, 2004.
15 Email, Sharon Colacino Oberg to FMN, November 25, 2006.
16 Interview, Sharon Colacino Oberg, October 13, 2004.
17 Ibid.
18 Interview, Milt Donin, September 1, 2004.
19 FHN, "Frank H. Netter, MD, Artist, Physician, Teacher," video, Ciba-Geigy, Summit, NJ, 1988.
20 Interview, Sharon Colacino Oberg, October 13, 2004.
21 Interview, Gina Dingle, February 15, 2006.
22 Interview, Phil Flagler, December 2, 2005.
23 Davis, Susan E., "Birth of an Anatomy Atlas," *Step by Step Graphics*, vol. 6, no. 1, January 1990, Dynamic Graphics Inc., Peoria, IL.
24 Agur AM, Dalley A., *Grant's Atlas of Anatomy*, Lippincott Williams & Wilkins, Philadelphia, 2004.
25 Interview, Sharon Colacino Oberg, October 13, 2004.
26 Interview, Phil Flagler, December 2, 2005.
27 *New York Times*, In Short; Reference, *Atlas of Human Anatomy*, by Frank H. Netter, reviewed by Lawrence K. Altman, May 13, 1990.
28 *JAMA*, vol. 263, no. 16, April 25, 1990.
29 *Journal of Bone and Joint Surgery*, vol. 72-A, no. 5, March 1990; *Mayo Clinic Proceedings*, vol. 65, March 1990.
30 *Journal of the American Dental Association*, vol. 120, March 1990, p. 238.
31 *Journal of Neurological and Orthopaedic Medicine and Surgery*, vol. 11, issue I, April 1990.
32 *Science Books and Films*, vol. 25, no 5, May–June 1990.
33 *New England Journal of Medicine*, vol. 323, no. 3, April 30, 1990, p. 619.
34 Interview, Sharon Colacino Oberg, October 13, 2004.
35 Letter, Frederick S. Kaplan to FHN, May 21, 1989.
36 Total hip replacement was developed by Sir John Charnley in the 1960s.

Chapter 28: Unfinished Business

1   FHN, CCMI, vol. 8, *Musculoskeletal System Part II*, Ciba, Summit, NJ, 1991.
2   Salter RB, *Textbook of Disorders and Injuries of Musculoskeletal Structure*, Lippincott Williams & Wilkins, Philadelphia, 1983.

3   Thompson GH, Salter RB, "Legg-Calvé-Perthes Disease," *Clin. Symp.*,
    vol. 38, no. 1, 1986.

4   FHN, op. cit., *Musculoskeletal System Part II*, Sec. I, "Congenital and
    Developmental Disorders," plate 39.

5   Hensinger RN, "Congenital Dislocation of the Hip," *Clin. Symp.*, vol. 31,
    no. 1, 1979.

6   Interview, Robert Hensinger, December 8, 2005.

7   Hensinger RN, Congenital Dislocation of the Hip. *Clin. Symp.*, vol. 31, no. 1,
    1979, in FHN, op. cit., *Musculoskeletal System Part II*, Sec. I, "Congenital and
    Developmental Disorders," plates 50–56.

8   Thompson GH, Salter RB, "Legg-Calvé-Perthes Disease," *Clin. Symp.*,
    vol. 38, no. 1, 1986; in FHN, op. cit., *Musculoskeletal System Part II*, Sec. I,
    "Congenital and Developmental Disorders," plates 57–65.

9   Ernest U. Conrad.

10 Enneking WF, Conrad EU III, "Common Bone Tumors," *Clin. Symp.*,
    vol. 41, no. 3, 1989; Conrad EU III, Enneking WF, "Common Soft Tissue
    Tumors," *Clin. Symp.*, vol. 42, no. 1, 1990; in FHN, op. cit., *Musculoskeletal
    System Part II*, Sec. II. "Tumors of the Musculoskeletal System," plates
    1–34. The volume included additional sections. For the part on dwarfism
    (FHN, op. cit., *Musculoskeletal System Part II*, Sec. I, "Congenital and
    Developmental Disorders," plates 1–16), Frank worked with Charles Scott,
    at Thomas Jefferson University Jefferson Medical College in Philadelphia.
    That material appeared also in a 1988 issue of *Clinical Symposia* (Scott CI
    Jr, "Dwarfism," *Clin. Symp.*, vol. 40, no. 1, 1988), published during the time
    that Frank was working on the *Musculoskeletal System Part II*, the pictures
    and text doing double duty. Dr. Freyberg served as guest editor for the
    section on rheumatic diseases. He was emeritus professor of medicine at
    Cornell University Medical College and emeritus director of the Division
    of Rheumatic Diseases at the Hospital for Special Surgery. They reused
    several plates on rheumatoid diseases and juvenile arthritis that Frank
    had done previously for a *Clinical Symposia* issue (Calabro JJ, "Rheumatoid
    Arthritis: Diagnosis and Management," *Clin. Symp.*, vol. 38, no. 2, 1986)
    and updated only the text. Chester Fink at the University of Texas
    Southwestern Medical School in Dallas prepared the text for the piece
    on juvenile arthritis (FHN, op. cit., *Musculoskeletal System Part II*, Sec. III.
    "Rheumatic Diseases," plates 17–20), and Dr. Freyberg prepared the text for
    the piece on rheumatoid diseases and others on arthritis (ibid., plates 1–13,
    21–37).

11 Swanson AB, "Congenital Limb Defects Classification and Treatment,"
    Clin. Symp., vol. 33, no. 3, 1981; in FHN, op. cit., *Musculoskeletal System Part II*,
    Sec. I, "Congenital and Developmental Disorders," plates 99–111.

12 Swanson AB, "Reconstructive Surgery in the Arthritic Hand and Foot"
    Clin. Symp., vol. 31, no. 6, 1979; in FHN, op. cit., *Musculoskeletal System Part II*,
    Sec. III. "Rheumatic Diseases," plates 62–73.

13 Program, 34th Hogden Memorial Lecture, Blodgett Memorial Medical Center, Grand Rapids, MI, November 21, 1989.

14 Email, Genevieve de Groot Swanson to FMN, March 22, 2006.

15 Interview and email, Genevieve de Groot Swanson to FMN, June 23, 2007.

16 Email, Hugo Keim, December 13, 2005.

17 Keim HA, "Low Back Pain," *Clin. Symp.*, vol. 25, no. 3, 1973; Keim HA, "Scoliosis," *Clin. Symp.*, vol. 30, no. 1, 1978; Keim HA, Kirkaldy-Willis W.H., "Low Back Pain," *Clin. Symp.*, vol. 32, no. 6, 1980; Keim HA, Kirkaldy-Willis WH, "Low Back Pain," *Clin. Symp.*, vol. 39, no. 6, 1987; Keim HA, Hensinger RN, "Spinal Deformities. Scoliosis and Kyphosis," *Clin. Symp.*, vol. 41, no. 4, 1989.

18 FHN, op. cit., *Musculoskeletal System Part II*, Sec. I. "Congenital and Developmental Disorders," plates 29–34.

19 The piece on hip replacement, with additional text by Paul M. Pellicci, was also published in a 1987 *Clinical Symposia* issue that Frank prepared in collaboration with Stuart Kozinn and Philip Wilson (Kozinn SC, Wilson PD Jr, "Adult Hip Disease and Total Hip Replacement," *Clin. Symp.*, vol. 39, no. 5, 1987); in FHN, op. cit., *Musculoskeletal System Part II*, Sec. IV. "Total Joint Replacement," plates 1–14.

20 FHN, op. cit. *Musculoskeletal System Part II*, Sec. IV. "Total Joint Replacement," plates 15–24.

21 Interview, Russell E. Windsor, November 14, 2005.

22 Interview, Gina Dingle, February 15, 2006.

23 Ibid.

24 Rockwood Charles A, Green David P, Wilkins Kaye E, King Richard E, *Fractures*, Lippincott Williams & Wilkins, Philadelphia, 1984.

25 Interview, James Heckman, November 22, 2005.

26 FHN, *CCMI*, vol. 8, *Musculoskeletal System Part III*, Ciba-Geigy, Summit, NJ, 1993, Sec. I. "Injury," plates 26–32.

27 Interview, James Heckman, November 22, 2005; letter, James Heckman to Michael DeBakey, August 14, 1987; letter, Michael DeBakey to James Heckman, September 8, 1987.

28 Interview, William DeVries, September 7, 2004.

29 Interview, Michael DeBakey, June 30, 2004.

30 Interview, John Craig, March 16, 2006.

31 Interview, James Heckman, November 22, 2005.

32 FHN, op. cit., *Musculoskeletal System Part III*, Sec. I. "Injury," plates 41–68.

33 Ibid., plate 48.

34 Letter, Fred Corley to FMN, November 18, 2005.

35 Conwell HE, "Injuries to the Elbow," *Clin. Symp.*, vol. 21, no. 2, 1969.

36 Conwell HE, "Injuries to the Wrist," *Clin. Symp.*, vol. 22, no. 1, 1970.

37 For example, in FHN, op. cit., *Musculoskeletal System Part III*, Sec. I. "Injury," plate 41, posterior dislocation of the elbow; plate 53, reduction of Colles fracture; plate 55, fracture of the radius.

38 Letter, Fred Corley to FMN, November 18, 2005; same story also from an interview of James Heckman, November 22, 2005.

39 FHN, *CCMI*, vol. 8, *Musculoskeletal System Part III*, Ciba-Geigy, Summit, NJ, 1983, Sec. I. "Injury," plates 5–10.

40 Letters, Basil Pruitt to FMN, January 12, 2004, and November 14, 2005.

41 Mubarak Scott J, Hargens Alan R, Akeson Wayne H, *Compartment Syndromes and Volkmann's Contracture*, W.B. Saunders, Philadelphia, 1981.

42 FHN, op. cit., *Musculoskeletal System Part III*, Sec. I. "Injury," plates 1–16.

43 Interview, Scott Mubarak, December 7, 2005.

44 Letter, FHN to Harold E. Kleinert, February 8, 1982.

45 Letter, FHN to Harold E. Kleinert, June 28, 1987.

46 Letter, FHN to Harold E. Kleinert, May 3, 1988.

47 There were three additional authors who worked with Harold Kleinert: his son, James Kleinert, himself an assistant professor of orthopaedic surgery at Louisville, and two former fellows, Steve McCabe and Anthony Berger. The four of them worked on the text for that with Maria Erdélyi-Brown, the editor at Ciba-Geigy.

48 Letter, FHN to Harold E. Kleinert, received February 13, 1989.

49 Pictures of the anatomy of the arm and hand that were included in that *Clinical Symposia* issue were some that Frank had done in consultation with anatomist Russell Woodburne for the *Musculoskeletal System Part I* volume (*Musculoskeletal System Part I*, Sec. I. "Anatomy," plates 43, 50, 53, 55).

50 FHN, op. cit., *Musculoskeletal System Part III*, Sec. I. "Injury," plates 117–126.

51 Kleinert HE, Kleinert JM, McCabe SJ, Berger AC, "Replantation," *Clin. Symp.*, vol. 43, no. 2, 1991.

Chapter 29: Giving Life

1 Chobanian AV, Gavras H, "Hypertension," *Clin. Symp.*, vol. 42, no. 4, 1990.

2 Interview, Aram Chobanian, March 27, 2006.

3 Email, Aram Chobanian to FMN, March 23, 2007.

4 DeBakey ME, Cooley DA, Creech O Jr, "Surgery of the Aorta," *Clin. Symp.*, vol. 8, no. 2, 1956.

5 FHN, at unveiling of Nurses Week poster for the Tri-Council for Nursing, Washington, DC, May 4, 1989.

6 Mary Mills Causey to FMN, c. May 5, 1989.

7 Interview, Frederick S. Kaplan, December 18, 2005.

8 Ibid.

9 Letter, Frederick S. Kaplan to FHN, May 21, 1989.

10 Kaplan FS, eulogy for FHN, September 22, 1991.

11 Moseley HF, "Disorders of the Hip," *Clin. Symp.*, vol. 5, no. 2, 1953, cover.

12 Interview, Frederick S. Kaplan, December 18, 2005.

13 Interview, Gina Dingle, February 15, 2006.

14 Letter, Frederick S. Kaplan to FHN, May 21, 1989.

15 Interview, Gina Dingle, February 15, 2006.

16   Interview, Arthur Emmett, September 2, 2006.
17   Email, Douglas Watson to FMN, March 12, 2006.
18   Interview, Arthur Emmett, September 2, 2006.
19   Interview, Phil Flagler, December 2, 2005.
20   Letter, Michael DeBakey to FHN, March, 27, 1990.
21   Letter, FHN to Michael DeBakey, August 1, 1988.
22   Letter, Michael DeBakey to FHN, March, 12, 1989.
23   Letter, FHN to Michael DeBakey, April 10, 1990.
24   Interview, Frederick S. Kaplan, December 18, 2005.
25   Letter, Frederick S. Kaplan to Douglas Watson, April 18, 1990.
26   DeBakey ME, Cooley DA, Creech O Jr, "Surgery of the Aorta," *Clin. Symp.*,
      vol. 8, no. 2, 1956.
27   Letter, Michael DeBakey to Douglas Watson, April 23, 1990.
28   Interview, Arthur Emmett, September 2, 2006.
29   Letter, FHN to Frederick S. Kaplan, April 25, 1990.
30   Letter, Douglas Watson to Frederick S. Kaplan, April 30, 1990.
31   Interview, Phil Flagler, December 2, 2005.
32   FHN, *CCMI*, vol. 8, *Musculoskeletal System Part III*, Ciba-Geigy, Summit, NJ,
      1993, Sec. I. "Injury," plates 1–4, 23–25, 33–40, 152–155; Sec. III "Amputation,"
      plates 6, 9–11; Sec. IV. "Rehabilitation," plates 13–14, 16–17.
33   Interview, David Mascaro, March, 4, 2005.
34   Interview, Craig Luce, October 1, 2004.
35   FHN, *CCMI*, vol. 8, *Musculoskeletal System Part III*, Ciba-Geigy, Summit, NJ,
      1993, Sec. I. "Injury," plate 48.
36   Craig Luce painted 10 pictures from Frank's sketches: FHN, op. cit.,
      Musculoskeletal System Part III, Sec. I. "Injury," plates 47–51, 57–60; Sec. IV.
      "Rehabilitation," plate 15.
37   Interview, Craig Luce, October 1, 2004.
38   Interview, Patrick McDonnell, September 14, 2006.
39   FHN, "Anterior and Posterior Chambers of the Eye," *Atlas of Human
      Anatomy*, Ciba-Geigy, Summit, NJ, 1989, plate 83.
40   Vera Netter to FMN, c. June 1990.
41   Interview, Patrick McDonnell, September 14, 2006.
42   Email, Stephen Carmichael to FMN, June 14, 2006.
43   Interview, Gina Dingle, February 15, 2006.

Chapter 30: Drawing Conclusions
1   Interview, Phil Flagler, December 2, 2005.
2   The Vesalius Trust, established under the Association of Medical
      Illustrators in 1988, presented to Frank the inaugural Frank Netter Award
      for Special Contributions to Medical Education, which Phil Flagler
      accepted on Frank's behalf.
3   FHN, *CCMI*, vol. 8, *Musculoskeletal System Part II*, Ciba-Geigy, Summit, NJ,
      1990.

4   Letter, Ernest Conrad to FHN, November 4, 1990.
5   FHN, *CCMI*, vol. 8, *Musculoskeletal System Part II*, Ciba, Summit, NJ, 1991, Sec. I. "Congenital and Developmental Disorders," plate 75.
6   Interview, Gina Dingle, February 15, 2006.
7   Interview, Arthur Weisenseel, December 28, 2006.
8   Interview, Gina Dingle, February 15, 2006.
9   Interview, Peter Som, March 23, 2006.
10 FMN, March 21, 2011.
11 Interview, Phil Flagler, December 2, 2005.

Epilogue

1   Letter of transmittal, FHN to NYU, June 25, 1964.
2   FHN, CCMI, Vol. 8, *Musculoskeletal System Part III*, Ciba-Geigy, Summit, NJ, 1993.
3   FHN, *Atlas of Human Anatomy*, Saunders/Elsevier, Philadelphia, 2011.
4   Interview, Frederick S. Kaplan, December 18, 2005.
5   "A recurrent mutation in the BMP type I receptor ACVR1 causes inherited and sporadic fibrodysplasia ossificans progressiva," *Nature Genetics*, vol. 38, no. 5, 2006, pp. 525–527.
6   "Potent inhibition of heterotopic ossification by nuclear retinoic acid receptor-γ agonists," *Nature Medicine*, vol. 17, no. 4, 2011, pp. 454–460.

Acknowledgments

F IRST, I MUST THANK my father Frank H. Netter. He was an extraordinary person who made an extraordinary contribution to the world. So many of the people who helped me with this book did so not for my sake but because of their love and admiration for him. Only because of him did his friends, his colleagues, and my family give me the interviews, letters, and papers that are so indispensable to the telling of this story. Sadly, some of those who contributed to this book died during the nine years of its writing, and I regret they did not live to see its publication. I like to think they would have enjoyed reading it.

After Daddy's death, when the time came for my siblings and me to dismantle his studio, numerous boxes of his files came into my possession, among them his copious autobiographical notes. I gave those papers to the University of North Carolina Health Sciences Library. I thank the director, Carol Jenkins, and her staff, including Diane McKenzie (now retired), Jake Wiltshire, Pam Roberts, Christie Degener, Barbara Tysinger, and Robert Ladd. I also thank Anne Wood Humphries, who curated the Netter collection at the library and guided me through the boxes of papers and helped me make sense of them.

I owe thanks to Gary Lees, chairman and director of the Art as Applied to Medicine program at Johns Hopkins University, and to Beth Doschinger, formerly with John Hopkins Medicine Development office, who gave me their list of current addresses for many of Dad's colleagues and consultants. Gary also used his resources to convert the deteriorating 16-millimeter film of *The Doctor Draws a Picture* to DVD, making it readable and conserving its content.

For the splendid accounts from Dad's colleagues—physicians, practitioners, and scientists with whom he consulted—I thank

Michael E. DeBakey, MD; Arthur H. Aufses, Jr., MD; Sharon Colacino Oberg, PhD; George W. Mitchell, Jr., MD; Marvin Moser, MD; C. Everett Koop, MD, ScD; Lodewyk H.S. Van Mierop, MD; John H. Abel, Jr., PhD; James R. Malm, MD; Murray G. Baron, MD; Robert S. Litwak, MD; Abel Lazzarini Robertson, Jr., MD, PhD; Marvin B. Bacaner, MD; Norman E. Shumway, MD, PhD; Ben Pansky, PhD; Felix O. Kolb, MD, FACP; Aaron B. Lerner, MD, PhD; Robert E. Olson, PhD, MD; Calvin Ezrin, MD, FRCP; Earle B. Weiss, MD; Paul J. Cannon, MD; Alan S. Cohen, MD; Hugo A. Keim, MD, FACS; Charles Horton, MD; Suresh Patel, MD; Roger C. Duvoisin, MD; Robert N. Hensinger, MD; G. Dean MacEwen, MD; Carl T. Brighton, MD, PhD; James R. Urbaniak, MD; Alvin S. Teirstein, MD; James W. Ryan, MD, PhD; Una S. Ryan, MD; Dr. Murray D. Altose; Morton N. Swartz, MD; Jose F. Landa, MD; Victor J. Marder, MD; Henry J. Heimlich, MD; Barry W. Peterson, PhD; Jerome J. Sheldon, MD, FACR; Jay B. Angevine, Jr., PhD; Genevieve de Groot Swanson, MD; Albert B. Swanson, MD; Seymour Diamond, MD; H.F. Moseley, MA, DM, MCh; Aram V. Chobanian, MD; Stephen S. Scheidt, MD; H. Royden Jones, Jr., MD; Richard A. Baker, MD; Stephen R. Freidberg, MD; Louis R. Caplan, MD; Harold E. Kleinert, MD; William C. DeVries, MD; Lyle D. Joyce, MD; George H. Thompson, MD; William F. Enneking, MD; Ernest U. Conrad III, MD; Thomas L. Kemper, MD; William A. Friedman, MD; Marc A. Flitter, MD; Murray Epstein, MD; Henry J. Mankin, MD; Martin S. Wolfe, MD; Russell E. Windsor, MD; James D. Heckman, MD; Fred G. Corley, Jr., MD; Basil A. Pruitt, Jr., MD; Scott J. Mubarak, MD; and Stephen Carmichael, PhD, DSc. Special recognition goes to Frederick S. Kaplan, MD, or Freddie, as Dad called him. His descriptions of the times they spent together lend enormous appeal to those sections of this book, and I thank him for that and for his support and friendship. I also thank Arthur C. Weisenseel, MD, who treated Dad during the last days of his life.

I received many kind words from the families of colleagues: Ralph D. Alley, MD; Leonard E. Glynn, MD, FRCP, FC Path; Edmund S.

Crelin, PhD, DSc; G.A.G. Mitchell, OBE, TD, ChM, DSc, FRCS; Ward Neuschwander; Howard G. Worthen, MD, PhD; Richard L. Varco, MD; Crawford J. Campbell, MD; Alfred Gilman, PhD; Lawrence McCormack, MD, MS Path; Floyd L. Wergeland, MD; Frederick Yonkman, MD, PhD; and Max L. Som, MD. Grant Mitchell in Manchester, England, sent me biographical materials on his father, Professor G.A.G. Mitchell. Jesse E. Edwards, MD was too ill to be interviewed, but Mrs. Edwards and their son, Dr. Brooks S. Edwards, were kind enough to send me copies of Dr. Edwards's notes. Peter Som, MD, whom I have known since our childhood days, reminisced with me about our parents. His father, Dr. Max Som, was Daddy's dearest friend and to me like a dear uncle.

Several of Dad's consultants who did not work extensively with him yet encouraged me in the writing of this biography were Robert Jarvik, MD; Herbert Silverstein, MD; Rudolph Camishion, MD; Robert T. McCluskey, MD; Robert B. Salter, MD, FRCS; A. Stone Freedberg, MD; Lloyd H. Smith, Jr., MD; R. Michael Scott, MD; Martin S. Hirsh, MD; Daniel Dumitru, MD, PhD; John Gleave, MA, FRCS; James R. Jude, MD; Donald C. Ferlic, MD; Wallace T. Miller, MD; Mary Ellen Avery, MD; Alfred P. Fishman, MD; Joseph A. Buckwalter, MD; and Thomas D. Sabin, MD.

I am especially grateful to Barbara Niss at The Mount Sinai Hospital in New York; Colleen Bradley-Sanders, formerly at New York University; Sydney Van Nort and Claudia Lascar at City College of New York; Gerard J. Pelisson, formerly of DeWitt Clinton High School; and Arlene Shaner at the New York Academy of Medicine for their historical accounts of those illustrious institutions that illuminate Dad's experiences, as well as for the wonderful pictures they gave me. I am greatly indebted to Ms. Bradley-Sanders and New York University for the digitized images of *Life of a Doctor*. Richard Berensen at the Society of Illustrators gave me the image of the glazed tile, *Girl with Pen,* which I love. I thank also Ruth Reininghaus at the Salmagundi Club; and Mark Mitchell at the National Academy of Design School. Thanks in particular to Dr. Marc A. Flitter and Barbara Niss for helping me track down

Rudolph Drosd, MD. Dr. Drosd was in his nineties when I spoke to him and told him that the little girl whose life he saved is now a grandmother.

I extend my special thanks to Gina Dingle and Phil Flagler, who were at Ciba and worked with Dad for years, for their many stories about my father. Also from Ciba were Milton Donin, PhD; Arthur Emmett, MB, BS, Medicine; Roy Ellis, MD; and Douglas Watson, who each freely shared with me their remembrances, and I am most appreciative.

Ray Olivere was in the army with Dad during World War II, and I thank him for filling in details of those years. Ray pointed me to the Sanford School and Merrilee Mose. I thank also medical illustrators Steve Harrison; David Mascaro; Craig Luce; John Craig, MD; and Patrick McDonnell, who not only told me about their experiences with Dad but also taught me a little about their craft.

Jacob Mordecai Netter's book is genealogically and historically rich. Rabbi Joan Friedman made the English translation, and her annotations were most helpful to my understanding that difficult book. My correspondence to Vienna about Solomon Netter prompted replies from Dr. Helmut Kretschmr and Katharina Smola in the magistrate's office, which my brother, Jonathan Netter, graciously translated from German for me. What a remarkable experience it was for me subsequently to visit the apartment house in Vienna where my great-great-grandfather Solomon lived, and even more so to visit his grave, so beautifully kept by the city of Vienna. Kathy Saudino guided me there and shared that emotional adventure with me, and I will always feel a special connection with her.

I obtained a wealth of information on family history from the United States census records; birth, marriage, and death records in the offices of the City of New York and in New York State archives; United States military and draft records; and other government documents. I am indebted to cousins Kathryn Mills, Oscar Lee McFadyen, Jr., Robert Marrazzi, and Adele Bendes and to Adele's son, Charles Bendes, and son-in-law, Graydon Wood, for accounts and pictures. By far the greatest encouragement and contribution to family background information came from cousin Richard Netter, who became to me a beloved family patriarch after my father's death, and from Richard's dear brother Edward, who championed this book and introduced me to John Lahey, PhD, then president of Quinnipiac University. It was Quinnipiac University Press who published the first edition of *Medicine's Michelangelo* in conjunction with the opening there of the Frank H.Netter MD School of Medicine.

Thanks go also to Joanne DelRio at Novartis and to Elyse O'Grady at Elsevier. I am deeply indebted to Elsevier for giving me the digital images of some of the medical illustrations in the Netter collection that lend so much to the meaning and appeal of this volume. Thanks also to Graydon Wood, who photographed *The Netter Children*, *Dellie*, and *The Artist's Mother*; Zachary Lemle and www.oldlongisland.com for the photo of Folly Farm; Brian Allen at Officina Briani, who created a letterpress print from the original plate of Netter's *Folly Farm* Christmas card; David L. Dawson for the photo of Frank Netter with Stephen Carmichael; and Doug Mokaren and Paul Braly at the University of North Carolina, who digitized holdings in the University of North Carolina Health Sciences Library. Joseph Kitterman, MD, and Suzanne Purrington read through early versions of the original manuscript with fresh eyes, and I thank them for their time, their comments and edits.

From the start, Patrick Inman worked with me as editor, reading revision after revision of the manuscript, tirelessly offering insight and suggesting changes all along the way. His encouragement has been steadfast and his professional insight, invaluable. His encouragement and wise counsel is largely responsible for my going forward with this second edition. I owe him a great deal.

To William L. Roper, MD, MPH, I owe a debt of gratitude for his contribution in preparing the foreword. I am deeply appreciative of his belief in this project and in my ability to take it from concept to completion.

I am enormously grateful to my literary agent, Robin Miura, an enthusiastic believer in this book and who suggested the title. I thank also gifted book designer Dick Margulis, who coordinated all the editorial efforts and guided this second edition to publication. Thanks also to proofreader Gregory Zelchenko, who combed through the manuscript with an eagle eye. Carol Roberts prepared the index, which although tied to the text is really a separate creative work; and I thank her for doing it.

Above all I thank my children, Jonathan, Caroline, and James, and my husband, Ralph, for their love and faith.

INDEX

Note: Page references in italics refer to illustrations. "FHN" refers to Frank Netter.